Statistics as Applied to

Economics

and Business

Statistics as Applied to Economics and Business

REVISED EDITION

ROBERT H. WESSEL
University of Cincinnati

EDWARD R. WILLETT
Northeastern University

ALBERT J. SIMONE
Boston College

HOLT, RINEHART and WINSTON, INC.

New York   Chicago   San Francisco   Toronto   London

July, 1965

Copyright © 1959, 1965
by Holt, Rinehart and Winston, Inc.
Library of Congress Catalog No: 65-10140
29313-0415
Printed in the United States of America

To HELEN, FRANCES, CAROLIE

Preface

The course in Statistical Methods should be one of the most valuable and useful in the program of study of the student of economics and business. Unfortunately, not only does it frequently fail to achieve this status, but it often becomes the most feared and disliked part of the entire curriculum. The reason for this is not hard to find. Many of the students of economics and business have had insufficient training in mathematics, and they have little aptitude for it. In not a few instances this fact is influential in their choice of these fields of study in preference to engineering or science. These students require a statistics text that presents the full force of statistical method without drawing on a deep background in mathematics.

It is to meet this problem that our text was written. The authors feel that even though mathematical notation is essential to a precise statement of most statistical concepts the basic ideas can often be explained verbally or by means of simple examples. The authors have attempted to present this explanation in such a way that the underlying statistical theory is fully exposed and the relation between theory and application thoroughly understood. In this way, rigor has not been sacrificed. Obviously, it would not be feasible to dispense entirely with formulas and equations. Nevertheless, in this text they are kept as few in number and as simple in form as possible. More complex mathematical statements that may prove useful in some courses are supplied in footnotes. In addition, a brief review of such concepts as simple equations and logarithms is presented in Appendix A. This appendix is included not only because the operations described will be required throughout the text, but also because it provides an opportunity for the student once again to become familiar with quantitative concepts.

Some people may be disenchanted with the basic approach just outlined. They may argue that statistics is a branch of applied mathematics and should therefore be treated, symbolically and analytically, from a strict mathematical point of view. They may argue that the student should be *made* to think mathematically. There is merit in this train of thought. However, it really begs the question because it does not explicitly recognize and deal with the fact that the typical business student today has an insufficient mathematical background for this type of approach. Because of this weak background, the wide range of topics typically covered in the required statistics course offered all business students, and the objective of this course—namely, *to provide the student with a set of statistical tools that he can apply in his functional area of concentration*—it is not possible to make the one- and perhaps even the two-semester statistics course meaningful and useful for the student if a predominantly mathematical approach is taken. At least this is the judgment of the authors, who have tried both approaches over a period of more than thirty years of combined teaching. After all, the course is characteristically entitled "Statistics" and not "Mathematics and Statistics." The student of business and economics needs a sound training in mathematics if he is to master the new quantitative methods, but this should occur in a separate mathematics course—not in the traditional statistics course, which should teach the student statistical, not mathematical, method. To demonstrate that this distinction can meaningfully be made, we have only to cite the great many highly successful practicing statisticians who are currently designing samples and running multiple regressions and analyses of variance, and who readily admit to a background in mathematics which turns out to be no stronger than that of the typical undergraduate student of business and economics.

The observations just made paraphrase the opening remarks that appear in the preface to the first edition. This is as it should be, because the problem and need identified in the first paragraph existed then, and the objective and orientation of the text, as indicated in the second paragraph, do not represent a change over the first edition.

However, in many ways this second edition is quite different from the first. With the increased emphasis on quantitative methods, as indicated by the expanding literary activity in the fields of management science, operations research, econometrics, and probabilistic model building in general, the student of business and economics, even on an introductory level, requires more work in analytical as opposed to descriptive statistics. It is in this area, then, that the major revision has occurred. The chapters on statistical inference have been completely rewritten and greatly expanded, and the basic concepts applied throughout the book. For example, in the core chapters (Chapters Six and Seven) relating to statistical inference, the basic concepts of probability, the sampling distribution of the mean, and the standard error of the mean are treated much more fully, and additional concepts, such as type I and II errors and Student's t distribution, are integrated with this basic material. Chapter Eight continues the introduction of additional topics, treating the binomial probability distribution, the normal curve approximation to the binomial, the sampling distribution of a proportion, and the Chi-square distribution. Chapter Nine presents an essentially descriptive discussion, in contrast to the detailed treatment of computational procedures in Chapters Six through Eight, of quality control and sample design. Correlation analysis

(Chapter Ten) is now examined immediately after the chapters on statistical inference, so that these concepts can be applied in this area as well. For example, this edition treats the question of the significance of the coefficient of correlation by introducing the very general z transformation.

These are the major changes in this second edition. There are, of course, other rather minor, but nonetheless important, additions and changes. For example, a brief discussion of kurtosis is introduced, formulas for the various index numbers are presented, problems have been added to each chapter, the two introductory chapters in the first edition have been combined in the new Chapter One, and the first edition's Chapter Three on arithmetic and algebraic techniques has been made into an appendix.

The organization of the table of contents, with a major section on statistical inference and one on forecasting, shows the added emphasis on analytical as opposed to descriptive statistics. It is hoped that a detailed reading of the text, with its continued emphasis on clear verbal exposition aided by the introduction and development of many examples, will persuade the instructor that the teachability of the first edition has been maintained despite the inclusion of more advanced topics. It should be pointed out, in addition, that because Chapters One through Seven, and Ten through Fourteen are independent of Chapters Eight and Nine, the latter chapters may be viewed as optional material to be covered dependent on the time availability and/or objectives of the individual instructor. Furthermore, within the basic chapters, most of the more difficult material is presented so that the basic material is independent of it (for example, the discussion of the z transformation is the next to the last section in the chapter on correlation).

Thus this text has flexibility. It can be adapted to either a one- or two-term course. The omission of selected topics and problems should suffice for the former, whereas their inclusion will make the text serve in the latter instance. Many questions and problems are included at the end of each chapter to enable the instructor who so desires to rely on this text as the sole material in the course. All of the areas conventionally included in a course in economic or business statistics are covered in this text. However, the more advanced aspects of some topics are intentionally omitted. Among the omissions are such topics as the harmonic mean, standard errors of several sample statistics, ideal index numbers, second- and third-degree trend equations, and curvilinear and multiple correlation. It is felt that topics such as these are appropriate to more advanced courses.

Though all three authors deserve an equal share of any credit due this text, Professor Simone, who did not collaborate on the first edition, must take primary responsibility for any criticism directed at the basic revisions noted above.

The authors are indebted to the late Sir Ronald A. Fisher, F.R.S.,

Cambridge, and to Messrs. Oliver and Boyd, Ltd., Edinburgh, for per-
mission to reprint, in abridged form, Table V-B from his book, *Statistical
Methods for Research Workers;* and to the late Sir Ronald A. Fisher, F.R.S.,
Cambridge, Dr. Frank Yates, Rothamsted, and Messrs. Oliver and Boyd,
Ltd., Edinburgh, for permission to use Table III from their book, *Sta-
tistical Tables for Biological, Agricultural, and Medical Research.*

In addition to the debt just acknowledged, the authors express their
gratitude to the many individuals whose suggestions and comments contributed to this project. Outstanding among these is Professor Alfred Kuhn
of the University of Cincinnati. Others to whom the authors are indebted
are Robert F. Pitt, Fairfield University; P. John Lymberopoulos, University of Colorado; and Richard Perlman, Adelphi College. They are
particularly indebted to Helen Mueller, Frances Willett, Helen Wessel,
and Carolie Simone for the typing, preparation of drawings, and assistance
in the many tasks attendant on the preparation of a manuscript. In addition, they are grateful for the understanding and sympathetic attitude of
their families that made this project possible.

Cincinnati, Ohio   R. H. W.

Boston, Massachusetts   E. R. W.

Chestnut Hill, Massachusetts   A. J. S.

Contents

Preface   vii

Part One.   INTRODUCTION

CHAPTER I   Conducting a Statistical Investigation   3

INTRODUCTION   3
The nature of statistics · Statistics and forecasting · Statistics and control · Statistics and exploration

CONDUCTING AN INVESTIGATION   7
Defining and limiting the problem · Definition of terms · Primary and secondary data and sources · Collecting primary data · Sources of inaccuracy in sampling results · Techniques of securing information · Forms of questions · Tabulation

CHAPTER II   Tables and Charts   28

GENERAL RULES   28
TABLES   29
CHARTS AND GRAPHS   35
Bar charts · Line charts · Pie charts · Semilogarithmic chart

CHAPTER III   Frequency Distributions   52

CONSTRUCTING A FREQUENCY DISTRIBUTION   55
Selecting the class interval · Defining class limits · Tabulation of frequencies

FREQUENCY DISTRIBUTIONS FROM DISCRETE DATA 59

CUMULATIVE FREQUENCY DISTRIBUTIONS 59

GRAPHING FREQUENCY DISTRIBUTIONS 60

The histogram · The polygon · The curve · Ogives

TYPES OF FREQUENCY DISTRIBUTIONS 64

The normal curve · The J-shaped distribution · The U-shaped distribution · The Lorenz curve

Part Two: DESCRIPTIVE MEASURES

CHAPTER IV Measures of Central Tendency 75

ARITHMETIC MEAN 76

Calculation of the arithmetic mean—ungrouped data · Weighted arithmetic mean · Calculation of the arithmetic mean—grouped data · When to use the arithmetic mean

GEOMETRIC MEAN 87

Calculation of the geometric mean—ungrouped data · Calculation of the geometric mean—grouped data

MEDIAN 91

Calculation of the median—ungrouped data · Calculation of the median—grouped data

MODE 97

Calculation of the mode—ungrouped data · Calculation of the mode—grouped data

COMPARISON OF MEASURES 101

CHAPTER V Measures of Dispersion and Skewness 108

DISPERSION 108

Range · Quartiles · Percentiles · Average deviation · Standard deviation · Relative dispersion

SKEWNESS 120

Calculation of skewness

KURTOSIS 122

Part Three.   STATISTICAL INTERFERENCE

CHAPTER VI Probability, the Normal Curve, and Sampling
Theory   133

PROBABILITY   134
Terminology · Probability situations · Predetermined situations · Incomplete-experiment situations · Complete-experiment situations · Probability situations and their applications · Range and
limits of the probability ratio

THE NORMAL CURVE   142
The normal curve in business · The normal curve
and the standard deviation · The Table of Areas ·
Probability and the normal curve

SAMPLING THEORY   148
Learning about the population from a sample ·
Simple random sampling · A simple experiment ·
The sampling distribution of the mean · Mean of
the sampling distribution of the mean · Shape of
the sampling distribution of the mean · Standard
deviation of the sampling distribution of the mean

SUMMARY   164

CHAPTER VII Sampling Applications: Confidence Intervals and
Tests of Significance   170

CONFIDENCE INTERVALS   170
Determination of a confidence interval · Interpretation of the confidence interval · Possible confidence levels · Relation between the confidence level
and the size of the confidence interval · The standard error of the mean and confidence intervals ·
Sample size and confidence intervals · Summary

TESTS OF SIGNIFICANCE   184
Sampling variation · A significant difference · The
significance level · Areas of acceptance and rejection · One-tailed versus two-tailed tests · Type I
and type II errors · Significance of a difference between two means

SAMPLING APPLICATIONS: UNKNOWN σ AND LARGE n   202

SAMPLING APPLICATIONS: UNKNOWN σ SMALL n, AND THE t DISTRIBUTION 206

t distribution · Confidence intervals · Tests of significance · Summary

CHAPTER VIII *Further Sampling Applications: Qualitative Data* 223

TWO PROBABILITY THEOREMS 223

BINOMIAL DISTRIBUTION 225

A general formula · Some applications · Mean and standard deviation of the binomial distribution · Normal curve approximation to the binomial

PROPORTIONS 239

Tests of significance · Confidence intervals

CHI-SQUARE DISTRIBUTION 244

A theoretical example · An example from personnel · An example from marketing · An example from production · Sample size

CHAPTER IX *Statistical Quality Control and Sample Design* 260

STATISTICAL QUALITY CONTROL 260

"Piece-to-piece" variation · Recognition of a pattern · Ability to predict · Relation between sample and universe · Control charts

SAMPLE DESIGN 267

Unrestricted random sampling · Restricted random sampling · Directed samples · Statistical inference and other sample measures

Part Four. FORECASTING

CHAPTER X Correlation 277

THE SCATTERGRAM 279

THE REGRESSION LINE 281

ACCURACY OF ESTIMATES 285

Standard error of estimate

CALCULATION OF MEASURES OF CORRELATION   288

The coefficient of determination · The coefficient of
correlation

OTHER RELATIONS   293

SHORT-CUT METHODS   295

SIGNIFICANCE OF r: THE z TRANSFORMATION   296

Some examples · The z transformation · Tests of
hypotheses concerning values of r other than 0 ·
Sample size and significance of r

CORRELATION AND FORECASTING   299

CHAPTER XI Index Numbers   309

METHODS OF CONSTRUCTION   310

Relative of aggregates price index · Average of relatives price index · Relative of weighted aggregates
price index · Average of weighted relatives price
index

PROBLEMS IN CONSTRUCTION   316

Defining purpose · Deciding commodities to be in-
cluded · Determining weights · Collecting data ·
Deciding the form of the index · Choosing the base ·
Deciding on form of average

QUANTITY AND VALUE INDEXES   322

COMMOM INDEX NUMBERS   322

Consumer price index · Wholesale price index · Index of industrial production

CHAPTER XII Times-Series Trend   331

THE IMPORTANCE OF TIME-SERIES ANALYSIS   331

ELEMENTS OF TIME-SERIES VARIATION   383

The secular trend · Seasonal variations · Cyclical
variations · Irregular or random factors · Problems
of classification · Mathematical statement of the
composition of time series

METHODS OF MEASURING TREND   338

Manual trend-fitting · Moving averages · Fitting least squares lines · Conversion of annual trend values to monthly values · Fitting a geometric straight line

SELECTION OF THE TYPE OF CURVE TO BE FITTED   347

CHOICE OF THE TREND PERIOD   348

THE EXTRAPOLATION OF TREND   348

CHAPTER XIII   Measuring Seasonal Variations   356

PRELIMINARY EDITING   356

THE PROBLEM OF ISOLATING SEASONAL VARIATIONS   357

THE RATIO-TO-TREND METHOD   357

Adjusting seasonal indexes to total 1200 percent · Appraisal of the ratio-to-trend method

THE RATIO-TO-THE-MOVING-AVERAGE METHOD   360

THE MEDIAN-LINK-RELATIVE METHOD   365

SELECTING THE PERIOD   368

AVERAGE IN COMPUTING SEASONALS   369

CHANGING SEASONALS   369

ELIMINATING SEASONAL INFLUENCES   370

SEASONAL INDEXES AND PLANNING   371

CHAPTER XIV   Measuring Cyclical Movements   377

THE RESIDUAL METHOD OF MEASURING CYCLES   378

Limitations of the residual method · Comparing cyclical variations

THE NATIONAL BUREAU METHOD   380

Specific cycles · Reference cycles

FORECASTING THE BUSINESS CYCLE   385

APPENDIXES

A. Arithmetic and Algebraic Techniques   395

B. Tables   415

    I. COMMON LOGARITHMS (FIVE-PLACE) OF THE NATURAL NUMBERS 1 TO 10,000   415

    II. RANDOM NUMBERS   434

    III. SQUARES, SQUARE ROOTS, AND RECIPROCALS   435

    IV. TABLE OF AREAS UNDER THE NORMAL CURVE   435

    V. TABLE OF "STUDENT'S" DISTRIBUTION—VALUES OF t   437

    VI. TABLE OF THE DISTRIBUTION OF CHI-SQUARE   438

    VII. TABLE OF VALUES OF r FOR VALUES OF z   439

Index

Part One

INTRODUCTION

Conducting
a Statistical
Investigation

INTRODUCTION

The Nature of Statistics

Statistics is the science that deals with the analysis of masses of quantitative data. It includes the collection, classification, summarization, presentation, and interpretation of such data. Because statistical conclusions are based on masses rather than on individuals, they apply only to masses and not to unpredictable individual items. This principle underlies the often-heard statement that although life insurance companies can accurately predict the number of policy holders who will die during the next year they are totally unable to identify them. Because statistical generalizations seldom are entirely accurate, uncertainties exist when they are applied. Hence the probabilities of error assume importance. In addition, when the masses of data under study are very large—which is often the situation—it becomes either impractical or impossible to examine every individual item. Under these circumstances a representative group of items is subjected to study and the conclusions derived therefrom are assumed to characterize the entire mass of data. This procedure, known as sampling, now occupies a place of central significance among statistical techniques.

Statistics is usually not studied for its own sake; rather, it is widely employed as a tool—and a highly valuable one—in the analysis of problems in both the natural and social sciences. In the latter area statistics often assumes its greatest importance in the study of economics and business.

Statistical methods are used by governmental bodies, private business firms, and research agencies as an indispensable aid in (1) forecasting, (2) controlling, and (3) exploring.

Statistics and Forecasting

Economic and business forecasting is usually based on a projection of past behavior into the future, an analysis of existing conditions, or a combination of the two. Both past experience and current factors must be measured, and as a result they are expressed in quantitative terms. Thus statistical analysis is an essential part of any forecasting attempt. Although a discussion of the techniques of forecasting will be reserved for later chapters, a comment on the use of business and economic forecasts is in order.

Almost everyone is interested in the over-all level of economic activity. Few businesses fail to enjoy the profits that are so widespread during prosperity and even fewer avoid the losses that accompany depression. Therefore the sales projections of most individual firms are necessarily tied to what general business conditions are expected to be. The industrial laborer, the white collar worker, the professional man, and the housewife also cannot escape the consequences of good or bad times. To government, which is committed to stabilization, high prosperity presents the constant threat of inflation and the attendant need for action to curtail price increases. Incipient depression carries with it the specter of mass unemployment, which must be prevented. General economic forecasts serve to forewarn both business and government of impending changes, thus enabling firms to make appropriate adjustments in their plans and providing government an opportunity to initiate necessary countermeasures.

All businessmen forecast. They may do so explicitly by making specific predictions of sales, costs, and other critical magnitudes, or implicitly by ordering goods, constructing plant, and procurring supplies. Obviously, the building of a new factory implicitly assumes that future sales will be sufficient to absorb its output. Adequate forecasting enables management to have the proper workers, supplies, and fixed facilities on hand when needed to meet sales demand. Thus makeshift and costly arrangements that are typically employed when management is taken by surprise are avoided. Forecasts governing the construction of fixed plant and equipment necessarily cover long periods of years; in contrast, only short-term projections are needed in planning purchases or hiring.

Although almost all firms are influenced to some extent by general business conditions, each industry and company within an industry has problems of its own. Hence individual forecasts for specific firms and industries are required in addition to over-all projections.

The insurance business is an interesting example of total dependence on statistical forecasts. Insurance companies collect small sums, called premiums, from a large group of people. The total amounts so collected must be sufficient to pay for the losses that actually occur and in addition defray the operating expenses of the company. In order to do business in such a manner, insurance companies must be able to predict with reasonable accuracy what losses can be expected. These predictions are made possible by an analysis of the frequency of occurrence of losses among large groups in the past. This particular branch of statistics is known as actuarial science.

Statistics and Control

As a result of the growth of large organizations, both in business and government, it has become impossible for those entrusted with managerial responsibility to observe directly and evaluate the activities of their subordinates. The master craftsman of old, working in the presence of few employees in a small shop, could easily oversee the quality of product, amount of waste, rate of production, and other critical factors concerning his apprentices or journeymen; the modern executive cannot. As a consequence, a new means of evaluation known as statistical control has developed. Generally it involves establishing standards of performance deemed to represent efficient operation. When actual results are compared with these standards, failure to achieve expected levels of performance stand out and serve as a basis for managerial action. Because statistical control is only as good as the standards employed, management should be continuously revaluating and, if necessary, revising its control standards.

Statistical controls are employed in all phases of business and governmental activity. Quality control establishes ranges of acceptable product characteristics and determines compliance through periodic sampling. Standard cost systems set up norms against which actual costs are tested. Quotas are often employed to measure results in both sales and production. Reports detailing experience with the use of different materials or sources of supply are invaluable to the purchasing agent or procurement officer. Test scores and other quantitative personnel records have become an indispensable part of personnel management, both civilian and military. Governmental agencies must rely on statistical material in promulgating their rules and regulations. For example, the Board of Governors of the Federal Reserve System would change the legal reserve requirements of member banks only after a careful study of statistical compilations concerning the supply of money, wholesale and consumer prices, bank loans and discounts, interest rates, and many other important elements in the national economic picture. It is no exaggeration to say that the large-scale operations—both private and public—that characterize the modern era could not exist without statistical controls.

Statistics and Exploration

Statistical methods are very frequently employed in projects designed to expand the frontiers of human knowledge. Such projects may take the form of scientific investigation designed to throw more light on important topics, they may seek to determine the validity or worth of some idea or process, or they may attempt to provide market or production data for business.

The inquiry of the National Bureau of Economic Research into the problem of the business cycle is of the first type. Here, approximately one thousand individual time series have been subjected to intensive study in order to lean more about the nature and workings of business fluctuations. Each individual cycle is compared to the cycle of general business in an attempt to determine its relation to the over-all pattern and is examined for individual characteristics that may be of significance. As a result of the work of the National Bureau, much more is now known about business cycles, and several promising approaches to cycle forecasting have been developed.

The second type of exploratory investigation is exemplified by the study that preceded the public release of the Salk vaccine. After Dr. Salk had developed the vaccine it was necessary to determine its effectiveness in preventing polio and to uncover any undesirable side effects that might accompany its use. Consequently, the vaccine was administered to a group of children and the incidence of polio among that group compared with other groups that had not been inoculated. In this way both its effectiveness and safety were clearly demonstrated. Similar studies usually precede the release of all new drugs.

Finally, business undertakes many types of research designed to improve production methods, product characteristics, and marketing techniques. The reader has probably received telephone calls asking what radio or television program he has been listening to or viewing. In addition, many people have had the experience of being interviewed regarding the magazines they have read and the advertisements that caught their attention. In both instances data were being gathered to improve marketing methods. An interesting example of this general type of statistical exploration is found in the market research that precedes the introduction of a new product. Many characteristics of a product are not technically fixed and may be varied at the discretion of the manufacturer. Consequently, the market-wise firm will attempt to achieve a combination of these characteristics most suited to the desires of the consuming public. The nature of this combination is determined by interviewing a representative group of consumers. Sometimes they are asked to state their preferences; at other times, various samples of the product are presented to them for evaluation. If the survey has been carried out scientifically, the results when tabulated should provide management with a fairly clear picture of what the public wants and will buy.

The foregoing examples were merely designed to show how wide-spread the use of statistical methods in business and economics is. Many more pages could have been filled with similar illustrations. At this point, however, it is necessary only to make clear to the reader that statistics is not a dry, abstract, and unrealistic pursuit followed by a small group of highly trained mathematicians, but rather a vitally important part of the economic and business life of the community. The usefulness of statistics to the reader depends to a great part on his ability to use his imagination in applying this tool to his own particular situation.

CONDUCTING AN INVESTIGATION

A statistical investigation is undertaken in order to secure information that otherwise would not be available. It may serve either to supply data on the topic of interest or to confirm or refute propositions that have been advanced previously. For example, a study might, on the one hand, inquire into the wage structure in a certain city, and, on the other, seek to deny or sustain the assertion that wages in that city are above or below the national average. A statistical investigation usually includes the following seven steps.

1. Determination of the information wanted
2. Definition of terms
3. Securing the data from
   (a) secondary sources or
   (b) primary sources by either census or sampling
4. Assembly and tabulation of the results
5. Organization of the data into convenient form, usually into tables and graphs
6. Analysis
7. Presentation of summarized data and conclusions in a final report

The first four of these steps will be considered in the present chapter. The last three will be taken up at length later.

Defining and Limiting the Problem

The purpose of the project should always be spelled out as precisely as possible. This will ensure the collection of the proper information and spare the expense and trouble of handling irrelevant data. Usually the investigator is fully aware of the reasons why he has been called on to undertake a study. A firm's sales may be declining, waste in production could be on the increase, or the public might be reacting adversely to certain policies or conditions. All these are problems that may call for statistical investigation. If they can be clearly defined and limited, the job of the investigator is made much easier. At the same time a clear definition of purpose also minimizes the doubts and confusions that sometimes hinder the progress of an investigation.

For example, if an investigator is informed that there is considerable unrest over rental costs around Boston and sets out to analyze this situation by stating his purpose as "A Study of the Level of Rents in the Boston Area," his road will be fraught with difficulties. In the first place, he has not found out enough about the problem to know which specific rentals are to be considered, and as a result the term "rent" is not precisely defined. Typewriters, boats, automobiles, aircraft, and clothing, in addition to real estate, are frequently rented. Even if the term "rent" is restricted to real estate alone, this limitation will not be sufficiently precise, because the types of real estate subject to lease are many and diverse. Furthermore, the investigator does not know exactly whose rental problems are his concern. Consequently, the specification "Boston Area" in the statement of the problem is by no means precise. Does it encompass only the city of Boston itself or should neighboring towns be included? If so, how many and which ones? Here a case could be made for considering as part of the Boston area all places from which individuals commute into the city. This interpretation could lead to the inclusion of parts of New Hampshire, Rhode Island, and even Maine. In addition, this statement of purpose makes no mention of the period or point of time considered by the investigation. As a result of the vagueness, vast quantities of irrelevant data probably would be collected and processed at considerable expense. If, on the other hand, the investigator finds out that the reason for his employment is that civic leaders are concerned over possible serious overcharges for unfurnished apartments in South Boston, and he states his problem as "A Study of Rentals of Unfurnished Apartments in South Boston, during 1957," most of the aforementioned difficulties can be avoided. He will have determined his exact purpose and limited it properly by defining it in correct and accurate terms.

A precise definition of purpose can be obtained in several ways. First, it may be possible to describe the exact manner in which the data will be employed. If this is the situation, both the information wanted and the most convenient form of presentation can usually be specified. Frequently, when it is impossible to spell out the objective of an investigation in such detail, a satisfactory statement of purpose can be derived by formulating a series of questions for which answers are sought. Obviously, the questions should be as specific as possible.

Nevertheless, the exact purpose of an investigation often cannot be stated in detail beforehand, because sufficient information relating to the problem is not available. The investigation itself then must break new ground and provide the knowledge on which more precise definitions can be based. Such exploratory studies are frequently undertaken and are in some ways the most important type of statistical inquiries. Because under these circumstances it would be foolish to attempt a precision of definition greater than available information really permits, it is best to proceed from a broad general statement of purpose at the outset to narrower and more specific statements as the investigation progresses. Thus a process of exploration and redefinition would continue until enough is known to formulate a precise and valid statement of the objective.

Definition of Terms

Statistical observations deal with magnitudes of variables; therefore it is imperative that the variables themselves be carefully defined. This caution is necessary if meaningful comparisons of observations are to be made. When variables are not clearly defined, observed differences may result from the fact that essentially unlike items have been included in the study. Suppose, for example, that a series of businessmen is asked to state the amount of the capital of their firms, and that no specific definition of capital is included in the question. There are many concepts of capital. Among these are a stock of wealth, goods used in producing other goods, a sum of money, total assets, total tangible assets, total net worth, capital stock, and capital stock plus paid-in surplus. Because one respondent may report his net worth, another his total assets, and a third the figure for capital stock, it is apparent that the items will not be comparable and the study will be worthless.

Unfortunately, many terms, like capital, are defined in a number of different ways. The very important economic concept of income is another case in point. It has been variously defined as a flow of want satisfaction (Fisher), a flow of commodities and services (Hewett), factor payments (U.S. Department of Commerce), and a sum derived after many elaborate computations (Director of Internal Revenue). A moment's reflection should be sufficient to convince the reader that this multiplicity of definition is found with most terms employed in economics and business. And he really should not be surprised, because the same term is used by different persons in different ways to serve different purposes. For the statistician, however, the situation creates two problems. First, he must choose among the various definitions, or propound new definitions if no existing concept fits his needs. In so doing he should select or formulate a definition best suited to the purpose of the investigation. Second, great care must be taken to be sure that all observations relate to the variable as defined. Consequently, the definition selected must be clear not only to the investigator but to everyone supplying information.

Defining terms presents practical as well as conceptual problems. Suppose unemployment is conceived of as a status of involuntary idleness—in other words, not working but willing to accept employment. Although the fundamental idea is clear, many decisions, some quite arbitrary, will have to be made in determining who should be counted as unemployed and who should not. Is an individual who is working only part time but would like to work full time unemployed? If the answer to this question should be "yes," then ought a distinction be made between a worker who is employed only a few hours each week and one who is working almost full time? Apparently some line of division on the basis of hours worked will have to be drawn, and its exact location will probably be arbitrary. Similar problems are encountered in applying the "willing to accept employment" criterion. Obviously, many housewives and retired persons would be willing to work if the pay were sufficiently high. This fact, however, ought not lead to the inclusion, among the ranks of the unemployed, of society matrons who are now idle but would be willing to offer their services at $5000 per week or more. On the other hand, a woman who would work for $25 and cannot find a job certainly should be counted in this category. It is clear that a decision is needed regarding the wage an individual demands as a condition of accepting employment. A similar decision will also be required concerning the type of work a person will accept. Although an obstetrical nurse ought not to be considered voluntarily idle because she refuses employment as a strip-tease dancer or a coal miner, she might well be considered to be so if she were unwilling to do special-duty nursing. Again, a line must be drawn. Although it might be possible to formulate a list of rules that could be employed in marking off categories, it is apparent that in each instance the informed judgment of the investigator is required. It is essential that problems of this type not take him by surprise and be given ill-considered and haphazard treatment, but rather be anticipated, analyzed, and intelligently resolved.

Care must be taken that the definition when applied will produce the information really wanted. If the prices consumers pay for new automobiles are under investigation, figures quoted by dealers will usually represent a considerable overstatement. The explanations is that dealers customarily grant trade-in allowances in excess of the market value of the old car turned in. Consequently, the real price paid by the consumer is the quoted price less the amount of the "over-allowance" on the trade-in. A knowledge of the institutional patterns and arrangements surrounding the data under study, such as the pricing practices of automobile dealers, will help the investigator avoid many pitfalls that could render a study worthless.

At times, information will not be available in the exact form needed for the investigation. In such circumstances, data that are on hand or can be collected might be adapted or corrected so that they will serve the purposes of the study. Most price data, for example, are expressed in current dollars—

in other words, prices are enumerated during each period without any allowance for the changing purchasing power of the dollar. If the purpose of the investigation is to study the movement of relative prices, the influence of changing price levels is undesirable. This influence can, in large part, be removed by converting the data to a constant dollar basis, which means that prices are expressed in dollars of the same purchasing power. The technique involved will be explained in a later chapter. When data are adapted or corrected, the problem of definition is obviously more complex. Definitions must be developed both for the collection of the original data and the process of correction or adaptation.

Primary and Secondary Data and Sources

Once the purpose of the investigation has been clearly defined, the problem of collecting the data arises. Here two alternatives exist: either an original investigation may be undertaken or data gathered by someone else may be employed. Data originally collected in the process of the investigation are known as *primary data;* those collected by other persons are called *secondary data.* If secondary data are employed, the source from which the information is taken may itself have conducted the original investigation; in this case, it is known as a *primary source.* If on the other hand the source did not itself collect the data but took them from some other primary source, it is known as a *secondary source.* The same source may at once be both primary and secondary. For example, the *Federal Reserve Bulletin* is the primary source of the banking statistics collected by the Board of Governors of the Federal Reserve System, but it is also a secondary source because it reports data collected by many other agencies. A distinction is sometimes drawn between data collected from the records of a single firm and data that encompass many economic units. The former are called "internal data" and the latter "external data."

Whenever possible, secondary data are employed. For the small investigation, operating on a limited budget, an attempt to collect national statistics on important magnitudes such as wages, income, or prices would not only be financially impossible but also foolish. Large agencies, both governmental and private, do an excellent job of gathering and reporting information of this sort. Even if conducting an original investigation is within the financial scope of the project, undertaking it is unwise if satisfactory data are already available. Among the more important sources of economic and business data are the various units of governments and governmental agencies, research organizations such as the Committee for Economic Development or the National Bureau of Economic Research, business firms, trade associations, trade journals, business periodicals, and reports of individual research projects.

Great care, nevertheless, should be exercised in using secondary data.

The purpose of the investigation that led to the collection of the data in the first place and the definition of terms employed should be known in order to ensure applicability to the problem at hand. In addition, the nature and reputation of the collecting agency should be considered. Technical errors of collection, tabulation, or analysis in the primary investigation usually will carry over into the other studies in which these data are used. Bias in the primary investigation may also cast doubt on the value of many statistics, especially when interest groups such as trade associations, unions, or business firms issue reports that use statistical data to substantiate or support some particular position or claim. Not long after World War II the CIO published the famous Nathan Report, which purported to show that substantial wage increases could be granted without significant price changes. Shortly thereafter a similar study prepared by statisticians employed by groups of manufacturers reached a diametrically opposite conclusion. Obviously, at least one of these reports was subject to serious question. At times overly zealous protagonists of particular causes or interests even go so far as to create statistics out of thin air. False polls used for political purposes or fake cost studies designed to influence public bodies are by no means unknown. Needless to say, the investigator must have sufficient confidence in the integrity of his sources to use their data without fear of undue bias or misrepresentation. Although it is sometimes possible to make allowances or corrections for bias, difficult value judgments are required and the study is still of doubtful worth.

Collecting Primary Data

Undertaking an original investigation poses two important problems: who will be called on to supply information, and how will the information be elicited from those contacted. If the group of items under study is relatively small or if vast financial resources are available, a *census* may be conducted. Every member of the group is then approached to provide data. In technical language, the entire population of the universe is included in the study. When, for example, the prices charged for penicillin by retail druggists in a small- or medium-sized community are analyzed, it is feasible to approach every druggist. If, however, such a survey were extended to cover the entire United States, the census would become almost a practical impossibility. To attempt it would be both unwise and unnecessary.[1] A complete census is virtually never attained. Some items or individuals would almost inevitably elude the census taker. Because these items or individuals usually are those most difficult to contact—stores in remote areas would be examples—and as the cause of their inaccessibility may also be influential in determining their responses, the conclusions drawn from

---

[1] In other cases, such as quality-control analysis where the items are destroyed in the process of the study, the census would be physically impossible.

the census may be distorted by the omissions. On the other hand, results obtained from a carefully selected group of druggists could well present a superior picture of the pricing policies pursued by all the druggists in the country. The procedure of selecting a limited group to represent a larger group is known as *sampling*. This procedure will be discussed at some length in subsequent chapters. However, it will be useful to describe, at this point, sources of inaccuracy in sample results.

Sources of Inaccuracy in Sampling Results

The purpose of sampling is to secure measures that approximate the characteristics of the entire universe.[2] Consequently, it is appropriate to consider elements which may cause sampling results to diverge from the true values that they seek to represent. In the first place, any of the parties to an investigation—either interviewers, respondents, or analysts—may make mistakes. Items may be accidentally omitted in compiling totals, figures may be transposed or otherwise recorded inaccurately, and so forth. Although mistakes usually cannot be eliminated entirely, reasonable care and accuracy in the conduct of the investigator can reduce this element to a minimum.

A much more insidious source of distortion of sampling results is found in *bias*. Bias causes certain items to have a much greater chance of being included in the sample than others have. As a result, the sample will be unduly influenced by the favored items, and sample measures will usually be artificially high or low. Bias in honest investigations is the result of inadequate planning and improper methods of collecting data.

Frequently, public-opinion polls conducted by newspapers are highly inaccurate for two reasons, both of which reflect substantial bias. In the first place, most newspapers have some political associations or leanings. As a result, their readership often contains a disproportionately large number of individuals with similar views. Therefore, when a newspaper polls its readers, the universe actually sampled—the readers of the paper— is not likely to be typical of the general public, the universe about which conclusions are sought. Second, newspaper polls are usually conducted by printing a ballot or questionnaire in the paper itself, which the reader who wishes to participate in the poll clips and mails in. Consequently, the poll reflects only the views of those who are sufficiently aroused to take this affirmative action. There is good reason to believe that the opinions of such a group may be significantly different from those of the population as a whole. For example, if an increase in real estate taxes were proposed, property owners would be seriously concerned and would be much more likely to respond to a poll on the issue. An accurate, unbiased survey of public opinion requires much more careful planning and execution than

[2] The terms "population" and "universe" refer to all the items in the group under study.

does the type of poll just described. Unfortunately, at times unscrupulous individuals deliberately introduce bias into statistical investigations so that the results of the investigation will bear out some preconceived conclusion. There are many sources of bias, several of which will be discussed in subsequent sections of this chapter. Because mistakes and bias are not inherent in the sampling process itself, they are often referred to as *non-sampling errors*.

On the other hand, sample results may differ from the true characteristics of the universe because of chance. If, for example, a universe is composed of half red and half black balls, a sample of 4 items might take the 16 possible forms shown below. The chances are 6 of 16 that the sample will correctly describe the universe by including an equal number of red and black balls. On the average, in 10 of 16 instances it will be incorrect, although in 8 of these instances it will err only by 1. The errors of the

Four black	Three black One red	Two red Two black	Three red One black	Four red
1	4	6	4	1
B B B B	R B B B	B B R R	B R R R	R R R R
	B R B B	B R R B	R B R R	
	B B R B	R B B R	R R B R	
	B B B R	R R B B	R R R B	
		R B R B		
		B R B R		

samples in these 10 instances are the result of chance selection alone. They are called the *random error of sampling*. The accuracy of sampling results and the inferences that can be drawn from them will be discussed at length in subsequent chapters. At this point it is sufficient to indicate that sampling errors are less if the universe itself is not widely dispersed and that random-sampling errors decline as the square root of the size of the sample increases. Thus sampling accuracy is doubled if the size of the sample is increased fourfold. The reasoning underlying these statements regarding the characteristics of random samples will be developed in detail in a later chapter.

Techniques of Securing Information

Having considered the selection of the items that will be included in the study, we can now focus attention on obtaining the specific information required. In collecting primary data either a direct or indirect approach may be taken. The direct approach requires that the documents or other tangible evidences of the data in question be examined by the investigator. In studying profits he would have to tabulate his information directly from the accounting records of the firms included, whereas an inquiry into the use of safety devices in industry would necessitate a physical check of the machines in the plants surveyed. When this direct approach is applied to behavior, the data gatherers must actually observe the individuals in the population or sample performing the act in question. On the other hand, the indirect approach merely requires that individuals possessing information concerning conditions, results, or behavior be questioned. Obviously, the direct approach has many advantages over the indirect. Conditions or behavior are objective facts, but responses to questions contain many subjective elements. Respondents may be unable to answer questions either because they do not understand them or because they do not have the information clearly in mind. They may be unwilling to supply correct information because of pride, fear, jealousy, and so forth. Consequently, what people do is usually much more significant than what they say. Nevertheless, direct examination is frequently quite expensive and may not permit the application of the sampling procedures desired. In addition, skill and care in interrogation can often greatly reduce the error or bias introduced by subjective factors.

Interviews or Questionnaires. Once it has been decided to secure the data by questioning, it is necessary to determine the way in which the questions will be asked. Either a printed form known as a *questionnaire* may be sent out in the hope that the recipients will fill it out and return it, or trained personnel may conduct interviews and record the information on forms known as *schedules*. An excellent questionnaire that reflects adherence to most of the principles detailed below is found in Figure 1-1.

The interview technique is definitely superior. It permits the investigator to control the selection of individuals from whom replies are received and makes the time of collection of the data definite. Usually a person will not refuse to answer questions directly put to him, whereas he often will ignore a questionnaire. Consequently, the returns received when a questionnaire is employed may contain a considerable bias that would not be present when interviews are used. This bias will result from the fact that individuals who are most intensely interested in the question are more likely to respond. The interviewer frequently can ask more questions and thus gather more data than would be possible with questionnaires. In addition, he can often secure answers to the difficult or offensive questions that would be left unanswered on a questionnaire. Finally, if the interviewer is skilled, he can evaluate replies for accuracy or bias, elicit information that otherwise would not be forthcoming, and perhaps obtain valuable information not included in the original schedule of questions.

Although the interview technique obviously is much more costly, results are so superior that its use is widespread. Most scientific public-opinion polling and market research rely quite heavily on interviewing. Although questionnaires are still employed frequently, results are suspect unless there is good reason to believe that the questions were adequate and

FIGURE 1–1.   *Questionnaire*

MERRILL LYNCH, PIERCE, FENNER & SMITH INC.
M. I. P. Research Department

January 20, 1960

WE NEED YOUR HELP IN IMPROVING THE M. I. P.

Six years ago this month we began selling the Monthly Investment Plan. Since then the plan has had minor changes but now after a half dozen years of operation we are going to make major changes to it.

Recently we have simplified the purchase order form and arranged for M. I. P. investors to receive reports from our Research Department on the companies whose stocks they own.

We would like to know what other changes you can suggest that would improve the Monthly Investment Plan from your standpoint. And we would also like to know more about you as an investor. Will you be kind enough to complete this questionnaire and drop it in the mail to us?

We appreciate your co-operation and hope that the results of this survey will enable us to give you better investment service in the future.

Sincerely yours,

M. I. P. Research Department

1. Which one of these three investment objectives is most important to you as a stockholder? Please check only one.
   ☐ Safety of capital   ☐ Liberal dividends   ☐ Price appreciation

2. Do you have a regular investment account in addition to your Monthly Investment Plan?
   ☐ Yes   No ☐

3. How long have you had your M. I. P.? ☐ less than 1 yr. ☐ 1-2 yrs. ☐ 2-4 yrs. ☐ 4-6 yrs.

4. Your sex: ☐ Male   ☐ Female

5. Your age: ☐ 21 to 30   ☐ 31 to 40   ☐ 41 to 50   ☐ 51 to 60   ☐ Over 60

6. Your approximate annual income:
   ☐ Under $4,000   ☐ $7,000-$10,000   ☐ $20,000-$50,000
   ☐ $4,000-$7,000   ☐ $10,000-$20,000   ☐ Over $50,000

7. Your occupation:
   ☐ Salaried employee   ☐ Proprietor of business   ☐ Retired
   ☐ Professional person   ☐ Housewife   ☐ Other

8. Your education:
   ☐ No formal schooling   ☐ Grammar School   ☐ High School   ☐ College

9. Did you own stock before you began your Monthly Investment Plan?   ☐ Yes   ☐ No

10. If you answered yes to the above question, how did you acquire this stock?
    ☐ Gift or inheritance   ☐ Investment Club
    ☐ Bought through broker   ☐ Employee stock purchase plan

11. How did you first hear of the M. I. P.?
    ☐ New York Stock Exchange
    ☐ Friend
    ☐ Broker
    ☐ Advertisement
    ☐ Other_____

12. What feature of the M. I. P. interests you most?
    ☐ Protection against inflation
    ☐ Dollar cost averaging
    ☐ Investing by mail
    ☐ Regular, scheduled savings
    ☐ Other_____

13. What prompted you to choose the stock you are buying through M. I. P.?_____

_____

14. In the past year has your account executive contacted you:
    In person ☐ Yes   ☐ No;
    By phone   ☐ Yes   ☐ No;
    By letter ☐ Yes   ☐ No?

15. Do you feel you are getting sufficient service from us? ☐ Yes ☐ No

16. If not what additional services would you like to have?_____

_____

_____

_____

_____

17. Do you have difficulty remembering when your next payment is due? ☐ Yes ☐ No. If not
    by what method do you remember?_____

_____

_____

18. What particular additional features would you like to have added to the M. I. P.?_____

_____

19. Are corporate income taxes paid before, at the same time or after corporate bond interest is
    paid? ☐ Before ☐ At the same time ☐ After ☐ Don't know

20. Common stocks are always purchased through stock exchanges? ☐ Yes ☐ No ☐ Don't know

SOURCE: Merril Lynch, Pierce, Fenner & Smith, Inc. Reprinted by permission.

the distribution of returns unbiased. One needs only to compare the forecasts of newspaper-conducted questionnaire polls with actual election results to appreciate this point. A partially, but by no means entirely, satisfactory way of avoiding the high cost of interviewing is found in the use of telephone interviews. This method contains some of the personal contact inherent to the interview and is sufficient if the questions are few and simple. Surveys designed to determine the audience of radio or television shows are often conducted in this manner.

Proper Questioning Procedure. Some differences in questioning procedure are encountered when interviews rather than questionnaires are employed. The differences center around the ability of the interviewer to rephrase or explain questions that the respondent does not clearly understand. Nevertheless, the same general principles of good questioning technique apply in both situations.

In the first place, the questions should be directed to individuals who are most likely to be in possession of the information desired. If, for example, data concerning a company's borrowing plans for the next few months are sought, the person interviewed or to whom the questionnaire is sent should be a financial officer of the company—usually the comptroller or treasurer—not a district office credit manager. All too frequently if the

17

wrong person is questioned he will not, for reasons of pride, admit to the error, but rather will attempt to answer. Such responses will ordinarily be an odd combination of a little knowledge, a good portion of rumor, and a great deal of fancy. Any significant number of such responses will render the entire study worthless.

Second, the questions should make known exactly what information is wanted. The respondent should understand all the words in the questions as well as their over-all meaning. Unless the person being interrogated is technically trained, technical terms should be avoided. Words, such as "capital" or "income," that have different meanings for different people should not be used unless a clear definition is included in the question. Questions preferably should be kept short and concise, because long and involved sentences reduce both the ability and desire of the respondent to answer. Usually such questions can be broken up into a number of shorter and simpler inquiries.

Third, the questions should be such that the respondents *can* answer, and answer as accurately as needed. It would be foolish, for example, to ask the average motorist detailed questions regarding the performance of his car. Typically, he does not check such things as mileage per gallon at various speeds, acceleration in feet per second, or compression ratios. By the same token, the typical housewife probably could not remember where she made all of her purchases during the past month, and she usually will not have computed the average number of cubic feet of gas used for cooking each week during the past year. Questions of this sort the respondent ordinarily cannot answer accurately, if at all, even though he possesses the basic information or might have it available. When information of this type is needed, simple questions, easily answered, from which the desired data can be deduced or inferred should be formulated. For example, gas consumption while cooking might be estimated from the answers to such questions as "How long do you spend cooking breakfast?" and "How often do you bake?"

Finally, the questions should be such that the respondent *will* answer, and answer correctly. Some types of questions make businessmen feel that they are under investigation or that the answers may be used against them at some future time. Such questions are not likely to be answered truthfully, if at all, because of this fear. Pride frequently can result in unwanted distortions. For example, many persons, when asked about their incomes, job responsibilities, or social status, are likely to exaggerate. Embarrassment often leads to erroneous results. For this reason, investigators conducting surveys concerning sexual behavior not only have difficulty obtaining responses but also have cause to believe that many statements of virtuous conduct are motivated by the respondent's being ashamed to reply truthfully. On the other hand, such studies are also plagued by those who are too willing to supply lurid accounts of erotic conquests. Prejudice also will frequently reduce the willingness of individuals to supply correct information. People often, either consciously or unconsciously, distort their statements regarding persons, races, religions, or ethnic groups that they do not like. Although it is impossible to avoid emotional responses entirely, the investigator should formulate his questions and questioning technique in such a way that he lessens this influence. Words such as "un-American," "Fascistic," and "Socialistic," which in addition to being vague are likely to arouse an emotional response, should, if possible, be avoided. Assurances that the information will remain entirely confidential or that the respondents may answer anonymously will help overcome fear and embarrassment. Indirect questioning may reduce the bias resulting from prejudice or pride. Experience and conscientious effort on the part of the investigator can go a long way toward minimizing these influences.

Sometimes a respondent will fail to reply completely or accurately because of a lack of interest. This difficulty can be dealt with in several ways. First, the series of questions should be kept as short as possible, to reduce the fatigue element. In addition, it may be possible to make the questions stimulating through the use of clever illustrations or provocative statements. Finally, incentives such as money, pens, or lighters may be offered for replies or may accompany a questionnaire. These devices are often successful in overcoming apathy, but if care is not taken, numerous biases may result. In some instances the respondent may feel obligated to give a certain answer because he is receiving compensation.

Forms of Questions

Although there are many different ways in which types of questions may be classified, the following is felt to be most useful for the beginning student. Observe that this classification deals only with the mechanical way in which the question is asked, not with the subject matter or content sought.

Multiple-Choice Question. A multiple-choice question suggests several answers among which the respondent may choose. For example:

How do you travel to work?
        ( ) Private auto
        ( ) Bus, subway, or streetcar
        ( ) Cab
        ( ) Train
        ( ) Walk
        ( ) Other   ....

This type of question is excellent if most of the possible answers are both known and few in number. Questions eleven and twelve in Figure 1-1 are of this type because all the alternatives are both known and can be precisely defined. The "other" category usually is required to take care of infrequently encountered answers. However, when the possible answers are numerous, a limited list—even if accompanied by an "other" category—may elicit a response different from that which otherwise would be forthcoming. The multiple-choice question leads or suggests. It may either cause the respondent to organize his thoughts on the basis of correct alternatives, thus improving his answer, or, by posing false alternatives, induce him to reply incorrectly. Hence the use of multiple-choice questions is indicated only when the investigator is confident of the existence of a limited group of important alternatives, it should be avoided when there are many possible responses of relatively equal significance. Multiple-choice questions are easily tabulated as long as "other" responses are not too frequent.

"Yes or No" Questions. The "yes or no" questions pose a simple alternative to the respondent. Although the choice usually takes the "yes or no" form, it is not uncommon to find such questions stated as "for or against," "right or wrong," or "true or false." This is an excellent technique of interrogation if applied to situations where a clear-cut alternative exists. The question "Did you vote in the 1956 Presidential election?" can have only a "yes" or a "no" answer because either the respondent voted or he did not. Similarly, questions such as "Do you own a car?" or "Are you employed in Boston?" can be answered only with a "yes" or a "no." However, when the alternative is not clear-cut, the "yes or no" type question should be avoided. A question such as "Are you in favor of the policies of the Republican party?" usually cannot be answered with a single reply. The Republican party has many policies, and only the most radical partisan would favor or oppose them all. A typical citizen would endorse some, have no opinion on many, and reject others. The "yes or no" question in this situation compels him to compress a variety of opinions into a single alternative that may, in reality, not exist.

Sometimes a respondent cannot give a single "yes" or "no" answer either because he has not as yet made up his mind or because he lacks information on the topic. The question "Do you favor increased dividend exclusions in computing Federal Personal Income Tax Liability?" might create both situations. Because the issues are technical, the respondent may be uniformed regarding them. On the other hand, even though he may be aware of the points of controversy he may not as yet have arrived at a conclusion. In such instances a "do not know" or "undecided" answer should be possible.

The Specific-Information Question. The specific-information type of question calls for a specific item of information. "How old are you?," "How many children have you?," and "What kind of a car do you own?" are examples. These questions are simple and direct and are well adapted to securing information of this type. Care should be taken to use this type of question only where the respondent can answer and will answer correctly. As was pointed out before, questions concerning piston displacement or gear ratios in the family car will probably produce only a blank stare or a wild guess, whereas an interrogation regarding the size of income or job status may carry the person interviewed into the realms of egotistic fancy.

The Open Question. The open question does not pose alternatives or request specific information. "What action should be taken to stabilize the economy?" is a question of this type. It leaves the respondent free to make whatever reply he chooses. In many ways this fact makes the open question superior to the other types, because the danger of being overly restrictive, suggesting answers, posing false alternatives, and introducing some biases is absent. The open question also may serve to interest the respondent in the interview itself, especially if he is asked his opinion at the outset. The great weakness of the open question lies in difficulty of tabulation. Because no restriction is placed on the variety of answers, many will often be forthcoming. Thus it is necessary to establish numerous classifications of answers and to define the boundaries of each. Often it is very difficult to decide in which category a given reply should be enumerated. Classifying replies not only increases the labor involved but frequently leads to improper tabulation.

Tabulation

After the data have been collected they must then be tabulated. Tabulation proceeds according to classifications that have been established in advance and that naturally follow from the nature of the questions. Thus the answers to "yes or no" questions will be tabulated into "yes" and "no" categories. With multiple-choice questions a classification is established for each possible answer. When a person is asked the make of his automobile, each of the various brands (Ford, Chevrolet, and the like) becomes a category. With the open question, as was noted above, serious problems of classification may arise. Similar problems appear with multiple-choice questions when too many items fall into the "other" category. If this difficulty arises, it is evident that the classification is not sufficiently comprehensive or that the question itself was unsatisfactory.

At times data are cross-classified—in other words, classified on the basis of the answers to two or more questions. For example, if a questionnaire asked both your age and the make of your car, categories such as men between 30 and 35 owning Fords could be employed.

The actual job of tabulation can be performed manually or by machines. The choice will depend on the amount of the data and the number of sortings required. A large mass of data that will be cross-classified in detail requires many sortings and is best handled by mechanical means. Smaller studies where the need for elaborate cross classification is absent can easily be tabulated manually.

Once the problem and the terms have been defined, the data collected, and the results tabulated, the investigator faces the challenging tasks of analysis and interpretation. Our attention will now be directed to these important topics.

SUGGESTED READINGS

Hanson, K. O. *Managerial Statistics*. Englewood Cliffs, N.J.: Prentice-Hall, Inc., 1955, chaps. 1, 2, and 3.

Mills, F. G. *Introduction to Statistics*. New York: Holt, Rinehart and Winston, Inc., 1956, chap. 16.

Neiswanger, W. A. *Elementary Statistical Methods* (rev. ed.). New York: The Macmillan Company, 1956, chaps. 1, 3, and 4.

Riggleman, J. R., and I. N. Frisbee. *Business Statistics* (3rd ed.). New York: McGraw-Hill Book Company, Inc., 1951, chaps. 1, 2, 3, and 4.

QUESTIONS

1. Why are statistical controls needed by the management of a modern business firm?
2. Of what importance to the department store executive is a forecast of the volume of Christmas business?
3. Why would an executive be interested in correctly anticipating an oncoming depression?
4. Suggest three topics for statistical investigations that you feel would add to our knowledge of the nature of the economic system.
5. Suggest three topics for statistical investigations that would enhance a firm's knowledge of the market in which it sells.
6. For what reasons are statistical studies made concerning the effects of new drugs on experimental groups of patients?
7. As an advisor to the President of the United States, what statistical information would you desire in formulating a recommendation for or against increased public spending?
8. Statistics is said to be a tool of the economist and businessman. What is meant by this statement?
9. Evaluate the following statements. Do you feel they are true, false, or a combination of truth and falsehood?

   (a) Statistical investigations make a unique contribution to human knowledge. Because the information collected is expressed in quantitative form, the element of human judgment, always a source of weakness in scientific inquiries, has been removed; so too have the biases and prejudices that distort the way in which we report observed phenomena. Although verbal accounts must necessarily reflect the subjective opinions of the investigator, statistical compilations present objective facts.

(b) Although the techniques of statistical analysis to some may seem sterile and lacking in human understanding, by facilitating the study of the results of the actions of masses of human beings they make possible a truer and deeper insight into man's basic nature.

(c) Before introducing a new product, most firms attempt to determine the tastes and preferences of the consuming public with respect to the type of goods under consideration. Once they have done so, the product-development division adapts the new item to the public's specifications. Usually this work is followed by actually testing the product on a limited group of consumers. If the tests indicate that the product will be well received, the firm can proceed with nation-wide distribution, confident that the product will be successful.

(d) By carefully analyzing the behavior of three or four individuals, firms may obtain conclusions valid for large groups. The conclusions will be valid, however, only if the utmost care and precision are taken at every step and if erratic actions are discounted.

(e) Should the prospects for the next few months seem to indicate the start of a business recession, every firm should reappraise its own forecasts. Many will have to expect their own sales and profits to fall as the level of business in general falls. Nevertheless, some favorably situated industries and firms can still anticipate sales advances and handsome profits.

10. Point out the errors in the following statement.

Statistics cannot be employed in the preparation of meaningful forecasts because all quantitative data must necessarily be drawn from past happenings. At the same time, this very factor enhances the usefulness of statistical data for purposes of control and consequently makes statistics an invaluable tool of management. When used properly, statistical controls will always pinpoint the sources of difficulty in a manufacturing process, sales program, or personnel policy. Nevertheless, when research programs are being evaluated, statistics can be of little assistance, because past results usually are unavailable in the area under study.

11. Evaluate the following definitions of purposes for statistical investigations:

(a) To determine the average money receipts of small farmers (those tilling between 5 and 25 acres) in Arkansas during 1958.

(b) To evaluate the influence of taxation on production incentives.

(c) To determine average depreciation charges in the chemical industry during World War II.

12. When may the unit "dollar" be employed without further definition in a statistical investigation?

13. Which of the following terms would require substantial definition if used in a statistical inquiry?
    (a) Gross national product
    (b) Rent
    (c) Short-term capital gain
    (d) Businessman
    (e) Taxpayer
    (f) Obstetrician
14. Assume that you are conducting a statistical investigation and that you employ the following data:
    (a) Department of Commerce estimates of personal income taken from the *Federal Reserve Bulletin*
    (b) Tabulations from schedules used in interviews that you yourself conducted
    (c) Corporate financial statements that were supplied by the companies themselves
    (d) Corporate financial data found in *Moody's Manual of Industrials*
    Which of the above are primary data and which would be classified as secondary data? Which of the secondary data were taken from primary sources and which from secondary sources?
15. How does a census differ from a sample?
16. Why may a census prove unsatisfactory?
17. Under what conditions may a questionnaire prove as satisfactory as a personal interview?
18. Why are personal interviews usually preferred to questionnaires?
19. Comment on the following questions that have been found on questionnaires or asked in interviews directed to average citizens.
    (a) Do you believe McCarthyism is un-American?
    (b) What make and model of car do you own?
    (c) Are you employed in a supervisory capacity?
    (d) Do you prefer Product A or Product B?
    (e) Have you ever falsified information on your income tax return?
    (f) Will the introduction of turbines in motor vehicles reduce gasoline consumption in motor vehicles?
    (g) How much did you spend on clothing last year?
20. A survey presumably designed to discover workers' attitudes asked the following question:

    Do you feel that your wages are   Excellent   ☐
                                         Good   ☐
                                         Only Fair   ☐

    When a majority of workers elected the third option, a publication reported that most workers felt that they were receiving fair wages. Comment on both the question and the conclusion drawn.
21. The following questions appeared in a questionnaire mailed to the

subscribers to *Consumer Reports*.[3] Classify each question for type (multiple choice, "yes or no," and so on). Evaluate each question on the assumption that typical respondents will be middle-income working people.[4]

(a) What is the year and make of your car? (If you have more than one, please list only your latest model.)

               Year   Make

(b) All things considered, do you feel that dealer service and parts supply for the car you have listed are satisfactory?

               Yes   No

(c) When you are ready to replace the car you have listed do you plan to buy the same make again?

        Yes   No   Don't know

(d) Please check which of the following have given you significant trouble or required major repairs since you bought the car listed above:

Automatic transmission   Radiator
Body noises   Rain leaks
Brake overhaul   Ring job
Carburetor   Valve and carbon job
Engine bearings   Wheel alignment
Front-end rebushing   None
Other major repairs (list)..............................

(e) On your next car, suppose all of the following were extra-cost optional equipment. Which would you want to purchase?

Power steering   Power seating
Power brakes   Power windows
Radio   Automatic transmission
Heater   White-wall tires
Air conditioner   Windshield washer
Seat belts   Fuel-injection system
Overdrive   Air suspension

(f) If your present car is a sedan or hardtop, do you think you will seriously consider replacing it (for your next car) with a station wagon instead of with another sedan or hardtop?

    Yes   No   Don't know   Have station wagon now

(g) If you were going to have two cars, which combination of the following would you be most likely to choose? (Check 2.)

Sedan   Small foreign-type sedan

[3] From 1957 Questionnaire. By permission of Consumers Union.

[4] In the actual survey, 35 percent of those responding checked "professional or related services" as the principal field of employment of the head of the household.

Station wagon	Small foreign-type
Hardtop coupe	station wagon
Convertible	Other
Sports car	Don't know

22. Of the procedures listed below, which would provide the best sample for determining the distribution of income within a community?
    (a) Mailing a questionnaire to every tenth person listed in the telephone directory
    (b) Recording the adjusted gross income from every tenth return filed with the Bureau of Internal Revenue office in the community
    (c) Interviewing every tenth person passing a given street corner on a given day
    (d) Calling at every tenth house on every tenth street listed in the city directory

23. Which one of the following questions is least likely to elicit a meaningful and correct answer?
    (a) Are you in favor of sales taxation?
    (b) Is space travel desirable and feasible?
    (c) Are the provisions currently being made for national defense adequate?
    (d) Are you emotionally mature?
    (e) Are you in favor of civil rights?

24. Assume that you are attempting to predict business-investment expenditures for the next 3 months. Which of the sources of information enumerated below would you consider most reliable? Which would be least satisfactory?
    (a) Statements made by management during negotiations with labor unions
    (b) Construction contracts currently in effect but not yet complete
    (c) Advertisements in the press
    (d) Projections in financial reports

25. Are the following statements true, false, or a combination of truth and falsehood?
    (a) Bias is not undesirable if it contributes to the reporting of results that the investigator has anticipated.
    (b) Inaccurate responses to questionnaires create no serious problems for the investigator as long as they result from inability to reply correctly rather than from bias.
    (c) Interviews introduce more bias than does the use of questionnaires.
    (d) "True or false" or "yes or no" questions should not be used on questionnaires unless only one of the two answers is possible.
    (e) Errors in tabulation are usually of little significance, because they tend to cancel out.
    (f) Sampling is superior to the census as a technique of collecting data.

(g) Open questions are more difficult than most other types to tabulate.

(h) The random errors of sampling are the result of chance and are therefore unimportant.

26. Which of the sources of error listed below will almost certainly carry through the entire process of the collection and analysis of data and consequently distort the conclusions obtained?

(a) Inability of respondents to answer questions

(b) Selective bias influencing the make-up of the group responding to a questionnaire

(c) Errors in tabulating individual responses

(d) Improper definition of the purpose of the investigation

(e) Use of ambiguous terms without precise definitions

(f) Failure to tabulate several items

(g) Inclusion of the same item in the sample more than once

27. Of the purposes below, indicate which cannot be achieved by means of the collection of primary data.

(a) The determination of the wage pattern in Detroit in 1959

(b) A forecast of the styling of automobiles in 1975

(c) Testing the efficiency of a production-control system

(d) Determining the political party most capable of governing

(e) Estimating income tax collections in 1976

28. Special projects. Prepare (1) a statement of purpose, (2) a definition of terms, (3) a sampling plan, (4) a questionnaire or schedule, and (5) a tabulation system for a statistical investigation covering any of the following topics:

(a) The average income of students at your university holding part-time jobs

(b) The amount of unemployment in your community

(c) The job opportunities for graduates of your university

(d) The prospective sales of a new product yet to be introduced

CHAPTER TWO

Tables
and Charts

Because statistical data are usually presented in the form of tables and charts, the ability to prepare good tables and charts is extremely valuable. This fact has led to the publication of a great deal of material concerning the proper techniques and rules that should be followed in their preparation. Unfortunately, however, excessive preoccupation with details of table and chart construction often leads to poor results. All too frequently readers become lost in a forest of regulations and completely neglect certain basic principles with which most of them are already familiar. The method of this chapter will be to present certain very basic rules, plus many examples. The few rules should be sufficient to indicate proper procedures, and the many examples should emphasize the fact that, especially regarding charts, adherence to the rules must be mixed with an ample supply of imagination if really outstanding results are to be obtained.

GENERAL RULES

The two basic principles of successful chart and table construction are (1) to present data in as clear a manner as possible, and (2) to present data as attractively as possible.

Although it is true that the need for clarity applies more directly to tabular presentation and that attractiveness is most essential for graphic presentation, both must be considered in every instance of table or chart creation. Because these principles state general objectives, they must be elaborated by specific rules. Even though the idea of presenting data in as clear a manner as possible may seem to be self-evident, the following rules should be observed in order to ensure clarity.

1. Every chart or table must have unity of subject matter—that is, contain one unified set of relations.

2. Every chart or table must have a title. The title should tell the casual reader what data are included—specifically answering the questions "what?" "when?" "where?" and "how?"

3. Every chart or table must have a statement concerning the source of information.

4. Every chart or table must have footnotes and/or references explaining anything that is not self-evident.

5. The headings for both the vertical and horizontal columns in a table must be clearly worded.

6. The axis, lines, bars, and the like in a chart or graph must be properly labeled.

Concerning the second principle—presenting data as attractively as possible—it must be admitted that the ability to present information in an eye-pleasing manner varies with a person's artistic talent and imagination.

TABLES

A table consists of data presented in labeled columns. After numerical items are collected they must be edited, checked, sorted, and compiled. When these operations have been completed, the problem becomes one of placing the figures on paper in such a manner that they can be more easily handled and understood. A good table achieves this end.

Table 2-1 is an example of a simple table. In this example, all the individual necessary parts have been labeled. If all these parts are included in the construction of a table, the information presented in its body should be clear. A reader can then use the data more intelligently and efficiently.

Tables can be divided into groups according to the number of breakdowns employed. The simplest form of table, involving only two classifications, is illustrated by Table 2-2. Here petroleum production is classified according to year and country.

A slightly more complicated situation is presented in Table 2-3, where data are classified in three ways, according to year, sex, and type of personnel. In Table 2-4, which is just a little more complicated than Table 2-3, data are classified according to an amount of money, price or mortgage debt, and year.

The most complicated example is presented in Table 2-5. Here data are broken down into many classifications, which reveal the results of 14 separate studies concerning the relation of smoking and lung cancer.

All these tables have certain things in common. Each is fully explained in itself. Some of the more complicated tables need more explanation; nevertheless, all of them are clear as they stand, without supporting

Table 2-1. PARTS OF A TABLE
(*Fictitious Data*)
National Sales
of   ←——Major Title
Underground Aircraft Company—1964*

Subtitle——→ JET AND ION DRIVE AIRCRAFT BY MONTHS

		Millions of dollars		←— Designation of Units
Column Headings ——→		*Jets*	*Ion drive*	*Total*
	January	25	36	61
	February	38	46	84
	March	12	20	32
	April	10	18	28
	May	18	26	44
	June	15	23	38
Stub Column ——→	July	16	24	40
	August	26	34	60
	September	37	45	82
	October	40	48	88
	November	42	50	92
	December	36	44	80
	Totals	315	414	729

Footnote——→ * Includes Alaskan sales.
Reference to Source——→ SOURCE: Annual Reports of the Company.

material. The units employed are either self-evident because of their simplicity or are carefully defined. In every case the source of the data is indicated in a footnote or specified in accompanying material. Totals are provided whenever they are needed. All of these tables have titles and column headings that are definite and clear. Notice also that these tables are drawn from many different sources, a fact that suggests the common use of this method of presentation.

Table 2-2.   ESTIMATED FREE-WORLD PETROLEUM PRODUCTION
(Illustration)

| | Million barrels per day | | | | |
	1950	1955	1960	1965	1975
United States*	5.91	7.50	9.00	10.00	11.50
Canada	0.08	0.35	0.70	1.10	2.00
Venezuela	1.50	2.15	3.00	3.50	5.00
Other countries	0.78	1.10	1.60	2.40	4.50
Subtotal	8.27	11.10	14.30	17.00	23.00
Middle East	1.76	3.24	5.00	9.00	24.50
Total	10.03	14.34	19.30	26.00	47.50

* Including Natural Gas Liquids for the United States.

SOURCE: Petroleum Investment Forum for Insurance Company Executives, The Chase Manhattan Bank, p. 9.

Table 2-3.   LIFE INSURANCE PERSONNEL IN THE UNITED STATES
(Illustration)

	Home office	Agency cashiers and clerks	Agency managers and assistants	Full-time agents	Total personnel
1945					
Men	26,700	3,200	21,900	121,600	173,400
Women	53,800	26,800	100	7,100	87,800
Total	80,500	30,000	22,000	128,700	261,200
1954					
Men	41,900	4,100	35,400	176,500	257,900
Women	83,800	36,900	400	5,300	126,400
Total	125,700	41,000	35,800	181,800	384,300
1955					
Men	44,000	4,400	38,000	184,100	270,500
Women	83,800	38,000	500	5,500	127,800
Total	127,800	42,400	38,500	189,600	398,300

SOURCES: Institute of Life Insurance and Life Insurance Agency Management Association.

A word of caution must be mentioned concerning tables in which percentages are presented, as is true of Table 2-6. Such tables present a part-to-total relation, and the sum of the parts cannot be more than 100 percent. This table illustrates two additional points. First, even though the table violates a rule held sacred by many writers—namely, that the number of horizontal divisions should not exceed the number of vertical

Table 2-4. HOUSE PURCHASES CLASSIFIED BY PRICE AND MORTGAGE DEBT,
1947–1949 AND 1954–1956*
(Illustration)

PERCENTAGE DISTRIBUTION OF NEW AND EXISTING NONFARM
HOUSES PURCHASED

	Price		Mortgage debt	
	1954–1956	1947–1949	1954–1956	1947–1949
Zero			16	22
$1 through $4,999	14	34	17	36
$5,000 through $7,499	12	19	20	22
$7,500 through $9,999	14	18	18	10
$10,000 through $14,999	35	18	24	7
$15,000 and over	25	9	5	(†)
Not ascertained	(‡)	2	(‡)	3
All cases	100	100	100	100
Median§	$11,390	$6,970	$7,920	$5,070

* Figures are based on averages of estimates of new and existing house prices and mortgage debt in 1947–1949 and 1954–1956. Debt is mortgage debt outstanding at time of interview (early in the year following year of purchase).
† No cases reported or less than one half of 1 percent.
‡ Amount assigned, not determined in interview.
§ Interpolated from bracket amounts.
SOURCE: 1957 Survey of Consumer Finances, *Federal Reserve Bulletin*, June 1957, p. 630.

divisions—a deviation from the rule as in this instance is not necessarily undesirable. Although in most instances it is true that a table such as this would be better presented if the market classifications were listed on the side and the 1950–1955 average and 1956 figures were recorded at the top, it can easily be seen that here there is good reason for violating the rule. The pictures representing the market classification make the table much more attractive and can be presented more satisfactorily horizontally than vertically. This table also clearly indicates that the possibility of achieving an attractive appearance is not restricted to charts and graphs.

Table 2-5. SUMMARY OF FINDINGS REPORTED BY FOURTEEN RETROSPECTIVE CLINICAL STUDIES ON THE ASSOCIATION OF SMOKING AND LUNG CANCER

(Illustration)

| Author | Country | Date | Number of cases | | Percentage who were nonsmokers among those | | Percentage who were heavy smokers among those | | Relative risk of lung cancer* | |
| 1 | 2 | 3 | With lung cancer | Without lung cancer | With lung cancer | Without lung cancer | With lung cancer | Without lung cancer | All smokers | Heavy smokers |
			4	5	6	7	8	9	10	11
Muller	Ger.	1939	86	86	3.5	16.3	50.0	10.5	5.4	22.2
Schairer & Schoniger	Ger.	1943	93	270	3.2	15.9	31.2	9.3	5.7	16.7
Wassink	Neth.	1948	136	100	5.0	19.0	55	19	4.5	11.0
Schrek et al	U.S.	1950	82	522	14.6	23.9	18.3	9.2	1.8	3.3
Mills & Porter	U.S.	1950	444	430	7.2	30.4			5.6	
Wynder & Graham	U.S.	1950	605	780	1.3	14.6	51.2	19.1	13.0	30.1
McConnel et al	Eng.	1952	93	186	5.4	6.5	38.5	23.8	1.2	1.9
Doll & Hill	Eng.	1952	1357	1357	0.5	4.5	25.0	13.4	9.4	16.8
Wynder & Cornfield	U.S.	1953	63	133	4.1	20.6	67.6	29.3	6.1	11.6
Sadowsky et al	U.S.	1953	477	615	3.8	13.2	46.8	30.7	3.8	5.3
Koulumies	Fin.	1953	728	300	0.6	18.0	65.8	25.0	36.4	79.0
Breslow et al	U.S.	1954	518	518	3.7	10.8	75.6	44.2	3.2	5.0
Levin	U.S.	1954	490	2365	8.0	26.9	52.7	22.7	4.2	7.8
Watson & Conte	U.S.	1954	265	287	1.9	9.7	73	57	5.5	6.5

* Relative risk of lung cancer is the ratio of the chances of a smoker developing lung cancer to those of a nonsmoker developing lung cancer. For example, the entry on line one of column 10, 5.4, means that the risk of a smoker developing lung cancer is 5.4 times that of a nonsmoker.

SOURCE: Harold F. Dorn, National Institutes of Health, "The Relationship of Cancer of the Lung and the Use of Tobacco," The American Statistician (Washington, D.C.: The American Statistical Association, December 1954) vol. 8, no. 5, p. 10.

Table 2-6. SHIPMENT OF STEEL PRODUCTS BY MARKET CLASSIFICATION (ILLUSTRATION)

	Distributors	Automotive	Oil and gas	Machinery and equipment	Construction and contractors' products	Forgings	Semi-finished for further steel processing	Household appliances and office equipment	Export	Transportation (air, rail, and shipbuilding)	Containers	All other markets	
Average 1950–1955 inclusive	19.1%	22.7%	8.8%	8.6%	7.7%	8.7%	4.1%	4.2%	2.9%	3.2%	3.7%	6.3%	100%
1956	21.0%	20.5%	10.4%	9.4%	8.1%	7.2%	4.4%	4.3%	3.8%	3.0%	2.6%	5.3%	100%

SOURCE: *U.S.A. Tomorrow*, Republic Steel Corporation, 1957, p. 37.

CHARTS AND GRAPHS

It is impractical to present in an introductory text all the possible types of charts and graphs. Hence only the more common types, plus a few examples to indicate the possibilities of the imaginative use of graphic techniques, will be presented. The construction of charts used to present frequency distributions will be discussed in Chapter 3.

A general rule which applies to any arithmetic-type chart is that the axis must begin at zero and vary by some constant amount away from zero. Thus a scale broken into units of 10 should proceed 0, 10, 20, 30, 40 for every quarter inch or other fixed measurement on the scale. In every instance where a scale does not begin with zero or where the scale "jumps," as 0, 10, 20, *30, 60*, 70, the fact must be clearly indicated on the chart by a break in the chart itself.

Bar Charts

One very common method of graphic presentation is the bar chart, where, as the name suggests, the information is depicted by bars. Usually the size of the bar indicates the magnitude of the data. Bar charts are of two general types; vertical and horizontal.

A simple vertical bar chart is presented in Figure 2-1. Here the bars, which depict the production of steel in Canada and Latin America at three different dates, clearly indicate the increasing trend over the 1957–1962 period.

Figure 2-2 presents the same type of bar chart coupled with a pictograph (picture graph) type of presentation.

Figure 2-3 is more complicated because more than one vertical bar is used at each date. Death benefits, living benefits, and total benefits are indicated for every year. Although the picture in this chart is not as simple as those presented in the other bar charts, the information is still clearly apparent.

Figure 2-4 presents a type of vertical bar chart in which the bars themselves are divided into parts. In this chart, estimated world steel production is presented according to producing country at three different dates. The comparison of the totals at each date and the manner in which the totals are distributed are much more evident than they would be if the material were presented in tabular form.

Horizontal bar charts present just as many possibilities as do the vertical charts already considered. The simplest possible horizontal bar chart is presented in Figure 2-5. In this chart, the market saturation of various types of household appliances is indicated by solid horizontal bars. Each bar can be compared in length with every other bar. It is clear from

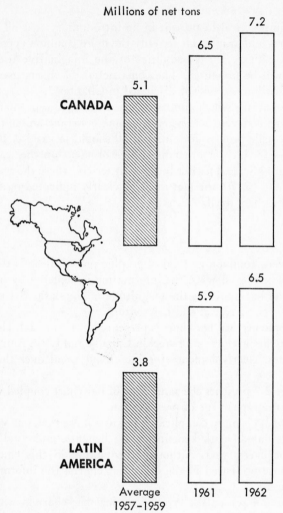

FIGURE 2–1.   *Steel Production in Canada and Latin America*

SOURCE: *Charting Steel's Progress*, American Iron and Steel
Institute, 1963, p. 37.

this presentation that the appliance facing the most saturated market is
the refrigerator, and that facing the least saturated market, the air
conditioner.

One of the many other ways the horizontal bar chart may be presented is illustrated in Figure 2-6. Here male life expectancy at birth is

FIGURE 2–2.   *Tin Plate and Metal Can Shipments*

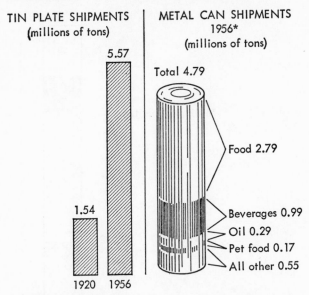

TIN PLATE SHIPMENTS
(millions of tons)

5.57

1.54

1920   1956

METAL CAN SHIPMENTS
1956*
(millions of tons)

Total 4.79

Food 2.79

Beverages 0.99
Oil 0.29
Pet food 0.17
All other 0.55

* Based on data from U. S. Department of Commerce.

SOURCE: *Charting Steel's Progress*, American Iron and Steel
Institute, 1957, p. 39.

FIGURE 2–3.   *Payments to Policy Owners and Beneficiaries over the
Past Ten Years (Millions of Dollars)*

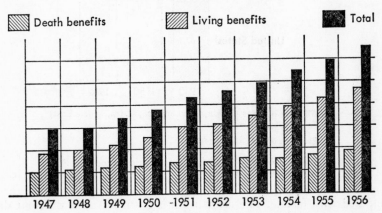

Death benefits   Living benefits   Total

1947   1948   1949   1950   -1951   1952   1953   1954   1955   1956

SOURCE: *97th Annual Report, 1956*, The Equitable Life Assurance Society of the
United States, p. 5.

FIGURE 2–4.   Estimated World Steel Production

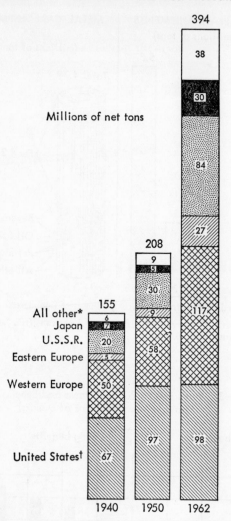

*All other includes Canada, Latin America, Africa, Middle East,
 Far East (excluding Japan), and Oceania.

†Excludes foundry steel castings.

SOURCE: *Charting Steel's Progress*, American Iron and Steel
Institute, 1963, p. 36.

compared with female. The comparison is given for three different dates.
The white bar at each date indicates male expectancy and the darker bar
indicates female.

Quite often a single bar is used and separated into various parts, as in
Figure 2-7. A single bar divided into parts can be used when a total is to be

FIGURE 2–5. *Market Saturation—Household Appliances—1956*

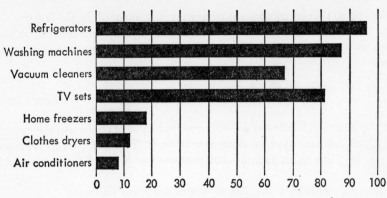

Percentage of wired homes having given appliances

SOURCE: *U.S.A. Tomorrow*, Republic Steel Corporation, 1957, p. 26.

FIGURE 2–6. *Expectation of Life at Birth in the United States*

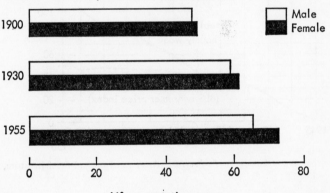

Life expectation, years

SOURCE: *Life Insurance Fact Book, 1957,* Institute of Life Insurance, p. 97.

FIGURE 2–7. *Assets of U.S. Life Companies, 1956*
$96,011,000,000

U.S. government securities   Miscellaneous assets
    All other government bonds   Mortgages   Policy loans
        Securities of business and industry   Real estate

7.9% 3.5%   43.4%   34.4%   2.9% 3.7% 4.2%

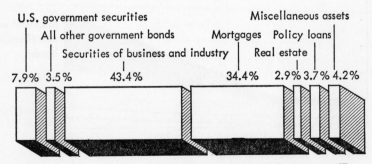

SOURCE: *Life Insurance Fact Book, 1957.* Institute of Life Insurance, p. 57.

broken up so that its component parts may be compared. In the illustration, total assets of United States life insurance companies are divided so that a reader may easily see the specific types of assets which comprise the total.

Line Charts

Figure 2-8 illustrates another common type of chart, usually called a line chart. On this type of chart one or more lines are used to represent values. In a line chart such as that presented in Figure 2-8 the movement

FIGURE 2–8.   *Rise in Wages and Prices Compared*

Percentage of increase,
1945 – December 1956

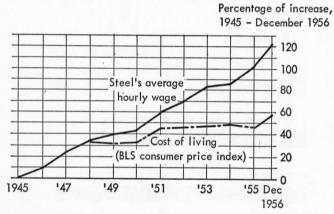

SOURCE: *Charting Steel's Progress,* American Iron and Steel Institute, 1957, p. 52.

FIGURE 2–9.   *Distribution of Securities of Business and Industry Owned by U.S. Life Companies*

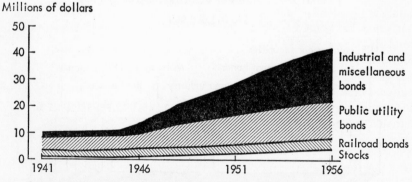

SOURCE: *Life Insurance Fact Book, 1957,* Institute of Life Insurance, p. 67.

of values is clear. In this illustration the lines indicate that the percentage rise in wages in the steel industry since 1945 has been greater than the percentage rise in consumer prices.

A modified type of line chart is found in Figure 2-9. Such a modification is useful to show the shift over time in the absolute size of a particular total and also the shift in the importance of its component parts. In the illustration, a picture of securities owned by United States Life Insurance companies is presented. The change in total securities owned is clear, as is the change in the relative importance in the total of the particular type of security.

Pie Charts

It would indeed be a mistake to leave a discussion of charts without presenting a sample of a pie chart. An example of one is found in Figure

FIGURE 2–10.   Ordinary Policies Purchased in the United States, 1956

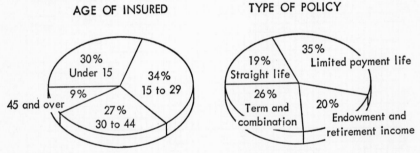

SOURCE: *Life Insurance Fact Book, 1957*, Institute of Life Insurance, p. 20.

2-10. The pie chart is probably the most common of all methods of presenting a picture of a total divided into its component elements. In the example, both "pies" are of the same diameter because both represent the same total—the ordinary policies purchased in the United States in 1956. This is an important fact, and should be well noted. If two different totals are used to prepare two separate pie charts so that the size of the parts may be compared, the size of the pie should vary with the size of the total. If, for example, the division of the national income in the United States is to be compared to the division of the national income in the Soviet Union, the size of the pie will be determined by the size of the national income in the particular country. To make both pies of the same size would be quite misleading, because it would then appear that the two national incomes are equal.

Semilogarithmic Chart

A type of chart that could quite frequently be used more advantageously is the semilog chart. It does not enjoy more extensive use because it is not as widely understood as a chart where an arithmetic scale is employed on both axes. On this type of graph an arithmetic scale is used on the horizontal axis and a logarithmic scale on the vertical axis. Such a scale causes the chart to show clearly a ratio or percentage change.

The vertical axis on the sample sheet of semilog paper presented in Figure 2-11 is a logarithmic scale. When actual values are plotted on such

FIGURE 2–11.   Portion of Sheet of Semilog Paper

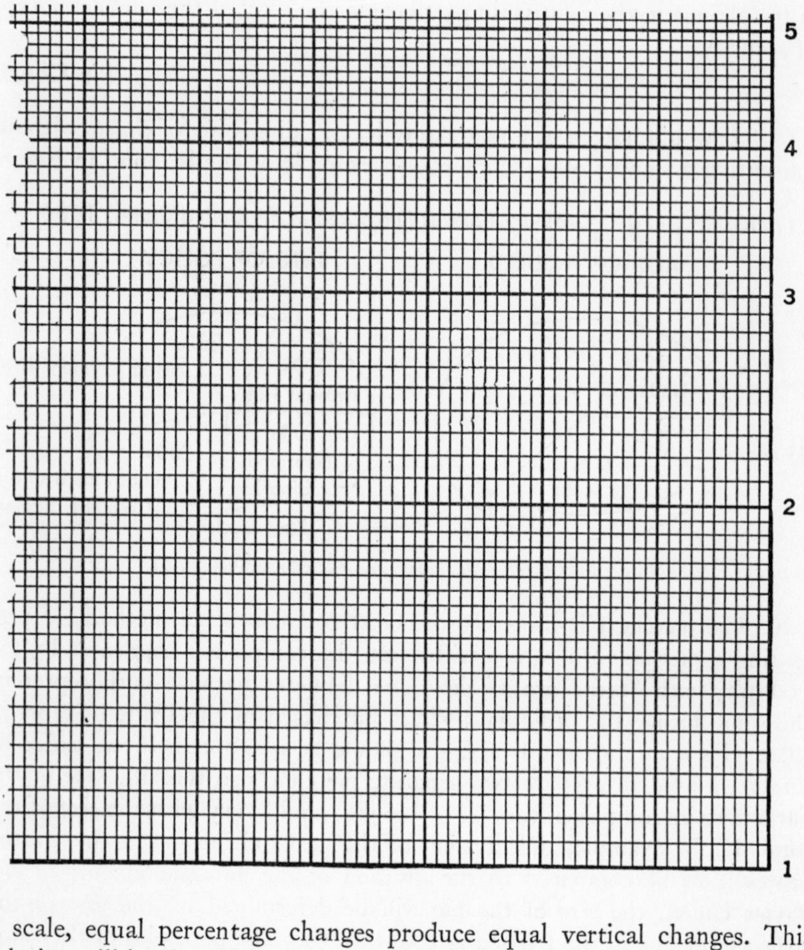

a scale, equal percentage changes produce equal vertical changes. This relation will be clear if the vertical scale in the figure is carefully examined. An increase on the scale from 1 to 2 is a 100-percent increase, as is an increase from 2 to 4. For this reason the distance between the 2 and 4 lines is the same as the distance between the 1 and 2 lines.

Any number can be used to start such a logarithmic scale, but it must be remembered that the number will be added onto itself 10 times, with the result that the number at the top of the scale is 10 times the original number. Thus, if the scale starts with 1, it would read 1, 2, 3, 4, 5, 6, 7, 8, 9, 10, but if it started with 4, it would read 4, 8, 12, 16, 20, 24, 28, 32, 36, 40. The explanation is that a log scale represents a logarithmic (percentage) increase, and each complete cycle represents an increase of one power of 10, such as from 1 to 10 and from 4 to 40.

An example of such a chart is presented in Figure 2-12, which uses the figures for the population of the United States presented in Table 2-7.

FIGURE 2–12. Growth of Population of the United States, 1947–2077 Semilog Chart

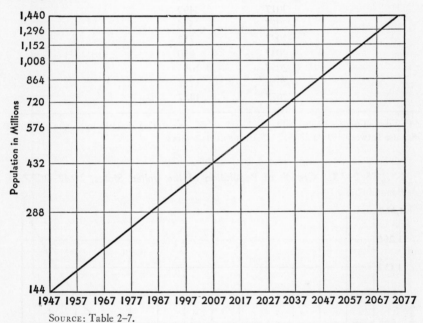

SOURCE: Table 2–7.

The population has increased about 19.4 percent between 1947 and 1957. Figures in the table representing the total population at the end of each 10-year period from 1957 to 2077 were obtained by assuming that the percentage increase remains constant and by increasing the total population by this percentage amount every 10 years. Though the assumption may be unwarranted, such an increase is not impossible, and the resulting problems are fascinating to consider. The important point here is that Figure 2-12 shows the constant percentage increase as a straight line. The chart clearly indicates that under these assumed conditions the 1947 population of 144 million persons will have doubled before 1987 and will have increased to 10 times its size before 2077.

Table 2-7. TOTAL POPULATION OF THE UNITED STATES*

	Population (millions)
1947	144
1957	172
1967	205
1977	245
1987	293
1997	350
2007	418
2017	499
2027	596
2037	712
2047	850
2057	1015
2067	1212
2077	1447

* Population figures in this table are based on the assumption that the approximate rate of increase between 1947 and 1957 (19.4 percent) continues.

FIGURE 2–13. Growth of Population of the United States, 1947–2077

Arithmetic Chart

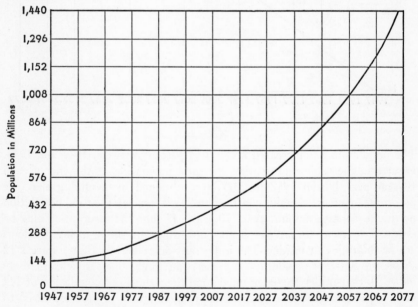

Source: Table 2-7.

In Figure 2-13 the same figures are plotted on a regular arithmetic scale. Now, if Figures 2-12 and 2-13 are compared, it is clear that a semilogarithmic chart shows percentage changes more effectively. Because the percentage increase is constant, the growth of the population is represented by a straight line on the semilog chart. On the arithmetic chart, however, this growth is represented by a curve. The arithmetic chart shows absolute increase and, if the percentage remains constant, the absolute increase will be larger each period as the population continues to grow larger. The larger

FIGURE 2-14. Total Energy Generated by Electric Utilities in Maine and Massachusetts, 1920-1950 (Hundred Millions of Kilowatt Hours)

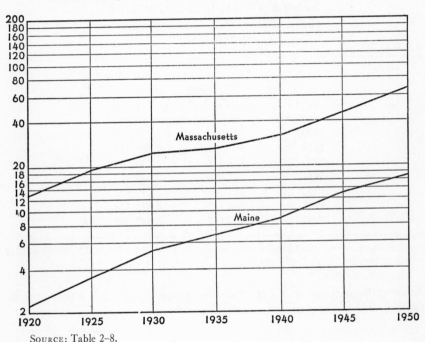

Source: Table 2-8.

absolute increase is indicated on the arithmetic chart by the increased steepness of the slope of the curve every 10-year interval.

Semilog charts can have more than one scale or cycle. Two or three cycle charts are necessary when a series being plotted has more than a 10-fold increase or when two series are to be compared and the largest value in one series is more than 10 times the smallest value in the other. Such a comparison is presented in Figure 2-14, which uses the figures for both Maine and Massachusetts presented in Table 2-8. By examining the two lines, we can see that although the amount of energy generated in Massachusetts is greater than that generated in Maine, the percentage

increase between 1920 and 1950 was greater in Maine than in Massachusetts. The larger percentage rate of increase is indicated on the chart by the
steeper slope of the line used to represent energy generated in Maine.

The use of the semilogarithmic scale facilitates the comparison of the
changes of unlike magnitudes, because, as mentioned above, equal percentage changes will show as equal vertical distances. This scale greatly
compresses higher values, thus it is possible to show two series widely
different in magnitude on the same graph. Such a representation would not
be possible on an arithmetic scale. When these graphs are being employed
to show relative changes only, it is also permissible to plot different series to

Table 2-8. TOTAL ENERGY GENERATED
Electric Utilities, Maine and Massachusetts
(1920–1950)

	Thousands of kilowatt-hours	
	Maine	*Massachusetts*
1920	205,099	1,332,832
1925	380,765	1,985,938
1930	554,321	2,564,742
1935	725,516	2,643,332
1940	923,242	3,418,207
1945	1,348,857	4,576,536
1950	1,680,457	6,587,882

Source: *Statistical Bulletin Electric Utility Industry in New England 1956*, Electric Council of
New England, July 1957, pp. 17 and 19.

different logarithmic scales on the same graph by using a different scale
on each side of the graph.

SUGGESTED READINGS

Croxton, F. E., and D. J. Cowden. *Applied General Statistics*. Englewood Cliffs, N.J.
    Prentice-Hall, Inc., 1939, chap. 5.
Crum, W. L., A. C. Patton, and A. R. Tebbutt. *Introduction to Economic Statistics*.
    New York: McGraw-Hill Book Company, Inc., 1938, chap. 8.
Hanson, K. O. *Managerial Statistics*. Englewood Cliffs, N.J.: Prentice-Hall, Inc.,
    1955, chaps. 10 and 11.
Neter, J., and W. Wasserman. *Fundamental Statistics for Business and Economics*.
    Boston: Allyn and Bacon, Inc., 1961, chaps. 4 and 5.
Riggleman, J. R., and I. N. Frisbee. *Business Statistics*. New York: McGraw-Hill
    Book Company, Inc., 1951, chaps. 5 and 6.

1. State the two basic principles of chart and table construction.
2. List the rules presented in the text that should be observed in order to ensure clarity in chart and table construction.
3. Discuss the usefulness of the semilogarithmic scale.
4. When is it necessary to use a semilog chart with more than one cycle?
5. Assume that you have just plotted two separate groups of data on a semilog chart. The line representing one series has a much steeper slope from the lower left of the chart to the upper right than does the line representing the other series. What does this indicate about the relative behavior of the two sets of data?

PROBLEMS

1. Prepare a simple table containing the following facts:
   One thousand two hundred and thirty-five persons taking the C.P.C.U. examinations in 1957 were insurance company personnel. Of this group 148 were Managers, 362 were Special and State Agents, 69 were Adjusters, 14 were engaged in Rating and Inspection, and 411 were Underwriters. Also in this group were 14 Engineers, 10 Lawyers, 24 Auditors and Accountants, 34 Trainees, and 149 Administrative and Clerical workers. (SOURCE: *Application, Study Group and Examination Statistics for 1957*, Philadelphia: The American Institute for Property and Liability Underwriters Inc.)
2. State verbally what the following sets of figures would look like if they were plotted on semilog charts: (a) 5, 15, 45, 135, 405; (b) 1, 2, 5, 15, 60; (c) 3, 9, 22, 46, 92.
3. State, with your reasons, the type of graph that in your opinion is most appropriate for portraying the following statistical data:
   (a) Sales of a wholesale electronics firm for March 1958 subdivided into the following categories: receiving tubes, cathode ray tubes, antenna equipment, parts, test equipment, and miscellaneous items.
   (b) Production of steel in the United States at 5-year intervals from 1928 to 1958.
   (c) Number of television receivers in use in the United States from 1948 to 1958 by years.
4. Prepare a table presenting the following facts:
   In a study made in Davenport, Illinois, and Fort Wayne, Indiana, a total of 8027 men and women were interviewed. In Davenport, 2669 men and 2680 women were interviewed; in Fort Wayne, 1316

men and 1362 women. In all, 3985 men and 4042 women were interviewed. (SOURCE: Appendix C, "Characteristics of the Davenport and
Ft. Wayne Samples," *NBC Study of Radio's Effective Sales Power*, New
York: National Broadcasting Company, September 1952, p. 55.)
5. Prepare a table depicting the data below:
    In a study of family ownership of heavy durable goods, it was
found that 84.5 percent of the people interviewed in Davenport owned
automobiles, in contrast to 85.1 percent of those interviewed in Fort
Wayne who owned automobiles. In Davenport 98.6 percent of the
people owned radios, but only 1.4 percent owned automatic dishwashers
in Fort Wayne 99.4 percent owned radios and .8 percent dishwashers,
Phonograph players were owned by 58.8 percent of the persons in
Fort Wayne and 51.1 percent of those in Davenport, and vacuum
cleaners by 82.9 percent of those in Davenport and 82.7 percent of
those in Fort Wayne. In total, 84.7 percent of the people interviewed
owned automobiles, 82.8 percent vacuum cleaners, 98.9 percent radios,
53.8 percent phonograph players, and 1.2 percent automatic dishwashers. (SOURCE: Appendix C, "Characteristics of the Davenport and
Fort Wayne Samples," *NBC Study of Radio's Effective Sales Power*,
New York: National Broadcasting Company, September 1952, p. 57.)
6. Present the following information in tabular form:
    In 1953, 64 persons took a total of 75 C.L.U. Management
Examinations and 35 completed the examinations. A year later 29
persons took 33 examinations and 14 completed them. In 1955, 21
persons took 27 examinations. That year, 8 completed the examinations.
The next year, 19 took a total of 25 examinations and 11 completed
them. In 1957, 53 persons took 69 examinations and 15 completed them.
(SOURCE: Table 9, "Significant Management Examination Data,"
Annual Report of the American College of Life Underwriters, Philadelphia: American College of Life Underwriters, 1957, p. 15.)
7. Construct a bar chart presenting the following facts:
    In 1952, N.B.C. studied the effect of radio advertising on the
purchase of Pet Milk and Carnation Milk. These companies are
nationally advertised competitors, but at that particular time "Pet
was advertised on an N.B.C. program ('Mary Lee Taylor'), while
Carnation was not then using network radio in these markets." At
the time, the study indicated that "among non-listeners to this program sales of Pet and Carnation were approximately the same: 16.7
percent vs. 17.0 percent," "However, 21.7 percent of the listeners
bought Pet ... while only 13.1 percent of these same listeners bought
Carnation." (SOURCE: "Pet Milk: Advertiser vs. Competitor," *NBC
Study of Radio's Effective Sales Power*, New York: National Broadcasting Company, September 1952, p. 40.)
8. Using the facts presented as follows, prepare a bar graph.

AVERAGE ANNUAL AUTOMOTIVE EXPENDITURES
BY ANNUAL HOUSEHOLD INCOME

Annual household income *(dollars)*	*Spending on* *automotive* *products* *(dollars)*
under 2,000	206
2,000 through 2,999	375
3,000 through 3,999	554
4,000 through 4,999	621
5,000 through 6,999	797
7,000 through 9,999	925
10,000 or more	1,156
Average U.S. Household	591

SOURCE: "Average Annual Household Expenditures by Annual Household Income," *Life Study of Consumer Expenditures* (New York: Time, Inc., 1957), p. 113.

9. Present the following data as (a) a bar chart, (b) a pie chart.

The Ford Foundation reports that between 1951–1956 its spending in the general area of "Economic Development and Administration" totaled $19,516,000. Of this total $4,172,000 was provided for Resources for the Future, Inc., $1,806,000 for the dissemination of economic information, $4,209,000 for training for careers in research, teaching, and administration, and $9,329,000 for research on central economic problems. (SOURCE: *The Ford Foundation Annual Report 1956*, New York: The Ford Foundation, 1956, p. 72.)

10. Construct a line chart depicting the following data.

ANNUAL COST OF WAGE SUPPLEMENTS
IRON AND STEEL INDUSTRY—1945–1956
(millions of dollars)

	Vacations	*Pensions, ins., S.U.B.,* *Soc. Security, holidays*	*Total*
1945	39.4	50.4	89.8
1946	39.3	41.9	81.2
1947	50.2	49.2	99.4
1948	55.6	51.4	107.0
1949	60.2	44.2	104.4
1950	65.5	165.7	231.2
1951	79.2	191.4	270.6
1952	96.1	162.1	258.2
1953	106.3	242.9	349.2
1954	98.2	209.8	308.0
1955	111.6	281.5	393.1
1956	129.4	315.3	444.7

SOURCE: *Charting Steel's Progress* (New York: American Iron and Steel Institute, 1957), p. 54.

11. Construct a simple line chart, using the following information:

ENPLANED PASSENGERS ON SCHEDULED AIRLINES
UNITED STATES—1948–1955

	Passengers (*in thousands*)
1948	13,060.4
1949	14,732.7
1950	16,937.0
1951	21,895.6
1952	24,350.3
1953	28,004.3
1954	31,657.9
1955	37,226.4

SOURCE: U.S. Department of Commerce, Civil Aeronautics Administration.

12. Present the figures on the following page on a graph, using (a) an arithmetic scale, (b) a semilogarithmic scale.

TOTAL NUMBER OF C.P.C.U.
EXAMINATIONS TAKEN
(1943–1957)

	No. of *examinations*
1943	206
1944	263
1945	452
1946	556
1947	861
1948	1449
1949	2194
1950	3066
1951	2651
1952	2252
1953	2602
1954	2865
1955	2819
1956	2697
1957	2997

SOURCE: Application, Study Group and Examination Statistics for 1957 (Philadelphia: The American Institute for Property and Liability Underwriters Inc.).

13. Present the following information on an arithmetic chart and on a semilog chart.

GROUP AND INDUSTRIAL
LIFE INSURANCE PURCHASES IN
THE UNITED STATES
(millions of dollars)

	Group	Industrial
1940	691	3,350
1941	1,117	3,460
1942	1,612	3,210
1943	1,826	3,250
1944	1,642	3,200
1945	1,265	3,430
1946	2,093	4,340
1947	2,689	4,575
1948	2,945	4,600
1949	2,877	4,930
1950	6,068	5,402
1951	4,031	5,461
1952	5,253	5,987
1953	6,243	6,506
1954	13,324	6,846
1955	11,258	6,342
1956	12,407	6,531

SOURCE: Life Insurance Purchases in the
United States, *Life Insurance Fact Book* (New
York: Institute of Life Insurance, 1957), p. 18.

CHAPTER THREE

Frequency
Distributions

The investigator frequently is interested in finding out how often certain values or ranges of values of the variable occur. Teachers, for example, want to know how many of their students are receiving passing grades, how many are doing good work, and how many are excelling. Consequently, a description of the pattern of the distribution of grades in the class is desired. Similarly, the economist who is studying the distribution of income needs information concerning the number of families receiving income between $2000 and $3000, $3000 and $4000, and so on. For purposes such as these the data are organized into a frequency distribution where the items are grouped into classes, each of which represents a range of values of the variable. In this way the frequency of occurrence of items in each class is brought to light. The assembly of masses of data into frequency distributions is one of the most useful techniques in the entire field of statistics. It not only enables the investigator to obtain a much clearer picture of the nature of the distribution, but at the same time arranges the data into a form that will greatly facilitate further analysis. In the chapters that follow, most of the discussion of measures of central tendency and dispersion will refer to data that have been grouped into frequency distributions.

    The following illustration should make the nature of frequency distribution clear. Assume that the objective of the investigation is to study the pattern of weekly wages received by the 60 production workers of Cincinnati Metals Company. For purposes of the study the pay-roll records for the week ending December 14, 1964, were employed. The wage figures for each of the workers, which represent their gross wages before deductions of any kind, have been rounded to the nearest dollar. In Table 3-1 the wage data are recorded as they were transcribed from the pay-roll sheets on which the employees were listed alphabetically. It is apparent that only a vague notion of the nature of the pattern of wages can be obtained by inspecting Table 3-1, and that consequently some other technique of presentation is called for.

Table 3-1.   WAGES OF PRODUCTION WORKERS
Cincinnati Metals Company
(Week of December 14, 1964)

Dollars per week

78	83	90	88	89	47
75	88	92	73	73	76
60	67	84	70	94	97
92	80	77	77	74	84
93	78	65	56	71	84
74	72	79	90	81	69
72	62	79	74	77	78
68	88	86	72	72	67
83	94	73	62	88	89
88	53	74	56	82	66

Table 3–2.   ARRAY OF WAGES OF PRODUCTION WORKERS
Cincinnati Metals Company
(Week of December 14, 1964)

Dollars per week

47	67	73	77	83	89
53	68	73	78	84	89
56	69	74	78	84	90
56	70	74	78	84	90
60	71	74	79	86	92
62	72	74	79	88	92
62	72	75	80	88	93
65	72	76	81	88	94
66	72	77	82	88	94
67	73	77	83	88	97

In Table 3-2 these same wage items are arranged in the order of their magnitudes. Such a list is called an *array*. As a result, more meaningful observations can be made. The over-all range from $47 to $97 per week stands out, as do some of the general characteristics of the distribution. However, the array still offers only a very cumbersome description of the pattern.

If the range of wages is broken down into class intervals of $10 each and the number of workers falling in each class tallied, a simple and informative description of the wage distribution results. This frequency distribution is found in Table 3-3. When the data are presented in this manner, it is immediately apparent that the greatest concentration is found in the $70-to-$80 dollar range and that the number of individuals falling in each 10-point class declines at successively higher or lower wage levels. In addition, it is clear that the number of workers drops off more rapidly in the lower wage ranges than it does at higher wage levels. These are the essential features of the wage pattern in the particular company,

Table 3-3.   FREQUENCY DISTRIBUTION OF WAGES OF
PRODUCTION WORKERS
Cincinnati Metals Company
(Week of December 14, 1964)

	No. of workers
Wages (dollars per week)	
40 but under 50	1
50 but under 60	3
60 but under 70	9
70 but under 80	23
80 but under 90	16
90 but under 100	8

and the frequency-distribution technique presents them in a simple and easily understandable form. This advantage of the frequency distribution is not confined to this example alone. In most instances the use of this technique will clearly bring to light any central tendency that may exist, as well as the dispersion of items away from the central values around which they may cluster. As will be shown in a later chapter, use of the frequency distribution also greatly simplifies the computation of several numerical measures designed to summarize the characteristics of the data.

Not all data should be organized into frequency distributions. Items classified on the basis of the time of their occurrence do not lend themselves to this kind of treatment, because conditions often change over time; as a result, noncomparable data would be included in the distribution. Theoretically, a frequency distribution is supposed to depict conditions at a point in time rather than events over a period of time. Similarly, items classified on the basis of kind or place cannot be directly organized into frequency distributions. For example, the fact that the populations of Boston, Cincinnati, and Columbus are 800,000, 500,000, and 300,000 respectively cannot be recorded in this manner. However, once the population figures for a large number of cities have been collected, these figures themselves can be recorded in classes according to size. Nevertheless, in the process the individual identities of the cities are lost.

CONSTRUCTING A FREQUENCY DISTRIBUTION

The construction of a frequency distribution is essentially a simple matter involving only three important steps. First, an appropriate class interval must be selected. Second, this class interval must be clearly marked off, and, finally, frequency of occurrence of items falling in each interval must be recorded. Of the three steps, the first causes the most difficulty.

Selecting the Class Interval

The class interval selected greatly influences the usefulness of the frequency distribution both as a technique of presentation and as a basis for further computation. An improper statement of class intervals often obscures or distorts the true nature of the distribution and sometimes causes mathematical computations based thereon to be incorrect. In order to avoid the pitfalls of distortion and error, the following principles should be followed whenever possible.

1. *The intervals should be equal.* If intervals are not of uniform width, it is difficult to make meaningful comparison between classes. At times, however, extreme items may require the inclusion of so many class intervals that the frequency distribution will become unwieldy. The items are then grouped in "and over" or "and under" classes. These classes are called *open-end classes*, and the frequency distribution itself is known as an *open-end distribution*. When the frequency distribution is being employed as a technique of presentation only, open-end classes do not seriously reduce its usefulness as long as only a few items fall in these classes. However, use of the distribution for purposes of further mathematical computation is frustrated because a mid-point value, which can be used to represent the class, cannot be determined for an open-end class.

2. *The width of the interval chosen should make the true nature of the distribution apparent.* When a narrow class interval is employed, the number of classes is nesessarily increased, whereas a wide interval reduces the number of intervals required. The use of an excessive number of classes causes individual class intervals to be sparsely populated, but the use of too few classes may obscure vital characteristics of the data. In Table 3-4(a), for instance, when a class interval of 2 is employed, many classes are entirely empty and others have only one or two items falling therein. The

frequencies do not rise continuously to a single peak value and decline steadily thereafter. In fact, there is no single class that has the highest frequency. Because the absence of continuous rise and decline in frequency, as well as the lack of a central class exhibiting the greatest frequency, cannot be logically explained in terms of the nature of the data being studied, it follows that these idiosyncrasies are the result of the small

Table 3-4.   WAGES OF PRODUCTION WORKERS
Cincinnati Metals Company
(Week of December 14, 1964)

(a) Too many classes		(b) Too few classes	
	No. of workers		*No. of workers*
Wages (dollars per week)		Wages (dollars per week)	
45 but under 47	0	40 but under 60	4
47 but under 49	1	60 but under 80	32
49 but under 51	0	80 but under 100	24
51 but under 53	0		
53 but under 55	1		
55 but under 57	2		
57 but under 59	0		
59 but under 61	1		
61 but under 63	2		
63 but under 65	0		
65 but under 67	2		
67 but under 69	3		
69 but under 71	2		
71 but under 73	5		
73 but under 75	7		
75 but under 77	2		
77 but under 79	6		
79 but under 81	3		
81 but under 83	2		
83 but under 85	5		
85 but under 87	1		
87 but under 89	5		
89 but under 91	4		
91 but under 93	2		
93 but under 95	3		
95 but under 97	0		
97 but under 99	1		
99 but under 100	0		

number of items in the entire distribution. Consequently, the class interval of 2 is too narrow and should be expanded.

The opposite situation results when the class interval is too wide. As can be seen in Table 3-4(b), when the class interval is widened to 20, all the items fall into three classes. This, of course, conceals the important facts that in the 60–80 class the greatest concentration is found between 70 and 80, and in the 80–100 class many more items fall between 80 and 90 than between 90 and 100. Obviously, smaller class intervals are indicated. Although the frequency distribution in Table 3-3, where the class interval of 10 is employed, is satisfactory, this particular interval cannot be considered the only acceptable choice. In Table 3-5 the use of a class interval

Table 3-5. WAGES OF PRODUCTION WORKERS
Cincinnati Metals Company
(Week of December 14, 1964)

Wages (dollars per week)	No. of workers
45 but under 50	1
50 but under 55	1
55 but under 60	2
60 but under 65	3
65 but under 70	6
70 but under 75	13
75 but under 80	10
80 but under 85	8
85 but under 90	8
90 but under 95	7
95 but under 100	1

of 5 produces a distribution that is not only satisfactory but in some ways superior to that in Table 3-3. Here, for example, the much greater concentration of items in the lower part of the 90–100 range and the upper part of the 60–70 range becomes evident. Whether an interval of 5 or 10 is chosen will depend on the degree of precision required or possible. It is apparent that there usually is no one right width of the class interval which is always necessarily preferred to all others.

The selection of the width of the interval will be influenced by the number of items in the distribution and the range of the variable over which frequencies are found. A large number of items permits many more classes than a small group does, whereas wide over-all range of the data requires wider class intervals than might otherwise be chosen. Usually the number of classes will not be less than 5 or more than 25.

3. *The mid-points of class intervals should be reasonably representative of the values falling in each class.* Once the data are arranged into a frequency distribution, the identity of individual items is lost. As a result, the actual items are assumed to be distributed evenly throughout the class or to be concentrated at the mid-point, so that the mid-point value will serve satisfactorily as a single value to represent the entire class. This assumption is always made for purposes of mathematical computation. Since the mid-point lies half way between the upper and lower class limits, these limits must be carefully selected in order to give proper mid-point values. Should the class limits be improperly selected, serious error of interpretation and computation could result. This would occur in a study of the prices of drug-product items if class intervals of 10 to 20 cents, 20 to 30 cents, and so forth were employed. Because these items are typically priced at the upper limits of these ranges—19-cent, 29-cent, and 39-cent price tags being typical—the assumption that the values concentrate at the mid-points (25 cents, 35 cents, and the like) would be invalid, and computations based thereon could lead to erroneous conclusions. With these data the class limits should be stated as 24 and under 34 cents, 34 and under 44 cents, and so on, so that the mid-points will fall at 19 cents, 29 cents, and so on, which are close to the areas of concentration of the data.

If these three principles are employed in selecting class intervals, the frequency distribution should adequately represent the mass of data from which it is constructed either for the purpose of final presentation or for further mathematical treatment.

Defining Class Limits

The class limits should be clearly defined. If the class limits of two classes were stated as 10 to 20 and 20 to 30, an item with a value of exactly 20 could be included in either class. Such ambiguity is, naturally, highly undesirable. This problem can easily be avoided if limits of 10 to 20 are construed as 10 *to but not including* 20, or by stating the limits as 10 *but under* or *but less than* 20. Another means of avoiding ambiguity is to employ one more significant figure in defining limits than is found in the data. If prices are stated in whole cents, the limits could be defined as 10 to 19.9 cents.[1]

Tabulation of Frequencies

The third step in the construction of a frequency distribution is the tabulation of the occurrences of values falling in each of the classes. This

[1] If numbers are being rounded, care should be taken to see that the rounding process does not cause an item to be included in a different class. For example, if the class limit is stated as 10 but less than 20, an item such as 19.7 when rounded to 20 might be included in the 20 to 30 class. This difficulty can be avoided if rounding is restricted to one more significant figure than the last significant figure in the statement of the class limits. Thus, with limits of 10 but less than 20, 19.69 could be rounded to 19.7 but 19.7 should not be rounded to 20.

presents no important problems and may be handled in two ways. The items falling in each class may be tallied and then counted. This method has the advantage of being the faster and cheaper. On the other hand, each item falling in a class may be entered in a space assigned to that class. Although this technique is costlier, it permits the investigator to see the actual items in their classes and as a result enables him to detect errors in the statement of the class limits.

FREQUENCY DISTRIBUTIONS FROM DISCRETE DATA

Some economic and business data are *continuous*—that is, the variable may take any value within the limits of the series. For example, the average cost of producing a product can be $32.0653 per unit, or any other figure that results when total costs are divided by output. However, when data are *discrete or discontinuous*, only certain values are possible. The number of children in a family can be only 1, 2, 3, 4, 5, 6, and so on. Values such as 2.5 cannot occur, humorous comments notwithstanding. Although most economic and business series, such as prices, are, strictly speaking, discrete in that quotations are usually not carried to minute fractions of a cent, when the values are separated by very small amounts the series are frequently treated as though they were continuous. Any resulting inaccuracy is so small that it is of no consequence in most practical applications.

Discrete data do not present serious problems in constructing frequency distributions. However, care must be taken in interpreting class limits and in defining mid-points. If the class, 5 but under 10, is used in a distribution of the number of employees per retail store, the values that can fall within this class are 5, 6, 7, 8, and 9. Hence 5 but under 10 really means 5 through and including 9. In addition, the stated limits cannot be averaged to find the mid-point in this illustration, because the middle value is 7, not 7.5. The correct mid-point of 7 could, however, be obtained by averaging the real limits of 5 and 9.

CUMULATIVE FREQUENCY DISTRIBUTIONS

Often the investigator desires to know not only how many items fall in a given class but also how many lie above or below the limits of the class. A professor may be interested in determining the number of students who received grades above or below the passing mark of 60, the average mark of 70, and so on. The analyst of wage patterns wants information on the number of workers falling above or below a single wage or series of wage levels. This type of information is supplied by cumulative frequency distributions. Cumulative frequency distributions are constructed on either a *more than* or *less than* basis. A "more than" distribution shows a value for each class equal to the total number of frequencies which equal or exceed the *lower class limit* of that class. In Table 3-6 the "more than" value of 60 for the $40-to-$50 per week class indicates that all 60 workers received wages equal to or higher than $40, the lower class limit of that class. The value of 47 for the $70-to-$80 class shows that 47 items—the 23 items from 70 to 80, the 16 from 80 to 90, and the 8 from 90 to 100—equal or exceed the lower class limit of 70. A "less than" distribution measures the number of frequencies falling below the *upper class limit* of each class. The "less

Table 3-6.   WAGES OF PRODUCTION WORKERS
Cumulative Frequency Distributions

	No. of workers	Under	More than
Wages (dollars per week)			
40 but under 50	1	1	60
50 but under 60	3	4	59
60 but under 70	9	13	56
70 but under 80	23	36	47
80 but under 90	16	52	24
90 but under 100	8	60	8

than" value of 36 for the 70-to-80 class shows that the wages of 36 workers were below the upper class limit of $80.

GRAPHING
FREQUENCY DISTRIBUTIONS

Simple frequency distributions may be presented graphically by using either histograms, polygons, or smooth curves. In constructing each, the class intervals are measured along the X axis; frequencies are indicated by Y values.

The Histogram

The histogram, or column diagram, as it is sometimes called, is constructed by erecting vertical lines at each class limit to the height indicated by the frequency. A horizontal line then joins these vertical lines. Figure 3-1 is a histogram showing the distribution of wages at the Cincinnati Metals Company that has already served as our example. Observe how clearly the nature of the distribution stands out. It should be noted that, when frequencies are measured, the zero base must be shown for the Y axis. However, it is not necessary to show the zero base along the X axis. When a histogram is constructed for discrete data, a little space usually is left between the bars of the histogram to indicate that the variable cannot assume intermediate values.

FIGURE 3–1.   Distribution of Wages of Production Workers
(Histogram)

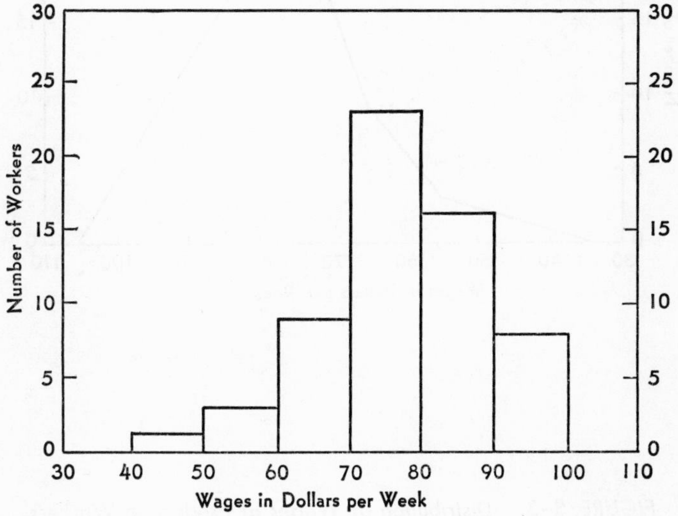

The Polygon

The frequency polygon is constructed by plotting the frequency of a class at the mid-point of the class and then joining these points with straight lines. The mid-points of the classes just beyond the limits of the series are included in order to enclose the figure. Figure 3-2 presents a polygon showing the distribution of wages of production workers. The polygon, in effect, interpolates the progression of frequencies from one class to another on a straight-line basis. In other words, when frequencies are rising, the polygon indicates more frequencies in the upper range of each class; in contrast, during the declining phase of the distribution it suggests a concentration of frequencies in lower parts of the class intervals. This grouping probably is characteristic of the real distribution of most data whose values show a tendency to concentrate in certain ranges. Another important advantage of the polygon is found in the fact that it facilitates the graphic comparison of two series. Two and sometimes three polygons can easily be interpreted and compared if plotted on the same graph. On

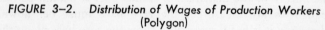

FIGURE 3–2.   *Distribution of Wages of Production Workers*
(Polygon)

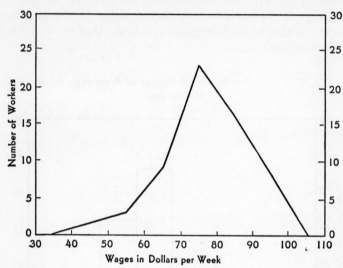

FIGURE 3–3.   *Distribution of Wages of Production Workers*
(Smooth Curve)

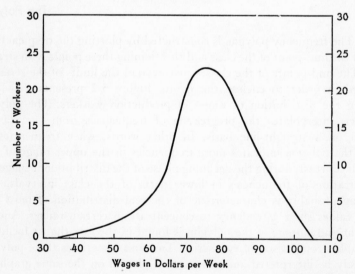

the other hand, two histograms on a single graph would probably be almost incomprehensible.

The Curve

If the investigator has reason to believe that deviations from smooth and continuous progression of the frequencies are caused merely by the fact that several of the items in the series are too small to permit a very large number of class intervals, a smooth curve can be drawn to represent the distribution. The curve should be drawn in such a manner that the areas under the curve in each class interval will be proportionate to the frequencies. In Figure 3-3 such a curve is drawn for the distribution of wages at the Cincinnati Metals Company. The smoothed curve can be used with continuous data only.

Ogives

Polygons depicting cumulative frequency distributions may be constructed. Such a polygon is known as an *ogive*. When a "more than"

FIGURE 3–4.   Distribution of Wages of Production Workers ("More Than" and "Less Than" Ogives)

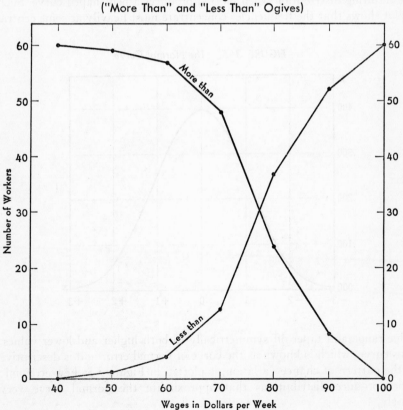

distribution is charted, the cumulative frequency for each class is plotted at the lower class limit of that class, because the "more than" values are computed from the lower class limit. "Less than" values are plotted to upper class limits for a similar reason. Figure 3-4 indicates the plotting of both "more than" and "less than" series for wage data in our example. It is interesting to note that the "more than" and "less than" curves intersect at the middle item of the series. As will be seen in the next chapter, the value of this item is known as the median.

TYPES OF FREQUENCY DISTRIBUTIONS

The Normal Curve

When many and diverse forces are affecting the values of the variable or when the difference between values can be explained in terms of chance, the resulting distribution when plotted produces a bell-shaped curve. Such a plot shows that the frequencies concentrate most heavily at some central

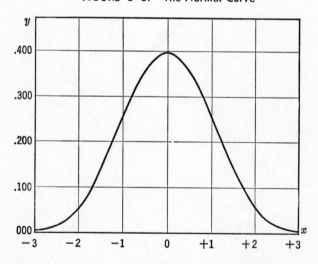

FIGURE 3–5. The Normal Curve

value range and taper off symmetrically to both higher and lower values. This curve, which is known as the curve of normal error and is descriptive of the pattern of chance variation, is plotted in Figure 3-5. Few economic series produce distributions that approximate the normal curve very closely.

The J-Shaped Distribution

Some series do not concentrate at central value ranges but exhibit continuously advancing or declining frequencies. Distributions dealing with income or wage levels would roughly describe such a pattern.[2] Obviously, at progressively higher income levels fewer individuals receive such income. When graphed, this type of distribution produces the J-shaped curve shown in Figure 3-6.

FIGURE 3–6.   Distribution of Income
(J-shaped Distribution)

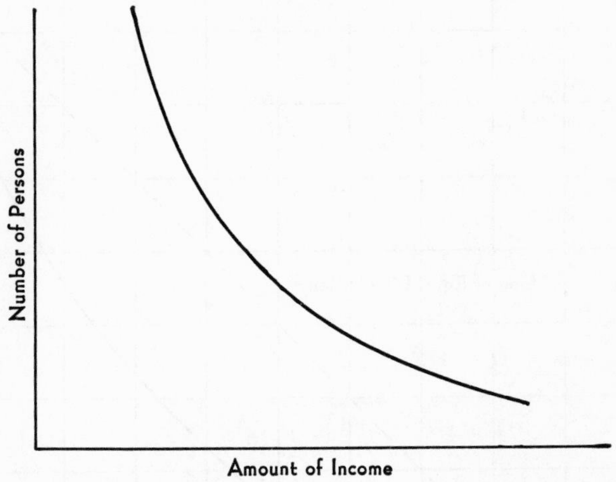

The U-Shaped Distribution

Sometimes a U-shaped frequency distribution is encountered. This may result first from the nature of the data themselves. For example, the distributions of grades on difficult problem-type tests often exhibit such a pattern, because typically the student can either answer the questions or he cannot. As a result, there will be relatively few mediocre papers, and grades will be either high or low. Often, however, the U-shaped distribution is the result of the inclusion of noncomparable data in the distribution.

The Lorenz Curve

A particularly useful type of cumulative frequency distribution is found in the Lorenz curve. When this curve is used to study the distribution

[2] Strictly speaking, income and wage data produce distributions that are skewed far to the right. This effect follows from the fact that a small number of individuals receive very low incomes or wages. If these few items are ignored, the distributions may be considered J-shaped.

of income, each point on it shows the percentage of total income received by a percentage of the population. Thus in Figure 3-7 the point corresponding to an X value of 30 and a Y value of 10 indicates that in 1954 the lowest 30 percent of the spending units received only 10 percent of the total income after taxes. Were income distributed absolutely

FIGURE 3–7.   *Distribution of Income in the United States in 1954 after Federal Income Tax*
(Lorenz Curve)

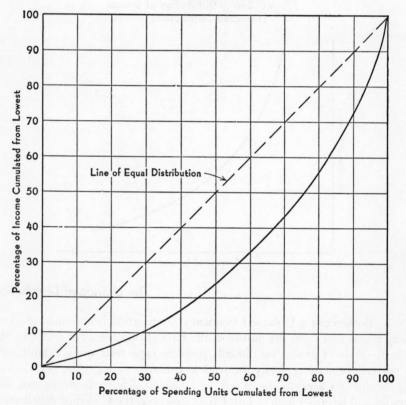

Source: Constructed from data compiled by Board of Governors of the Federal Reserve System.

equally, the Lorenz curve would become a straight 45-degree line. This would indicate that 10 percent of the spending units would receive 10 percent of the income, 20 percent would receive 20 percent, and so forth. The deviation of the curve away from the equal distribution line is indicative of the unequal income distribution in the country.

The use of Lorenz curves is not confined to studies of income. The distribution of sales within an industry can be analyzed in this way also.

Each point on such a curve would indicate the cumulative percentage of sales made by a percentage of the firms cumulated from the firms with the lowest sales. Many similar applications of the Lorenz curve can be found.

SUGGESTED READINGS

Croxton, F. E., and D. J. Cowden. *Applied General Statistics* (2d ed.). Englewood Cliffs, N.J.: Prentice-Hall, Inc., 1955, chap. 8.

Mills, F. C. *Introduction to Statistics*. New York: Holt, Rinehart and Winston, Inc., 1956, chap. 3.

Neiswanger, W. A. *Elementary Statistical Methods* (rev. ed.). New York: The Macmillan Company, 1956, chap. 8.

Riggleman, J. R., and I. N. Frisbee. *Business Statistics*. New York: McGraw-Hill Book Company, Inc., 1951, chap. 7.

QUESTIONS

1. How does a frequency distribution differ from other arrangements of statistical data?
2. When is the use of a frequency distribution advisable in statistical analysis?
3. What factors make a large number of class intervals necessary? When would they not be needed?
4. Why are more than cumulative frequencies plotted at the lower class limit when constructing an ogive?
5. List three possible uses of the Lorenz curve.
6. Explain two techniques of stating class limits that will ensure mutually exclusive classes.
7. What changes in the structure of a frequency distribution do the following conditions suggest?
   (a) All the items fall in three classes.
   (b) Many classes contain no frequencies.
   (c) Doubt exists concerning the class in which a given item falls.
   (d) The frequencies rise toward the center of the distribution, but the frequencies in the seven central classes are as follows: 7, 5, 9, 6, 12, 5, 10.
   (e) The items in most classes cluster near the lower class limit.
8. What different interpretations are suggested by the histogram and the polygon?
9. How can you justify smoothing a frequency curve?
10. Which of the following data are (1) clearly continuous, (2) really discrete but for all practical purposes continuous, or (3) discrete?
    (a) The retail price of coal per ton

    (b) The number of children per family
    (c) Time worked per week
    (d) Average cost per unit
    (e) Employees under a supervisor
    (f) Gross National Product
    (g) Index of Industrial Production
11. Criticize the following frequency distribution:

PRICES OF MILK PER QUART
IN SELECTED RETAIL
ESTABLISHMENTS
(1954–1964)

Prices (cents)	No. of stores
under 15	12
15 but under 17	3
17 but under 19	1
19 but under 21	5
21 but under 23	6
23 but under 25	7
over 25	15

12. By a normal curve is meant the bell-shaped curve that results when statistical investigations pertaining to business are properly conducted and plotted. Do you concur?
13. The word "normal" used in connection with the normal curve indicates that this type of distribution is superior to others that might be encountered. It also indicates that most actual frequency distributions will take approximately this form. Do you agree?
14. Are the statements below true, false, or a combination of truth and falsehood?
    (a) It is always better to have too few class intervals rather than too many.
    (b) The mid-point of a class interval should be representative of the values within the class not only when the items cluster around the mid-point but also when they are evenly distributed throughout the class.
    (c) It is immaterial in which class an item falling at the boundary between two classes is listed.
    (d) A histogram is more useful than a polygon.
    (e) "More than" and "less than" frequency polygons for the same series will intersect at the middle of the series.
15. Why on occasion do frequency distributions have two maximum points or assume the shape of the letter U?

1. The list below enumerates the salaries of the active players on the
   roster of a major league baseball club.

13,500	16,000	20,000	15,500	10,000
13,000	16,000	20,000	15,000	6,500
13,000	17,000	24,500	14,500	6,500
12,500	18,000	52,000	14,000	6,000
10,500	18,000	101,000	14,000	6,000

   Construct a frequency distribution. Be prepared to defend the number
   of classes chosen, the width of the interval, the location of the mid-
   points, and the definition of class limits.

2. The living expenses of 74 business executives in 1957 ran as follows:

Expenses (dollars)	No. of executives
1,000 but under 5,000	3
5,000 but under 10,000	5
10,000 but under 15,000	8
15,000 but under 20,000	12
20,000 but under 25,000	19
25,000 but under 30,000	10
30,000 but under 35,000	8
35,000 but under 40,000	6
40,000 but under 45,000	2
45,000 but under 50,000	1

   (a) Construct a histogram using the above data.
   (b) Construct a polygon.
   (c) Compute both a "more than" and "less than" frequency table.
   (d) Plot the "more than" and "less than" ogives on the same graph.

3. Convert the frequency distribution below to class intervals of 5 and
   then 10.

Class	Frequency
0 – 2.5	1
2.5– 5.0	0
5.0– 7.5	2
7.5–10.0	3
10.0–12.5	0
12.5–15.0	5
15.0–17.5	15
17.5–20.0	8
20.0–22.5	3
22.5–25.0	7
25.0–27.5	0
27.5–30.0	1

Which of the three sets of class intervals do you prefer?

4. The securities listed below comprise the portion of the bond portfolio of the Connecticut Mutual Life Insurance Company classified as "Miscellaneous" as of December 31, 1957.

Security	Coupon rate percentage
American University, Washington, D.C., First Mtge., 1955	4¼
Central Trust Co., Rochester, N.Y., Capital Notes	3½
Colorado Seminary (University of Denver), First Mtge. Rev., A, 1951	4
Colorado Seminary (University of Denver), First Mtge. Rev., B, 1951	3¾
Colorado Seminary (University of Denver), First Mtge. Rev., C, 1951	3⅝
First Trust Co. of Albany, N.Y., Capital Notes	4
Hardin College, Tex. (Midwestern Univ.), First Mtge. Bldg. Rev., 1949	4
Hudson Trust Co., Union City, N.J., Capital Notes	4½
International Bank for Reconstruction and Development	4½
Lutheran University Association, Ind., Valparaiso University, Stud. Union Bldg. First Mtge., 1954	4½
Lutheran University Association, Ind., Valparaiso University, Dorm. First Mtge., 1955	4
Merchants Bank of New York, N.Y., Capital Notes	4
Rocky River Realty Co., First Mtge.	3.15
Rocky River Realty Co., First Mtge.	3¾
Rollins College, Fla., First Mtge. & Collat. Inc. Rev., 1949	4¼
Rollins College, Fla., First Mtge. & Collat. Inc. Rev., 1957	5¼
Southern Methodist University, Tex., Stud. Union Bldg. Rev., 1953	4
Southern Methodist University, Tex., Colliseum Bldg. Rev., 1954	4
Trinity College, Conn., Dorm., 1953	4
Tulane University of La., First Mtge. Food Services Bldg. Rev., 1957	4⅞
Twin Lakes Reservoir & Canal Co., Ref.	4
Union County Trust Co., Elizabeth, N.J., Capital Notes	4½
University of Miami, Fla., First Mtge., 1954	5
University of Pittsburgh, Penn., First Mtge., Stud. Union Rev., 1957	5⅛

(a) Construct a frequency distribution from the above data.
(b) Justify your choice of class interval.
(c) What does this frequency distribution tell you about the distribution of yields on the "Miscellaneous Bonds"?
(d) Construct "more than" and "less than" cumulative frequency distributions.

5. Construct the before and after federal income tax Lorenz curves from the following data for 1954.

	Percentage of total money income before tax	Percentage of total money income after tax
Spending units ranked from the lowest (tenths)		
Lowest	1	1
Second	3	4
Third	5	5
Fourth	6	7
Fifth	8	8
Sixth	9	9
Seventh	11	11
Eighth	13	13
Ninth	15	15
Highest	29	27

Part Two

DESCRIPTIVE MEASURES

CHAPTER FOUR

Measures of
Central Tendency

A list of the consumption expenditures of all persons living in the United States would provide the viewer with little insight into the essential nature of the mass of data before him. Similarly, an enumeration of the net earnings of all firms in New England during 1964 could convey only a very vague notion of the profitability of carrying on business in that area. A management analyst seeking to discover the characteristics of the sales pattern of the Cincinnati Metals Company could gain virtually nothing by merely leafing through all of the invoices issued during any given year. Each of these examples demonstrates the point developed at the beginning of the preceding chapter—that unorganized masses of data in themselves are rarely of use in arriving at meaningful conclusions and, consequently, that processing is necessary. At that time it was pointed out that arraying the items in the order of their magnitudes helps somewhat and that organizing the data into a frequency distribution usually brings to light characteristics that otherwise would remain hidden. Often, however, it is desirable to go further and to summarize the entire mass of data with a single number. For example, when the consumption expenditures of residents of the United States are compared with the consumption expenditures of Canadians, or when the profits of New England firms are contrasted with those of companies in the Southwest, the advantages of using a single figure to represent the mass of data are apparent.

A number that can properly represent an entire series must reflect the tendency of the data to concentrate at, and be distributed about, certain central values. For this reason these summary numbers are frequently referred to as measures of central tendency. More commonly, however, they are known as *averages*.

Several statistical measures may be employed as averages. Each has its own individual characteristics, some of which may be advantages and

others disadvantages for the purpose at hand. The more important properties of most averages can be brought to light by answering the following
five questions with respect to the average under consideration.

1. Are all the items in the distribution employed in calculating the
average? If this is the situation, the value of the average will be influenced
by every item in the series that it represents.
2. If the average is multiplied by the number of items from which it
was computed, will the total be the same as the sum of the items of the
series? Should this condition be met, the average can be used to represent
the series in further computation.
3. Is the average affected by extremely large or small values in the
distribution? If so, these extremes may distort the average and reduce
its usefulness.
4. Is the average the middle item of the group? If it is, the same
number of items will have values above and below the average.
5. Is the average the value most frequently encountered in the
series? If it is, the average will be the most typical value of the data.

Actually, no one average will possess all the above characteristics.
The way each average meets this test will be considered below.

ARITHMETIC MEAN

The most common average is the arithmetic mean. The definition of
this measure is really a description of how to calculate it. The arithmetic
mean is the sum of the values in a group divided by the number of values
in the group. This type of average is the one that many incorrectly believe
provides a "yes" answer to the five questions given above. Actually, only
the first three questions can correctly be answered "yes" for the arithmetic mean.

1. The arithmetic mean does include all of the items in a distribution
in its calculation.
2. The arithmetic mean is a measure that, multiplied by the number
of items in the group from which it was derived, will give the original
total.
3. The arithmetic mean is affected by extremely large or small
values in the distribution from which it was derived. This characteristic,
in fact, is the greatest weakness of the arithmetic mean.

The last two questions must be answered "no" for the arithmetic
mean, except for certain special situations, notably the normal curve,
which will be mentioned later in the next chapter.

4. The arithmetic mean is not usually the middle value in a distribution.

5. The arithmetic mean is not usually the most commonly occurring value in the group.

Viewing the arithmetic mean with these answers in mind, it should be clear that, because of a "yes" answer for the first two questions, the arithmetic mean has a very definite relation to the total of the values in a distribution and therefore has a wide range of possible uses, but because it is affected by extremes it is often a very poor measure to represent a particular group.

Calculation of the Arithmetic Mean—Ungrouped Data

As an example, assume that a person went shopping and purchased 5 items, as given in Table 4-1.

Table 4-1

Item	Cost
1	$1.50
2	2.10
3	1.25
4	1.75
5	1.90
Total	$8.50

To arrive at a simple arithmetic mean would require only dividing the total of these purchases, $8.50, by the number of purchases, 5, resulting in an average of $1.70. The mean, in this example, indicates that the average purchase made by the shopper was $1.70.

Using this very simple example, certain characteristics of the mean can be illustrated. These characteristics are extremely simple points and they rank with many other statements that people read and immediately ignore as something they have always known. Despite their simplicity, these characteristics are important. Not only do they more fully describe the arithmetic mean, but they also provide a basis of comparison that can be used as a point of reference in comparing other averages with the arithmetic mean.

First, it should be noted that all 5 purchases were used to get the total from which the mean was calculated. All the items in the distribution affected the mean.

Second, multiplying the arithmetic mean by the number of items will produce the original total. Thus 5 times $1.70 gives $8.50.

Third, if the value of any of the items in the distribution is changed, the value of the arithmetic mean changes. For example, if the first purchase, instead of being $1.50, had been $2.50, the total would be $9.50 and the value of the arithmetic mean would change from $1.70 to $1.90.

Fourth, the arithmetic mean is clearly affected by extremes. For example, if the first item, instead of being $1.50, had been $11.50, the total would be $18.50 and the arithmetic mean $3.70. This mean, $3.70, would certainly not represent the group. Four of the 5 purchases were $2.10 or less and one of the 5, $11.50, was more than the mean. Certainly, $3.70 would not be indicative of the average purchase made by this buyer during the shopping trip.

Fifth, the sum of the deviations from the arithmetic mean is zero. Table 4-2 uses the same example to prove this statement.

Table 4-2

	Cost	Difference from mean
Item		
1	$1.50	−.20
2	2.10	+.40
3	1.25	−.45
4	1.75	+.05
5	1.90	+.20
Totals	$8.50	0

Although these are not the only characteristics of the arithmetic mean,[1] they seem to be the easiest to understand and the best for comparison with other measures of central tendency.

Weighted Arithmetic Mean

As a slightly more complicated example, assume that a recent high school graduate is considering the possibilities of becoming a television repair man. In his immediate neighborhood, he knows 5 men who do this sort of work. Three of them do the work on a full-time basis; the other two have additional jobs, repairing television receivers on a part-time

[1] Another important characteristic of the arithmetic mean is that the sum of the squared deviations from this mean will be a minimum—smaller than the sum of such deviations from any other average. Although this is certainly important, it is not as simple as the other characteristics and seems to be much less meaningful as a basis of comparison between averages.

basis after work and on holidays. From interviewing these men, the information presented in Table 4-3 is obtained.

A simple arithmetic average could be obtained from these figures by
dividing the total average hourly earnings, $10.98, by the number of men,
5, giving an average of $2.196 or $2.20. This would obviously be a misleading average because no attention has been given to the fact that the
wage which affects the mean the most because of its size, $3.15, was earned
only 40 times, whereas the smallest wage in the group, $1.73, was earned
200 times. To correct this situation a weighted mean should be found.
The purpose of weights is to give figures their proper relative importance.

Table 4-3

	Hours worked per month	Average hourly earnings
Man		
A	160	$ 1.85
B	200	1.73
C	120	1.80
D	40	3.15
E	60	2.45
Totals	580	$10.98

In this example, the hours worked per month by each man will satisfactorily indicate the relative importance of each of the average hourly
earnings. Two steps are necessary to get a weighted mean:

1. Multiply each of the values by their respective weights—in this
instance, average hourly earnings will be multiplied by the hours worked
per month.

2. Divide the total of the weighted values by the sum of the weights
—in this instance, the total weighted hourly earnings will be divided by
the total hours worked per month.

If we use Table 4-4, the first step would be to multiply each figure
representing hours worked per month by the corresponding value representing average hourly earnings. The second step would be to divide the
total weighted hourly earnings by the sum of the weights—$1131 by 580—
giving a weighted arithmetic mean of $1.95. This weighted mean represents
the earnings of the group much better than did the unweighted mean. The
unweighted mean in this example is $2.20 in contrast to the weighted mean
of only $1.95. The reason for the difference is that in the unweighted
average calculation the most important value was the $3.15 figure—the

largest average hourly earnings—whereas in the calculation of the weighted average the most important value is $346, representing the lowest average hourly earnings.

In such a small example, timesaving doesn't seem to be particularly important, but it must be emphasized that in larger problems involving more unwieldy figures any step toward making calculation easier is a

Table 4-4

Man	Hours worked per month	× Average hourly earnings	= Weighted hourly earnings
A	160	$1.85	$ 296
B	200	1.73	346
C	120	1.80	216
D	40	3.15	126
E	60	2.45	147
Totals	580		$1131

Table 4-5

Man	Hours worked per month	Weights	× Average hourly earnings	= Weighted hourly earnings
A	160	4	$1.85	$7.40
B	200	5	1.73	8.65
C	120	3	1.80	5.40
D	40	1	3.15	3.15
E	60	1.5	2.45	3.675
Totals		14.5		$28.275

step in the right direction. In the preceding paragraphs it was stated that the purpose of weights is to give figures their proper relative importance. In calculating the weighted arithmetic mean, it is not the absolute size of the weights that is of prime importance; it is their relative size. One simple way to reduce the size of weights is to find some common denominator that can be divided into each of the original weights. In the example, for instance, all the hours-worked numbers can be divided by 40 and a series of weights obtained. The weighted mean would be found through the same two steps—multiplying each of the average hourly earnings by these new weights and then dividing the total of the weighted values by the sum of these new weights. Table 4-5 illustrates this method.

Dividing the total of the weighted hourly earnings, $28.275, by the sum of the weights, 14.5, gives exactly the same arithmetic mean as before, $1.95. Notice how much smaller the weights have become and how much easier they are to multiply. In any sizable problem this would be a very worth-while feature.

The point to note in using reduced weights is that the relative, not the absolute, size of the weights is important. Before reducing the weights, repairman A had worked 160 hours per month—four times as many hours as repairman D. After the weights had been reduced, the weight for repairman A, 4, is still four times as great as the weight for repairman D, 1.

Calculation of the Arithmetic Mean—Grouped Data

As the preceding chapter stated, the frequency distribution is the most common means of presenting large groups of values. In instances where frequency distributions are presented, getting all the original values making up the distribution may be impossible or impractical. Yet it is

Table 4-6.   WAGES PAID TO WORKERS
Underground Rocket Company
(Plant A)

	No. of workers
Wages (dollars per week)	
40 but under 60	60
60 but under 80	70
80 but under 100	85
100 but under 120	110
120 but under 140	95
140 but under 160	80
	500

still evident that the average and other measures, which will be taken up in subsequent pages and chapters, are needed to provide more information about the distribution or to condense the information presented by the distribution itself so that various distributions can be compared more easily. To illustrate the method of computing the arithmetic mean from a frequency distribution, it seems best to create an easily understood distribution, as presented in Table 4-6.

It is immediately clear that a class interval of $40 up to $60 cannot be multiplied by a number of workers. For this reason, the mid-points of the class intervals are used to represent the various classes. A large X is most commonly used to designate mid-points.

The explanation of the calculation of the arithmetic mean from a grouped distribution will be broken down into three methods. In a sense, each of the first two methods helps to prepare the way for the third method, which is the shortest and most frequently used. Each of them, however, has its own peculiar uses.

It now becomes simpler to present methods in terms of formulas. Every attempt will be made to explain each formula carefully to indicate clearly that each is only a kind of shorthand notation of the method itself. $\bar{X}$ always designates the arithmetic mean.[2]

1. *Basic Method.* The crudest and most self-evident way to compute the arithmetic mean of the wages in the example would be to multiply the mid-point of each class interval by the number of workers in that interval, add these weighted values, and divide by the total frequency. If $\bar{X}$ signifies the arithmetic mean, Σ is a sign indicating addition, X indicates the mid-points, f the frequency in a class, and N the total of the frequencies, then in formula form this method would be

$$\bar{X} = \frac{\Sigma fX}{N}$$

With the use of this formula and the figures found in Table 4-7, the arithmetic mean is found to be

$$\bar{X} = \$52000/500 = \$104$$

This method is perfectly correct, but the arithmetic necessary is lengthy; hence any possibility of reducing the size of the figures used is an attractive one. This reduction can easily be achieved by multiplying the frequencies by differences from an assumed mean rather than by the mid-points.

2. *Actual-Deviations Method.* In the formula that will now be used, A indicates the assumed mean. This assumed mean is *any* one of the mid-points that might be selected. Usually the size of the numbers to be dealt with will be smaller if the mid-point used as the assumed mean is the mid-point beside the largest frequency, but the selection of any of the mid-points will give the same answer. Differences between each of the mid-points and the one selected as the assumed mean are indicated by the d in the formula.

---

[2] This is not strictly true. $\bar{X}$ commonly indicates the mean of a sample, whereas M indicates the mean of a universe. However, by this very fact, it should be evident that $\bar{X}$ appears most frequently as the symbol designating the arithmetic mean. Much more statistical work is done with samples.

Table 4-7.   WAGES PAID TO WORKERS
Underground Rocket Company
(Plant A)

Wages (dollars per week)	X	No. of workers f	fX
40 but under 60	$ 50	60	$ 3000
60 but under 80	70	70	4900
80 but under 100	90	85	7650
100 but under 120	110	110	12100
120 but under 140	130	95	12350
140 but under 160	150	80	12000
Totals		500	$52000

Table 4-8.   WAGES PAID TO WORKERS
Underground Rocket Company
(Plant A)

Wages (dollars per week)	X	d	f	fd
40 but under 60	$ 50	−60	60	$ −3600
60 but under 80	70	−40	70	−2800
80 but under 100	90	−20	85	−1700
100 but under 120	110	0	110	0
120 but under 140	130	+20	95	+1900
140 but under 160	150	+40	80	+3200
Totals			500	−8100
				+5100
				−3000

The formula is then

$$\bar{X} = A + \frac{\Sigma fd}{N}$$

In the example, the mid-point $110 will be used as the assumed mean. The calculation is presented in Table 4-8. With the use of the formula $\bar{X} = A + \Sigma fd/N$, the arithmetic mean is

$$\bar{X} = \$110 + (-3000/500) = \$110 - 6 = \$104$$

This short-cut method works because it is based on one of the characteristics of the arithmetic mean previously mentioned—namely, that the sum of the deviations from the arithmetic mean equals 0. If some midpoint is selected as the assumed mean and, as usually is the situation, it is not the actual mean, the sum of the deviations from this assumed mean will not be 0. But, adding or subtracting the average of these deviations from the assumed mean gives a corrected mid-point, a figure from which the sum of the deviations is 0—the actual arithmetic mean.

There is more saving of time in the second formula than in the first. The saving would, of course, be more evident if the problem involved larger numbers. One of these first two formulas would have to be used if the class intervals were unequal. However, if, as in the example, the class intervals are equal, a third formula, which makes a very definite reduction in work, can be used. As was stated in connection with the weighted average, it is not the absolute size of weights that is important but their relative size.

3. *Step-Deviations Method.* As long as the relative size of the differences remains the same, their absolute size is unimportant. In the example, each class interval is $20. If the d column, used to get the values for the previous formula, is examined, it will be seen that, because the class intervals are equal, the difference between each of the values in the d column is exactly the same as the class interval—$20. If each of these values were to be divided by some common value, they would all be divided by $20.

The third formula decreases the amount of arithmetic by stating differences from the assumed mean in terms of class-interval units (the number of class intervals each mid-point is from the assumed mean). These differences are indicated by d_s in the formula. Before the average of these differences can be compared to the assumed mean, the size of the class interval must be reinstated into the formula. For this reason, the average of these differences is multiplied by the size of the class interval, which is indicated by i in the formula. The formula is

$$\bar{X} = A + \frac{\Sigma f d_s}{N}\, i$$

The mid-point of $110 will still be used as the assumed mean so that the formulae may be more easily compared. The calculations needed to provide the required figures are presented in Table 4-9. With the use of this data, the formula[3] would read

$$\bar{X} = \$110 + (-150/500)20 = \$110 + (-3000/500) = \$110 - 6 = \$104$$

[3] The fact that these formulas are only a kind of shorthand must be emphasized. Business students, many of whom have had only a brief acquaintance with mathematics and symbols, may quite often be confused when symbols vary among teachers and textbooks. Sometimes, for example, x_1 is used instead of d_s. Nothing at all is changed in the method—it remains the same, regardless of the symbols used.

Table 4-9. WAGES PAID TO WORKERS
Underground Rocket Company
(Plant A)

	X	d_s	No. of workers f	fd_s
Wages (dollars per week)				
40 but under 60	$ 50	−3	60	−180
60 but under 80	70	−2	70	−140
80 but under 100	90	−1	85	− 85
100 but under 120	110	0	110	0
120 but under 140	130	+1	95	+ 95
140 but under 160	150	+2	80	+160
Totals			500	−405
				+255
				−150

Table 4-10. WAGES PAID TO WORKERS
Underground Rocket Company
(Plant A)

	X	d_s	No. of workers f	fd_s
Wages (dollars per week)				
40 but under 60	$ 50	0	60	0
60 but under 80	70	+1	70	+ 70
80 but under 100	90	+2	85	+ 170
100 but under 120	110	+3	110	+ 330
120 but under 140	130	+4	95	+ 380
140 but under 160	150	+5	80	+ 400
Totals			500	+1350

The calculations in Table 4-10 prove that the final answer, the arithmetic mean, is the same regardless of which mid-point is used as the assumed mean. Here $50, rather than the $110 previously selected, is used as the assumed mean. Although the arithmetic involved is slightly greater because the assumed mean is farther from the actual mean, the result is not affected. With the use of this data, the formula would read

$$\bar{X} = \$50 + (+1350/500)20 = \$50 + (+27000/500) = \$50 + 54 = \$104$$

The value of the arithmetic mean is precisely the same when found by any one of the three formulas given. Any one of the mid-points, not just the $110 used, could have been selected as the assumed mean in the last two formulas; the answer would still have been the same.

The last formula is for practical reasons the most important of the three. Although the first two are necessary whenever intervals are unequal, the final one is more commonly used elsewhere. Not only is the last formula one that is more common and one that reduces the amount of arithmetic involved, but it is also directly connected to the formula usually used to calculate the standard deviation explained in the next chapter. Thus a thorough comprehension of the technique used in this arithmetic-mean formula—a relatively simple measure to understand—will facilitate understanding of the calculation of the standard deviation—a relatively more difficult measure to grasp.

It should be noticed that nothing has been said concerning the choice of the formulas presented here over other possible formulas. The reason is that the arithmetic mean is one of the rigidly defined measures of central tendency. There may be differences in symbols used in the various formulas, but the basic method will remain the same. This characteristic is a great advantage of the arithmetic mean. It immediately eliminates any arguments concerning method and makes the mean a value that can be checked by anyone desiring to do so without any question about what method was used. In other words, it is a measure that can be used with confidence by a person other than the calculator.

Any measure computed from a frequency distribution will, of course, usually differ from the same measure computed from the same but ungrouped data. Proper care in constructing the frequency distribution will reduce the probable difference. At best, measures calculated from frequency distributions are, in a sense, careful estimates. This fact does not, however, reduce the usefulness of these measures. If the formulas used are sound mathematically and the frequency distribution carefully constructed, differences that may exist between measures calculated from grouped and ungrouped data will be unimportant. Also important are the great saving in time involved when grouped data are used and, of course, the fact that there are instances when the ungrouped data would be unavailable.

When to Use the Arithmetic Mean

At the beginning of this section it was noted that the arithmetic mean is the most widely understood and frequently used type of average.

The very fact that a statistical measure is known and can be comprehended by many readers is in itself a recommendation. In addition, because it is rigidly defined and all the values in the series are employed in its calculation, the arithmetic mean can be used in making further computations. The fact that the arithmetic mean multiplied by the number of items in the distribution results in a total equal to the sum of the items makes it especially useful for certain purposes. For example, if a department store is planning to open a new branch in a near-by city, one of the things management will want to know is the amount of additional weekly pay-roll expense this expansion will entail. If the same type of personnel will be employed and if wages and salaries in the near-by city are approximately the same as in the headquarters city, an accurate forecast of the additional pay roll can be prepared by multiplying the arithmetic mean of employees' weekly pay in the current store by the number of persons to be hired in the branch.

The values of extreme items do influence the arithmetic mean. In situations like that of the department store example above, this fact is not a disadvantage, because similar extreme items can be expected at the new branch. However, in some instances extreme values are not representative of the data under study and do distort the arithmetic mean in an undesirable manner. If further computations are not contemplated under these circumstances, some other average should be employed. The arithmetic mean should not be used to average ratios and rates of change. Here the geometric mean described below is most appropriate. Generally speaking, with the exception just noted, the arithmetic mean should be selected when the average will be used in further computation, and it may well be used for other purposes so long as the influence of extreme values is not important.

GEOMETRIC MEAN

The geometric mean is another rigidly defined average. Although it is employed less often than any of the other averages, it has its uses. There are two outstanding reasons why it is less frequently used, both of which are connected with the fact that logarithms are used to compute this average. The first reason is that, because of the use of logarithms, the arithmetic involved is naturally more laborious. The second is that any measure based on logarithms is more difficult to explain and is understood by a relatively small percentage of the population.

Referring to the five questions asked at the beginning of this chapter:

1. The geometric mean *is* a measure that includes all the items in a distribution in its calculation.

2. The geometric mean multiplied by the number of items in the group from which it was derived does *not* give the original total.

3. The geometric mean is *not* affected by extremely large values in the distribution from which it was derived.

4. The geometric mean is *not* the middle value in the group.

5. The geometric mean is *not* the most commonly occurring value in the group.

Only the first question, whether the geometric mean is a measure including all the items in a distribution in its calculation, was answered positively.

The two foremost advantages of the geometric mean are its rigid definition and the fact that it is not affected drastically by extremely large values. The geometric mean should be used in averaging ratios, in computing average rates of change, and in computing an average for a series distributed logarithmically.

Calculation of the Geometric Mean—Ungrouped Data

The definition of the geometric mean, like that of the arithmetic mean, is really a description of how to calculate it: The geometric mean is the antilog of the sum of the logarithms of the values in a group divided by the number of values in the group. The calculation of the geometric mean, though laborious, is not difficult. Really the only difference between the

Table 4-11

	Cost	Logarithm
Item		
1	$1.50	.1761
2	2.10	.3222
3	1.25	.0969
4	1.75	.2430
5	1.90	.2788
Total		1.1170

method of calculating this mean and the arithmetic mean is that the values in the former are changed to logs and it becomes necessary to find the antilog of the answer. The same examples that were used in explaining the arithmetic mean are employed here in order to facilitate a comparison of the computation techniques, although in reality the geometric mean would not in most instances be used with data of this kind. Table 4-11 refers to the items purchased by a shopper.

In calculating the geometric mean, the logarithm of each item is found and these logarithms are totaled and divided by the number of values. The average of these logarithms must then be converted to its antilog. In this example, the total of the logarithms is 1.1170. Dividing this by the number of values, 5, gives an average of .2234. The antilog of .2234 is $1.67. It should be noted that the arithmetic mean for the same items was $1.70. The geometric mean is smaller than the arithmetic one because the larger numbers do not have as much influence on the geometric mean. Because the values of these items are relatively alike in size, the difference between the two means is small.

The difference in the effect of extreme values can be seen more easily if the first item, instead of being $1.50, is $11.50, as in Table 4-12.

Table 4-12

Item	Cost	Logarithm
1	$11.50	1.0607
2	2.10	.3222
3	1.25	.0969
4	1.75	.2430
5	1.90	.2788
Total		2.0016

In this example, the geometric mean is found by first dividing 2.0016 by 5, which gives an answer of .4003, and then finding the antilog of this, $2.51. Though the geometric mean still does not represent this particular set of values adequately, it can easily be seen that the extreme value of $11.50 had much less effect on the geometric method, which resulted in a geometric mean of $2.51, than it did on the arithmetic method, which resulted in an arithmetic mean of $3.70.

Calculation of the Geometric Mean—Grouped Data

As with ungrouped data, the calculation of the geometric mean from grouped data is laborious but not complicated. In grouped data, the values are represented by mid-points; hence it is the mid-points that must be changed to logarithms. The major part of the effort required is multiplying these logs by the frequencies. The products are then totaled and divided by the number of frequencies. Finding the antilog of this value provides the final answer—the geometric mean. The formula for this method is

$$\log GM = \frac{\Sigma f \log X}{N}$$

Using the same frequency distribution that was used to illustrate the arithmetic mean makes comparison of the two means easier. The work necessary for the geometric mean is presented in Table 4-13.

With the use of the formula, $\log GM = \Sigma f \log X/N$ in this example

$$\log GM = 996.6665/500 = 1.9933$$

and the antilog of this, the geometric mean, is $98.47.

Table 4-13.   WAGES PAID TO WORKERS
Underground Rocket Company
(Plant A)

	X	log X	No. of workers f	f log X
Wages (dollars per week)				
40 but under 60	$ 50	1.6990	60	101.9400
60 but under 80	70	1.8451	70	129.1570
80 but under 100	90	1.9542	85	166.1070
100 but under 120	110	2.0414	110	224.5540
120 but under 140	130	2.1139	95	200.8205
140 but under 160	150	2.1761	80	174.0880
Total			500	996.6665

The arithmetic mean of this distribution is $104. Again the geometric mean is definitely smaller than the arithmetic mean because less emphasis is placed on large values. This fact can be even more easily seen if attention is given to the X and log X columns. The mid-point $150 is three times as large as the first mid-point $50, but the log of the mid-point $150, 2.1761, is definitely not three times the size of the log of the mid-point $50, 1.6990. The relative size of the larger value has then been reduced.

The usefulness of the geometric mean can also be illustrated in a brief example using price ralatives. To emphasize the situation, Boston and Houston will be used as points of comparison for two commodities. In the example presented in Table 4-14, Boston will be used as the base city, and the prices in Houston will be compared to the prices in Boston.

In this example, if the arithmetic average of price relatives is used, the answer indicates that the prices of these commodities in Houston are, on the average, 25-percent higher than the prices in Boston. If, however, Houston is used as the base, the arithmetic average of price relatives would indicate that the prices in Boston are 25-percent higher than the prices in Houston. Now, it is inconsistent to say that the prices of the same two commodities are 25-percent higher in Boston than in Houston and 25-percent higher in Houston than in Boston.

If the geometric mean is used, the average of the logarithms is 2.0000 and the antilog 100, regardless of which city is used as a base. This is a consistent answer. If the price of one commodity is twice as much in Boston as in Houston and the average of the other only half as much, the average of the relatives should remain at 100, as it does when the

Table 4-14. PRICES OF GASOLINE AND OIL IN BOSTON AND HOUSTON

	Boston			Houston		
	Price in cents	Price relative	Logs of relatives	Price in cents	Price relative	Logs of relatives
Commodity						
Gasoline (gal.)	.25	100	2.0000	.50	200	2.3010
Oil (qt.)	.60	100	2.0000	.30	50	1.6990
Total		200	4.0000		250	4.0000
Average		100	2.0000		125	2.0000

geometric mean is computed. As this statement implies, whenever relatives or ratios are to be averaged, the geometric mean should be employed.

MEDIAN

Often neither the arithmetic nor the geometric means provides a satisfactory measure of central tendency. An example of this difficulty is the situation in which the alumni department of a college found itself. The department planned to publish a story in its alumni magazine concerning alumni contributions. It seemed evident that an average was necessary to represent the data. By calculation it was found that the arithmetic mean was $17. This discovery was unfortunate. In the first place, no one had ever actually contributed $17 to the alumni fund, and hence it would be a very unrealistic figure to use. Secondly, a very small percentage of the contributors had ever given as much as $17. Most contributors gave $5 or $10. A few had given amounts in the hundreds, and these few extremes had served to pull the average upward. Now, if $17 was published as an average contribution, many of those who had given less in the past and could not afford to give more might decide not to give anything in the hope that they might eventually be forgotten.

Two measures of central tendency exist that are excellent to use in such a situation. One of these, the first to be explained, is called the median; the other the mode. The median is by definition the middle value in a distribution. Whenever the median is given as a measure, one half of the items in the distribution have a value the size of the median value or smaller, and one half have a value the size of the median value or larger.

It is revealing to apply to the median the same five questions that were applied to the arithmetic and geometric means.

1. The median is *not* a measure that includes all the items in a distribution in its calculation.

2. The median is *not* a measure that can be multiplied by the number of items in the group from which it was derived, in order to obtain the original total.

3. The median is *not* affected by extremely large or small values in the distribution from which it was derived.

4. The median *is* the middle value in a group.

5. The median is *not* the most commonly occurring value in a group.

Because the median does not use all the items in a distribution in its calculation, it can be calculated for an open-end frequency distribution. The arithmetic and geometric means cannot be calculated for open-end distributions because a mid-point value for each interval is necessary for their calculation. Naturally, no mid-point value can be found for an interval which has either no upper limit or no lower limit.

The fact that the median is not affected by extremely large or small values is also a distinct advantage. The arithmetic and geometric means are called "calculated averages" because they use all the items in their calculation and do not depend on the position of any particular item. The median is a positional measure because it is the value at a particular position in the distribution. It does not use all of the items in its calculation but is concerned only with items in the class intervals on each side of the middle item and in the class interval in which the middle item is located. That is to say, extremely large or small values do not at all enter into the calculation of the median.

Perhaps the greatest advantage of the median is, however, the fact that the median actually does indicate what many people incorrectly believe the arithmetic mean indicates. The median indicates the value of the middle item in the distribution. This is a clear-cut meaning and makes the median a measure that can be easily explained.

Calculation of the Median—Ungrouped Data

The calculation of the median from ungrouped data is extremely simple. The only possible complexity arises when an extremely large number of items is involved, and then the only problem is the amount of necessary labor. If we use the same ungrouped distribution that has already been used for the arithmetic and geometric means—the items procured by a shopper—rearrangement as in Table 4-15 is the only operation necessary. To find the middle value, the values must be arranged in order from the smallest to the largest.

Table 4-15

	Cost	Rearrangement
Item		
1	$1.50	$1.25
2	2.10	1.50
3	1.25	1.75
4	1.75	1.90
5	1.90	2.10

Table 4-16

	Cost	Rearrangement
Item		
1	$11.50	$1.25
2	2.10	1.75
3	1.25	1.90
4	1.75	2.10
5	1.90	11.50

When these values are arranged in numerical order, the third item has a value of $1.75. Thus the middle, or median, value in this group is $1.75. Two items had a value less than this, and two had a value higher. The arithmetic mean for this group was $1.70.

The fact that the median is not affected by extremes can easily be seen if the first cost is changed from $1.50 to $11.50. When the arithmetic mean was computed under these conditions it became $3.70, a clearly unrepresentative amount. The median, however, would still be the middle value, this time $1.90, and thus a representative value. This situation is given in Table 4-16.

The median value changed in this example only because one of the lowest values in the group was changed to one of the largest. It should be noticed that any variation in the values on each side of the median, as long as they remain either smaller or larger, as they were, will have no effect on the median whatsoever.

Although it is obvious that the third value in a group of 5 is the middle value, there is an arithmetic method for determining the mid-value, which is of use in working with larger figures. The rule is that in a group composed of an odd number of values, such as 5, add 1 to the total number of values and divide this by 2. Thus 5 + 1 would be 6, which, divided by 2, gives 3—the number of the value starting at either end of the numerically arranged group that will be the median value. In a large group the same method would be followed. In a group of 99 items the middle value would be the 50th value. This would be determined by $(99 + 1)/2 = 50$.

The procedure for determining the median of an even-numbered group of items is not as obvious. If there were, for instance, eight different values in a group, the median is really not determinable because both the fourth and fifth values are in the center. In practice, the median value for a group composed of an even number of items is estimated by finding the arithmetic mean of the two middle values—that is, adding the two values in the middle and dividing by two.

Calculation of the Median—Grouped Data

The formula for the median is

$$Me = L + (p/f)i$$

This formula assumes that the frequencies are cumulated starting at the smallest class values. The formula

$$Me = U - (p/f)i,$$

the same method, assumes that the frequencies are cumulated starting at the largest class values.

To give meaning to the letters used in these formulae, it is necessary to define the "median class." The median class is the class in which the middle item in the distribution lies. Dividing the total frequencies by 2 will determine which item is in the center, and cumulating the frequencies from either end of the distribution until the half-way item is reached will serve to locate the frequency in the middle. By referring to the corresponding class interval the median class is located.

In the formula first presented, L denotes the lower limit of the median class, f the frequency in that class, and i the class interval of that class. p is only slightly more difficult to explain. p represents the number of items needed in the median class in order to reach the middle item. For example, if there were 200 frequencies in a distribution, the 100th frequency would be the center, and the object would be to find the value associated with this 100th frequency. If, in cumulating the frequencies, 95 were cumulated up to the median class, only 5 more would be needed in the median class to reach the middle item. This 5 would be p in the formula.

In calculating the median of a frequency distribution there is no question of whether to add 1 to the total frequencies depending on whether the number is even or odd. This procedure was followed in the ungrouped distribution because specific items and individual values were involved.

Table 4-17. INCOME OF PERSONS PURCHASING ORDINARY LIFE INSURANCE—1956
(Ages 0–14 Excluded)

	No. of policies (in thousands)	Cumulated no.
Income (dollars)		
under 2000	175	175
2000 but under 3000	641	816
3000 but under 4000	1225	2041
4000 but under 5000	1225	3266
5000 but under 7500	1458	
7500 but under 10,000	408	
10,000 and over	699	
Total	5831	

SOURCE: *Life Insurance Fact Book, 1957; Life Insurance Buying, 1956* (New York: Institute of Life Insurance).

In a frequency distribution all the frequencies have lost their individuality. The effort now is not to find the value of one specific item but to find a particular point on a curve—the one value that will have 50 percent of the frequencies on one side of it and 50 percent of the frequencies on the other. The example in Table 4-17 will more clearly indicate the method.

If we use the first formula given, $Me = L + (p/f)i$, in this problem,

$$Me = \$4000 + (874.5/1225)\$1000$$

$$Me = \$4000 + \$710 = \$4710$$

These values were obtained by following the definitions of terms already given. Thus the median class was found by dividing the total frequencies, 5831, by 2, which gives 2915.5 as the middle frequency. Cumulating the frequencies proves that this frequency must be in the $4000 up to $5000 class interval, because before reaching that interval there are 2041 cumulated frequencies—not enough—and after including those in the next interval there are 3266, more than the 2915.5 needed. The 2915.5th frequency must be somewhere in that last interval; hence this interval becomes the median class interval. The lower limit of that class is $4000; the number of frequencies in it is 1225, and its class interval is $1000. Because 2041 frequencies had been cumulated before reaching that interval, by subtracting the 2041 from 2915.5—the number desired—it is found that 874.5 more frequencies are needed to reach the center, 2915.5th frequency.

This is, of course, a percentage system. The class interval for the median class in this example is $1000. The question is, "What percentage of the way through this interval must the middle value in the distribution be located?" Dividing the number of frequencies needed, 874.5, by the total number in the interval, 1225, gives the percentage of the frequencies needed—.71 or 71 percent. If 71 percent of the frequencies are needed to reach the middle item and the frequencies in that class are spread over an interval of $1000, it is estimated that 71 percent of this interval, or $710, is needed to reach the value of this middle item.

The second formula given, $Me = U - (p/f)i$, is the same method but starts cumulating from the higher values. U in this formula represents the upper limit of the median class. For this problem the values would be

$$Me = \$5000 - (350.5/1225)\$1000$$

$$Me = \$5000 - \$290 = \$4710$$

Regardless of at which end cumulating is begun, the value of the median will, of course, be the same.

In this example the median value is $4710. This value indicates that, as near as it can be estimated by this formula, one half of the policies purchased in 1955 were purchased by persons having an income of $4710 or less and one half by persons having an income of $4710 or more.

It should be noticed that neither the arithmetic nor the geometric means could have been calculated from this frequency distribution. Both of these measures require class mid-points for all the classes, and, as this is an open-end distribution, no mid-points can be found for the first and last class intervals.

The median, although not as commonly used as the arithmetic mean, is a fairly popular measure. One of the most familiar uses of the median is in the Dun & Bradstreet ratios.[4] Since 1938 Dun & Bradstreet has compiled its "14 important ratios" annually, and median ratios are one

[4] Roy A. Foulke, *The Genesis of the 14 Important Ratios* (New York: Dun & Bradstreet, Inc., 1955).

of the ways in which this information is presented. These ratios are provided for a five-year period for 70 different lines of business activity and offer excellent information for financial analysis.

MODE

In a discussion of fashions, the use of the word "mode" is commonplace. In this field it refers to the particular clothing that is in style—that is, popular. In statistics the mode means the same thing in a sense, as it refers to the most "popular" value. The mode, by definition, is the most frequently occurring value. In the alumni magazine article referred to in connection with the median, $10 was the mode of the alumni contributions. This means that more alumni gave $10 than gave any other amount.

Applying the same five questions to the mode that have been applied to the other measures of central tendency indicates the features of the mode as such a measure.

1. The mode is *not* a measure that includes all the items in a distribution in its calculation.

2. The mode is *not* a measure that can be multiplied by the number of items in the group from which it was derived and the original total thus obtained.

3. The mode is *not* affected by extremely large or small values in the distribution from which it was derived.

4. The mode is *not* the middle value in a group.

5. The mode *is* the most commonly occurring value in a group.

The mode, like the median, does not use all the items in a distribution in its calculation, and this fact gives it advantages similar to those of the median. The mode also can be calculated for an open-end frequency distribution, and the mode also is not affected by extremely large or small values. The mode is another measure that actually does indicate what many people incorrectly believe the arithmetic mean indicates. The mode is the most frequently occurring value. If the modal wage in a factory is $65, more workers receive $65 than receive any other wage. This modal wage is what many believe the "average" wage always indicates; actually, such a meaning is indicated only if the average used is the mode.

Calculation of the Mode—Ungrouped Data

The mode is an extremely simple measure to use. It is necessary, for an ungrouped distribution, only to pick out the number that occurs most often. Thus, if a store listed its sales for a particular day in order by value of sale as $5, 6, 7, 7, 8, 9, 9, 9, 10, 10, 11, the mode would be $9. The mode is most representative when there is one number that occurs a far greater number of times than does any other. In the example, 3 of 11 sales were $9. According to its definition, the mode here is $9. The mode would, however, be an even better average to use to represent this series of values if the $9 sale had occurred 6 of 11 times. The more often the modal value appears relatively, the more valuable the measure is as an average to represent data.

Calculation of the Mode—Grouped Data

A disadvantage of the mode is that it is not a rigidly defined measure. There are several formulas for calculating the mode, all of which usually give somewhat different answers. If this difficulty is overemphasized, the value of the mode as a measure is questionable. It should be remembered, however, that the mode is at its best as a measure of central tendency when there is a clear-cut situation—a situation in which there is clearly one value or one class that is outstanding in the frequency of its occurrence. If the mode is used only for situations for which it is best suited, the meaning of the answer obtained is clear and useful. In such instances, that there are different formulas does not injure the representativeness of the mode.

Again, the method and formula used here are not necessarily perfect, and some persons might not consider this method the best. It seems, however, to be just as good as any other; moreover, it is a fairly popular and easily computed method.

The formula for the mode is

$$M_0 = L + \frac{d_1}{d_1 + d_2} i$$

In this formula, L signifies the lower limit of the modal class. The modal class is the class that has the largest frequency. d_1 indicates the difference between the frequency of the modal class and the frequency of the preceding class. d_2 indicates the difference between the frequency of the modal class and the frequency of the following class. i stands for the class interval of the modal class. The example in Table 4-18 will illustrate the method.

Because the largest frequency is 2305, the corresponding class, $3,000 through $3,999, becomes the modal class. With the use of the formula,

$$Mo = L + [d_1/(d_1 + d_2)]i$$

$$Mo = \$3000 + [592/(592 + 651)]\$1000$$

$$Mo = \$3000 + (592/1243)\$1000 = \$3000 + \$480 = \$3480$$

Thus $3480 is the mode—the income received more often than any other income by these families. Notice that the d_1 in the formula is calculated by subtracting the frequency in the class preceding the modal class, 1713, from the frequency in the modal class, 2305; the result is a d_1 of 592. d_2 is calculated by subtracting the frequency in the class following the modal class, 1654, from the frequency in the modal class, 2305; the result is a d_2 of 651.

As the example indicates, the mode also can be calculated from an open-end frequency distribution. The mode can also, as in the example,

Table 4-18. INCOME AFTER TAXES FOR A SAMPLE OF
NONCONSTANT* INCOME FAMILIES
U.S. Urban (1950)

Income (dollars)	Sample frequency
under 1000	419
1000 through 1999	983
2000 through 2999	1713
3000 through 3999	2305
4000 through 4999	1654
5000 through 5999	931
6000 through 7499	627
7500 through 9999	333
10,000 and over	230
Total	9195

* Nonconstant indicates families not having the same income in the previous year and expecting a change in the following year.

Source: Irwin Friend and Irving B. Kravis, "Consumers in the American Economy," *American Economic Review, Papers and Proceedings* (Menasha, Wis.: American Economic Association, May 1957), p. 545.

be calculated from a distribution having unequal class intervals. However, careful examination of the data used in the sample will reveal that all the class intervals near the modal class are equal. Under these conditions —equal class intervals, at least in the classes around the modal class—the mode can be calculated without any great difficulty. If the class intervals on each side of the modal class are not equal in size, difficulty is encountered.

The formula for the mode is essentially a weighting formula. A percentage of the class interval in the modal class is added onto the lower limit of the modal class. How large this percentage is depends on the size of the frequencies on each side of the modal class. The differences between the frequencies on each side of the modal class and the frequency of the modal class become weights—weights that determine how much of the modal class interval shall be added onto the lower limit. If the frequencies in the classes on both sides of the modal class are to be used to produce weights, fairness requires that frequencies have the same opportunity to occur on both sides. If the class interval on one side of the modal class is smaller than the class interval on the other, obviously frequencies will not have the same opportunity to fall on both sides.

If we use this line of reasoning, a basic rule can be established: class intervals on each side of the modal class must be equal in size to each other. It is best if they are also the same size as the modal class interval, but at the very least they must be the same size as each other. Very often, by combining classes on each side of the mode, the mode can even be calculated in distributions that do not immediately meet this requirement. This calculation will work if, when the classes are combined, the resulting interval on one side of the modal class equals the interval on the other side.

Many rules can be found concerning the necessity of combining classes in distributions having two or more class frequencies, near each other in the distribution, of about the same size. The safest rule, however, is to remember that the mode is most meaningful when there is a clear-cut outstanding frequency. When this situation does not exist, reliance on some other measure of central tendency seems preferable.

In instances where combining classes will not produce a situation of equal class intervals on each side of the modal class, and where no clear-cut modal class exists, some other measure must be used. Another instance when the mode cannot be found is in a bimodal distribution—a distribution with two modes. If such a distribution were to be plotted, a double humped curve would result. The definition of the mode as *the* most frequently occurring value excludes the possibility of two values fulfilling this requirement.

If collected data produce a bimodal distribution, the data themselves should be questioned. Quite often such a condition is caused by the taking of too small a sample; the difficulty can be remedied by increasing the sample size. Another common cause is the use of nonhomogeneous data. If, for example, statistics had been gathered at the beginning of World War II relating to tire mileage, and both natural and synthetic rubber tires had been included, a bimodal distribution would have been the result. In this example the data would not have been homogeneous, and separate data should have been obtained for each of the two categories of rubber tires, natural and synthetic. In a situation such as this, the separation of the data into homogeneous groups will produce ordinary distributions with one mode, and the mode then can be considered as a possible measure of central tendency. In instances where a distribution is bimodal and nothing can be done to change it, the mode is obviously eliminated as a possible measure of central tendency.

COMPARISON OF MEASURES

Four measures of central tendency have been considered in this chapter: the arithmetic mean, the geometric mean, the median, and the mode. Each has its own peculiar meanings, advantages, and disadvantages. The selection of an average depends on how the measure is to be employed and the characteristics of the averages themselves.

If the measure is to be used further algebraically, the mode is necessarily eliminated because it is not a rigidly defined measure. For problems in probability or quality control the arithmetic mean is necessary. For an open-end distribution or any distribution containing extreme items the median is excellent. The mode is best for situations where there is an outstandingly large frequency.

If the measure is to be compared with averages already calculated for other distributions, it must be the same as those with which it is being compared. Should it be necessary to present data to a group relatively unfamiliar with statistical techniques, certainly one of the more understandable measures is needed—obviously not the geometric mean. Remembering the characteristics of each of the averages facilitates the selection of the proper one for the particular situation. Any businessman not appreciating the possibilities inherent in each of these measures of central tendency is neglecting valuable analytical tools.

SUGGESTED READINGS

Chou, Y. *Applied Business and Economic Statistics*. New York: Holt, Rinehart and Winston, Inc. 1963, chap. 6.

Griffin, J. I. *Statistics, Methods and Applications*. New York: Holt, Rinehart and Winston, Inc., 1962, chap. 5.

Lewis, E. V. *Statistical Aanalysis, Ideas and Methods*. Princeton, N.J.: D. Van Nostrand Company, Inc., 1963, chap. 3.

QUESTIONS

1. Compare the arithmetic mean, median, mode, and geometric mean to show the manner in which they are affected by extreme values.
2. Which is the best average?
3. Why must the class intervals on each side of the modal class be of equal size when the mode is calculated from a frequency distribution?

4. Would it be possible for more than one half of the workers in a plant to receive a wage lower than the arithmetic mean? Of what significance is your answer to the use of the mean by (a) the public relations director of the firm, and (b) the union business agent?

5. Why is the geometric mean smaller than the arithmetic mean when they are both calculated from the same distribution?

6. Why is the median rather than the mean called a "positional" value?

7. What is a "bimodal" distribution?

8. If the average weight of male babies at birth is $7\frac{1}{2}$ pounds, is it possible for the most common weight to be $6\frac{1}{2}$ pounds?

9. The greatest weakness of the arithmetic mean does not affect the median and mode. Why?

10. The dispersion of the data may be concealed by the use of an average. Discuss.

11. State clearly two of the three reasons given in the text for a bimodal distribution *and* the proper steps to take in calculating the mode in each instance.

12. Give a specific example of an instance in which
    (a) The median would be used in preference to the arithmetic mean
    (b) The arithmetic mean would not be as satisfactory as the geometric mean
    (c) The mode would be used in preference to the median.

13. State clearly, numbering each step, how to calculate the following measures from *ungrouped* data: (a) median, (b) arithmetic mean, (c) geometric mean.

14. In a particular distribution, there are two class intervals, each having an extremely large number of frequencies. They are located next to each other in the distribution. No other classes have as many frequencies. How would you calculate the mode?

15. What is the purpose of an average?

16. Explain the reason why the short-cut method of calculating the arithmetic mean produces the same answer that the long method produces.

17. In 1950, the median age of the people of the United States was 30.2 years. Explain the meaning of this statement. (SOURCE: *Census of Population*, U.S. Department of Commerce, Bureau of the Census)

PROBLEMS

1. From the following distribution, which depicts the sales of dentifrice in retail drugstores in Boston,
   (a) Calculate arithmetic mean, mode, median, and geometric mean.
   (b) Which average best summarizes the distribution? Why?

Daily sales (dollars)	No. of sales
10 but under 20	10
20 but under 30	30
30 but under 40	40
40 but under 50	15
50 but under 60	5
	100

2. Using the following figures,
   (a) Derive arithmetic mean, geometric mean, and median.

Sale number	Amount (dollars)
1	1.50
2	3.00
3	2.75
4	2.00
5	1.25
6	2.50
7	1.00
	14.00

   (b) Why are the values of two of these averages the same?
3. What is the class interval in the following distribution?

Earnings (dollars)	No. of workers
50.00 through 59.99	5
60.00 through 69.99	9

4. From the following frequency distribution, calculate
   (a) The arithmetic mean by each of the three methods presented in the text, (b) median, (c) mode, and (d) geometric mean.

Earnings (dollars)	No. of workers
40.00 through 44.99	3
45.00 through 49.99	9
50.00 through 54.99	15
55.00 through 59.99	27
60.00 through 64.99	18
65.00 through 69.99	12
70.00 through 74.99	9
75.00 through 79.99	7

5. Calculate the "best" average for the following frequency distribution.

SIZE OF ELECTRONICS DISTRIBUTORS
IN NORTHEASTERN UNITED STATES
1965

Volume group (dollars)	No. of distributors
under 100,000	84
100,000 but under 250,000	144
250,000 but under 500,000	98
500,000 but under 1,000,000	70
over 1,000,000	54
	450

6. Using the distribution of earnings of door-to-door appliance salesmen, below, calculate (a) arithmetic mean, (b) mode, (c) median, and (d) geometric mean.

Weekly earnings (dollars)	No. of salesmen
30 but under 35	2
35 but under 40	10
40 but under 45	18
45 but under 50	50
50 but under 55	70
55 but under 60	30
60 but under 65	18
65 but under 70	1
70 but under 75	1
	200

7. Examining the averages calculated in problem 6, state
   (a) Which average would be most significant to a young man considering this line of endeavor as a career?
   (b) Which average would be most useful to the Bureau of Internal Revenue?

8. Using the following distribution,
   (a) Calculate arithmetic mean, mode, median, and geometric mean.

LENGTH OF LIFE IN HOURS OF SAMPLE OF
BRAND X FLASHLIGHT BATTERIES

Hours	No. of batteries
150 but under 175	45
175 but under 200	54
200 but under 225	62
225 but under 250	75
250 but under 275	33
275 but under 300	25
300 but under 325	12
325 but under 350	9

   (b) If you were the purchasing agent for a large city whose police
   force used this type of battery, which average would you employ
   in calculating your requirements for the next year?
9. Using the following data, explain the five characteristics of the arithmetic mean presented in the text. Use an arithmetic illustration whenever possible.

ELEVATOR TRIPS PER DAY IN CYCLOP OFFICE BUILDING
(January 5 through January 11, 1965)

	No. of elevator trips per day
Monday	115
Tuesday	140
Wednesday	120
Thursday	130
Friday	145
Saturday	150
Sunday	110

10. Using the following information, calculate the average hourly earnings
    of construction labor.

	No. of hours worked	Average hourly earnings
Carpenter	500	$2.50
Plumber	50	2.80
Electrician	25	3.50
Bricklayer	100	3.00
Laborer	400	1.50

11. Calculate the most suitable "average" for the following data.

AGE OF TWO THOUSAND TWO HUNDRED AND TWENTY PERSONS
WHO TOOK THE C.P.C.U. EXAMINATIONS IN 1957

	No. of persons
30 and under	786
31 through 35	737
36 through 40	397
41 through 50	258
51 and over	42

SOURCE: Application, Study Group and Examination Statistics for 1957 (Philadelphia, Pa.: The American Institute for Property and Liability Underwriters Inc.).

12. Students in a statistics course had the following grades: Smith 73, McCarthy 53, Fogg 71, Hall 95, Richards 77, Seymour 69, Houghton 73, Paul 21, Michaels 66, Pressly 86, Floss 75, Howard 74, West 69, Foote 73, Jones 74.

Find (a) arithmetic mean, (b) median, (c) mode, and (d) geometric mean.

13. (a) Using the following figures, calculate the arithmetic mean receipts for the New England states.

NEW ENGLAND STATES'
TOTAL RECEIPTS
Amusement Recreation Services—1954
(thousands of dollars)

	Receipts
Maine	$ 14,709
New Hampshire	11,987
Vermont	5,747
Massachusetts	116,336
Rhode Island	21,360
Connecticut	44,021

SOURCE: U.S. Department of Commerce, Bureau of the Census, *Census of Business.*

(b) The arithmetic mean of these values clearly illustrates the basic weakness of this average. Discuss.

(c) Using the same values, calculate the geometric mean.

(d) Why are the arithmetic and geometric means of these values quite different?

14.   1964 PRICE RELATIVES OF SIXTY-TWO
                          SELECTED FARM COMMODITIES
                                  (1955 = 100)

	No. of relatives in each class
Price relatives	
40–60	10
60–80	30
80–100	10
100–120	5
120–320	3
320–720	2
720–1120	2

(a) The U.S. Congress would like to know how much the prices of farm commodities have, on the average, risen or fallen since 1955. Disregarding problems in weighting introduced by such questions as the number of farmers dependent for a livelihood on particular crops or the gross revenue contributed by different crops, which measure of central tendency do you think will best depict the true picture? Why?

(b) Calculate the measure selected.

15. Assume the following facts. The frequency of the modal class interval ("$10 and under $20") is 40. The frequency of the class preceding the modal class ("$0 and under $10") is 25. The frequency of the class following the modal class ("$20 and under $30") is 20. Calculate the mode.

16. Assume the following facts. The class interval that contains the assumed mean is "$20 and under $30." $\Sigma fd_s = +70$. $N = 100$. Calculate $\bar{X}$.

17.   WEEKLY ALUMINUM PRODUCTION
                            XYZ Company, 1965
                                  (tons)

	No. of weeks
1,000 but under 1,500	2
1,500 but under 2,000	5
2,000 but under 2,500	11
2,500 but under 3,000	20
3,000 but under 3,500	9
3,500 but under 4,000	4
4,000 but under 4,500	1
	52

Calculate the median.

18. Assume the following facts. $N = 101$. There are nine class intervals, all of equal size. The first class interval is "$10 and under $20." The cumulative frequencies of the fifth, sixth, seventh, and eighth classes are, respectively, 45, 78, 90, 99. Calculate the median.

CHAPTER FIVE

Measures of
Dispersion and Skewness

DISPERSION

The preceding chapter dealt with measures of central tendency—measures indicating the value around which the items in a distribution are clustered. Although these measures are important, for many purposes they do not give a complete indication of the nature of a distribution. For example, assume that the average wage in a plant is $75 per week and that the wages of all workers fall between $70 and $80. By knowing the average wage, a person could state confidently that a friend working in the plant earns about $75 per week. However, if the wages ranged from $40 to $120, no such confident statement concerning a friend's probable wage could be made based solely on the information given by the average of $75.

To make the picture complete, something else must be known about a distribution. The extent and nature of the spread of the values around their summary figure—around the average that indicates central tendency—should be ascertained. Measures that indicate the spread of the values are called *measures of dispersion;* those dealing with symmetry are referred to as *measures of skewness.* Four measures of dispersion will be presented. Two, the range and the quartiles, are called positional measures because they depend on the values at particular positions in the distribution. The other two, the average deviation and the standard deviation, are called calculated measures of deviation because all the values are employed in their calculation.

Range

A simple, crude, but extremely useful, measure of dispersion is the range. The range is simply the distance between the largest and smallest value in a group of values. It is found by subtracting the smallest value in the series from the largest or, in a frequency distribution, by subtracting the lower limit of the lowest class interval from the upper limit of the highest. If wages in a plant vary between $40 and $120, the range is $80. If they vary between $70 and $80, the range is $10.

The range was for some time presented in texts with considerable disdain. In a sense it is unfortunate that its calculation is so simple, because this fact prevents the devotion of any considerable number of pages to its explanation. The range has, however, in addition to its use in situations such as the range of wages in a plant and so forth, found wide use in quality control. As will be stated in the chapter on quality control, half of the usual control chart used is devoted to the range. The idea basically is that if the range—the difference between the largest and smallest mass-produced items—increases beyond a certain point, the production machinery should be examined to find out why the items produced have not followed their usual more consistent pattern. In some companies, once familiarity with the products and production methods has developed, the range is used to estimate the standard deviation, a much more complicated measure to calculate.

The range is certainly the most commonly used measure of dispersion in everyday living. Questions, from "How much does your husband make in a week?" to "How many tomatoes do you get to a plant?" to "How much water do you have in your cellar?" are all usually answered in the form of a range. Answers to questions such as these are usually given in the form of "Between such and such," and, regardless of the crudity of expression, the answer is still a range.

All this has been stated to emphasize the fact that, despite the relatively small amount of space devoted to the range, it is still an important concept. Although it does not consider the manner in which values are spread out within the distribution but concerns itself only with the top and bottom values, the range is still an extremely useful measure. Its great disadvantage is that it is so greatly affected by extremes.

Quartiles

The range is a positional measure of dispersion because it concerns itself only with the values at the top and bottom of the distribution— values at particular positions in the distribution. The quartiles are positional measures because they concern themselves with the three values in a distribution that divide the items into four equal groups. The second quartile is the median. This is the value that divides a distribution in half. The first quartile divides the lower half of the distribution in half, and thus it is the value that separates the first quarter of the items from the second. One quarter of the values in a distribution are as much as or less than that value, one quarter are between this value and the median or second quartile, and three quarters are as much as or more than the first quartile. Similarly, the third quartile divides the upper half of a distribution in half. One quarter of the values in a distribution are as much as or more than the third quartile, one quarter are between this value and the median or second quartile, and three quarters are as much as or less than this third quartile.

The distribution used to calculate the median in the preceding chapter, presented again in Table 5-1, will serve to illustrate the derivation of the quartiles.

Table 5-1. INCOME OF PERSONS PURCHASING ORDINARY
LIFE INSURANCE—1956
(Ages 0–14 Excluded)

		No. of policies (in thousands)	Cumulated no.
Income (dollars)			
under	2000	175	175
2000 but under	3000	641	816
3000 but under	4000	1225	2041
4000 but under	5000	1225	3266
5000 but under	7500	1458	4724
7500 but under	10,000	408	5132
10,000 and over		699	5831
Total		5831	

SOURCE: *Life Insurance Fact Book, 1957; Life Insurance Buying* (New York: Institute of Life Insurance).

The formula used for the median was $Me = L + (p/f)i$. The formula for the second quartile is exactly the same except that the symbol Q_2 is substituted for the symbol Me to indicate that quartiles are now being sought. This substitution, of course, does not affect the method of calculation.

In describing the calculation of the median, it was stated that all the symbols in this formula depended on first defining and locating the median class. L, for example, is the lower limit of the median (second quartile) class. This formula remains the same regardless of whether the first, second, or third quartile is sought. The only difference is that the definition and location of the class being used differs, and therefore the symbols in the formula refer to different classes, depending on which quartile is being considered. In finding the median, the first step was to locate the median class, defined as the class in which the middle item in the distribution lies. Similarly, in finding the first quartile, the initial step is to locate the first quartile class, which is defined as the class in which the item one quarter of the way through the distribution lies. In finding the third quartile, the first step is to locate the third quartile class, defined as the class in which the item three quarters of the way through the distribution lies.

Calculation of Q_2. In locating the median or second quartile, the median class is found by first dividing the total frequencies by 2, $5831/2 = 2915.5$, to get the middle frequency, and then cumulating the frequencies to find out in which class the 2915.5th frequency lies. This frequency is located in the $4000 up to $5000 class. Therefore L in the formula, the lower limit of the median class, is $4000; f, the frequency of the median class, is 1225; and i, the class interval of the median class, is $1000. p, the number of frequencies needed in the median class, is found by subtracting the cumulated number of frequencies up to the median class, 2041, from the number desired, 2915.5. This results in a p value of 874.5. If we substitute in the formula,

$$Q_2 = \$4000 + (874.5/1225)\$1000 = \$4000 + \$710 = \$4710$$

The second quartile or median value is $4710. Half the policies were purchased by persons having this income or less, and half by persons having this income or more.

Calculation of Q_1. In finding the first quartile, the first step is to find the class in which the item one quarter of the way through the distribution lies. This is done by dividing the total frequency by 4: $5831/4 = 1457.75$. Next it is necessary to find the class in which this frequency occurs. Examination of the Cumulated number column reveals that it must exist in the $3000 up to $4000 class, because before reaching this class there are 816 cumulated frequencies—not enough—whereas, after going through this class, there are 2041 cumulated frequencies—more than enough. This class is then the first quartile class. The formula now is

$$Q_1 = \$3000 + (641.75/1225)\$1000 = \$3000 + \$520 = \$3520$$

The lower limit of the first quartile class is $3000, the frequency in that class is 1225, and the class interval of that class is $1000. p in the formula is found by subtracting the cumulated number of frequencies up to the first quartile class, 816, from the number desired, 1457.75. This results in a p value of 641.75. If we use these values, the first quartile of this distribution is $3520.

Calculation of Q_3. In finding the third quartile, the first step is to find the class in which the item three quarters of the way through the distribution lies. This is done by dividing the total frequency by 4 and multiplying the answer by 3. Thus $5831/4 = 1457.75 \times 3 = 4373.25$. Next it is necessary to find the class in which this frequency occurs. Examination of the Cumulated number column reveals that it must exist in the \$5000-to-\$7500 class, because before reaching this class there are 3266 cumulated frequencies—not enough—whereas after going through this class there are 4724 cumulated frequencies—more than enough. This class is the third quartile class. The formula now is

$$Q_3 = \$5000 + (1107.25/1458)\$2500 = \$5000 + \$1900 = \$6900$$

The lower limit of the third quartile class is \$5000, the frequency in that class is 1458, and the class interval of that class is \$2500. p in the formula is found by subtracting the cumulated number of frequencies up to the third quartile class, 3266, from the number desired, 4373.25. This results in a p value of 1107.25. The third quartile of this distribution is \$6900.

Now all three quartiles have been found and the distribution divided into quarters:

$$Q_1 = \$3520$$
$$Q_2 = \$4710$$
$$Q_3 = \$6900$$

From these values we can determine the following facts. One quarter of the policies were purchased by persons having an income of \$3520 or less and three quarters by persons having an income of \$3520 or more. One quarter of the policies were purchased by persons having an income between \$3520 and \$4710, and another quarter were purchased by persons having an income between \$4710 and \$6900. One quarter of the policies were purchased by persons having an income of \$6900 or more, and three quarters by persons having an income of \$6900 or less. One half were purchased by persons having an income of \$4710 or less, and one half by persons having an income of \$4710 or more. It is also found that one half of the policies were purchased by persons having incomes between \$3520 and \$6900.

Quartiles provide much more detailed information concerning the distribution than would be supplied by the range. They also permit an interested person to discover much more about the distribution than the median alone or any other measure of central tendency by itself could reveal. By subtracting the first quartile from the second, it is found that this quarter of the policies is spread over an income range of \$1190 (4710 − \$3520). The quarter of the policies above the median is spread over an income range of \$2190 (\$6900 − 4710). This distribution indicates that the middle half of the policies was sold to an income group having a particular characteristic. These policies were more concentrated in the lower part of this income interval than in the upper part. The policies sold to persons just under the median income were spread over a smaller range of incomes than were policies sold to persons just above the median income.

Interquartile Range. The interquartile range is obtained by subtracting the first quartile from the third $(Q_3 - Q_1)$. In the example, $6900 - 3520 = 3380$. As previously stated, this interval includes 50 percent of the frequencies. If a range is desired to measure dispersion, the interquartile range has an advantage in that extremes at either end of the distribution will not be able to affect it. Both ends are eliminated from consideration because only the middle 50 percent is used.

Semi-interquartile Range. The semi-interquartile range (also called the quartile deviation) is found by dividing the interquartile range by 2: $(Q_3 - Q_1)/2$. This measure is useful, because the dispersion can be tied to the median by stating it as a variation from the median. In the example, $3380/2 = 1690$. If the distribution was normal, it can be stated that 50 percent of the frequencies lie within the range of the median plus and minus this semi-interquartile range. The median plus and minus this range includes 50 percent of the items only when the distribution is symmetrical. If the type of normal curve based on errors is used (it will be discussed in the chapter on the normal curve), this range is generally called the "probable error." In such a distribution, 50 percent of the items will fall within this range and 50 percent outside it. The chances are equal (50-50) that any item chosen at random will fall within this range.

Once the method of calculating quartiles is understood, it can be seen that a distribution can be divided into any number of sections by such a technique. The same method can be used to divide a group into five or ten parts that has been used to divide a group into four parts.

Percentiles

One measure important enough, especially in the field of education, to merit separate mention is the percentile. This is calculated in essentially the same manner as are the quartiles. There are 99 percentiles.

To find out, for example, what value separates the top 40 percent of the items (students) from the bottom 60 percent, the 60th percentile would be calculated. This practice is often followed in teaching when an educator wants to discover the particular values that separate the test scores of a group of students.

Because the manner of calculating percentiles is the same as that for the calculation of quartiles, very little need be said concerning details of calculation. The same formula would be used. The only difference is that instead of applying the formula to the class in which the 1st, 2nd, or 3rd quartile value lies, it would now be applied to the class within which the particular percentage value lies. For example, to find the 60th percentile, it would be necessary to apply the formula to the class in which the item 60 percent of the way through the distribution lies.

Average Deviation

The measures of dispersion discussed up to this point have been positional measures that depend on the position of certain values in the distribution. The average and standard deviations, however, are calculated measures that use all the values in the distribution.

The average deviation is sometimes called the mean deviation. It is the average difference between the items in a distribution and the median or mean of that series. Theoretically it might be better to use the median

Table 5-2

	Cost	*Deviation from median $1.75*	*Deviation from mean $1.70*
Item			
1	$1.50	$ .25	$ .20
2	2.10	.35	.40
3	1.25	.50	.45
4	1.75	.00	.05
5	1.90	.15	.20
Totals		5)$1.25	5)$1.30
Average		$ .25	$ .26

as the measure of central tendency,[1] but for all practical purposes either the median or the mean can be used. It is, of course, necessary to state clearly which has been used in a particular problem so that the meaning will be clear.

Average Deviation—Ungrouped Data. The calculation of the average deviation for ungrouped data can be demonstrated with the use of both the median and mean as a base. If the shopping example presented in the preceding chapter on measures of central tendency is used, Table 5-2 gives the necessary figures.

This calculation would be expressed as a formula by

$$A.D. = \frac{\Sigma|d|}{N}$$

The | | indicates that signs are ignored in deriving the deviations.

[1] The explanation is that the sum of deviations, when signs are ignored, is smaller from the median than from the mean.

The meaning of this measure is that the average deviation of the items from the median is $.25 and from the mean $.26. This information would be useful for comparison. If in another group of items the deviation from the median is only $.20, it can be said that the items in that group are more concentrated around the median. If the variation of a series from the measure of central tendency is large, the homogeneity of the data is questionable. A homogeneous group of items will fall compactly around a measure of central tendency.

Average Deviation—Grouped Data. Calculating the average deviation from the distribution presented in Table 5-3 and used in the previous chapter to calculate the arithmetic mean will indicate that the average

Table 5-3.   WAGES PAID TO WORKERS
Underground Rocket Company
(Plant A)

$\bar{X} = \$104$

	X	No. of workers f	$|d|$	$f\,|d|$	$|d_s|$	$f\,|d_s|$
Wages (dollars per week)						
40 but under 60	$ 50	60	54	3240	3	180
60 but under 80	70	70	34	2380	2	140
80 but under 100	90	85	14	1190	1	85
100 but under 120	120	110	6	660	0	0
120 but under 140	130	95	26	2470	1	95
140 but under 160	150	80	46	3680	2	160
Totals		500		13620		660

deviation is theoretically simple to calculate but that, in practice, it involves considerable labor.

The basic formula for calculating the average deviation from a frequency distribution is

$$A.D. = \frac{\Sigma f |d|}{N}$$

In this formula actual deviations are used. Thus, in Table 5-3, the $|d|$ column is obtained by subtracting the arithmetic mean of $104 from each of the mid-points, ignoring plus and minus signs. For this example, the formula would read $A.D. = 13620/500$ and the average deviation would then be $27.24 or $27. That is to say, the average difference between the wages paid to these workers and the mean wage is $27.

The disadvantage of this formula is the labor involved, because the multiplication of f times $|d|$ can be quite lengthy. For this reason the formula

$$A.D. = \frac{\Sigma f |d_s|}{N} i$$

is often used. In this method the $|d_s|$ values are the step deviations described in the calculation of the mean, except that now they must be from the mid-point of the median class. These "steps" are found by expressing the difference between the mid-point selected as the assumed mean and the other mid-points as a number of class intervals. The only difference is that now the plus and minus signs of the step deviations are ignored. For this example, this formula would read $A.D. = (660/500)20 = \$26$. This formula results in less accuracy but much less labor. Quite often the answer is accurate enough to be usable.

Usefulness of the Average Deviation. The average deviation is a much-criticized measure. The advantages of the measure are usually underemphasized and neglected, whereas the disadvantages often receive great attention.

The average deviation does have definite disadvantages. The ignoring of plus and minus signs is decidedly bad from the viewpoint of the mathematician and prevents further algebraic use of the measure.

The advantages of this measure are, however, important. By comparing the average deviation with the standard deviation, the other calculated measure of dispersion, it will be evident that the average deviation is far simpler to understand and often far easier to compute. Plus and minus 1 average deviation from the arithmetic mean under a normal curve would include 57.5 percent of the frequencies, and limits based on average deviations from the mean can be established, just as are limits based on the standard deviation. The National Bureau of Economic Research has found, in its work on forecasting business cycles, that the average deviation is the most practical measure of dispersion to use for this purpose.

The outstanding advantage of the average deviation is its relative simplicity. Anyone familiar with the concept of the average can readily appreciate the meaning of the average deviation. If a situation requires a measure of dispersion that will be presented to the general public or any group not thoroughly grounded in statistics, the average deviation is very useful.

Standard Deviation

Without a doubt, the most generally important measure of dispersion is the standard deviation. All work involving probability analysis involves the standard deviation. Because it is the only measure of dispersion that is not only rigidly defined but involves every item in its computation and adheres to accepted mathematical principles, it must be employed whenever the measure of dispersion is used in further computation. The basic measures underlying the techniques of quality control are the arithmetic mean and the standard deviation.

Finally, this measure of dispersion has a unique relation to the "normal" distribution.[2] This relation, as well as the "normal" distribution itself, will be described and utilized in Chapter 6. It will be seen that most of the analytical, as opposed to purely descriptive, applications of modern-day statistics depend on the mathematical relation between the arithmetic mean, the standard deviation, the concept of probability, and the normal distribution.

The symbol designating the standard deviation is σ. Computationally, it can be defined as the square root of the average of the squared deviations from the arithmetic mean of a distribution. Unfortunately,

Table 5-4

		Cost	d	d²
	Item			
$\bar{X} = \$1.70$	1	$1.50	$−.20	$.0400
	2	2.10	+.40	.1600
	3	1.25	−.45	.2025
	4	1.75	+.05	.0025
	5	1.90	+.20	.0400
				$.4450

this definition of the measure is not very useful; it helps only in stating the method by which the standard deviation is calculated, and is of no assistance whatsoever in bringing about an understanding of the measure. Such an understanding can be acquired only by example and use. Although a brief attempt will be made to explain the standard deviation in this chapter, full understanding should dawn only after the chapters on the normal curve and sampling have been completed.

Standard Deviation—Ungrouped Data. The standard deviation can now be calculated and compared with the average deviation, again with the use of the shopping example, as in Table 5-4. In this distribution, the sum of the squared deviations from the mean is $.445. The average of these squared deviations would then be $.445/5 = $.089. The square root of this

---

[2] In a normal distribution the items are spread out in such a manner that they form a normal curve, as described in the chapter on the frequency distribution, Chapter 3, and more fully in Chapter 6. Briefly, the normal distribution is represented by a bell-shaped, symmetrical curve having exactly the same number of frequencies and the same range of values on both sides of the arithmetic mean, the center point.

average is $\sqrt{.089}$ = $.30. Algebraically this calculation would be expressed as

$$\sigma = \sqrt{\frac{\Sigma d^2}{N}}$$

Notice that the standard deviation, $.30, of this group is larger than the average deviation, $.26, of the same group. The explanation is that the deviations were squared, and squaring an extreme difference will increase its importance in the measure calculated.

Table 5-5.   WAGES PAID TO WORKERS
Underground Rocket Company
(Plant A)

	X	No. of workers f	d_s	fd_s	fd_s^2
Wages (dollars per week)					
40 but under 60	$ 50	60	−3	−180	540
60 but under 80	70	70	−2	−140	280
80 but under 100	90	85	−1	− 85	85
100 but under 120	110	110	0	0	0
120 but under 140	130	95	+1	+ 95	95
140 but under 160	150	80	+2	+160	320
				−405	1320
Totals		500		+255	
				−150	

Standard Deviation—Grouped Data.   Using the same example that was used in the calculation of the average deviation will again permit a comparison of the two measures of dispersion. Actually, of course, the calculation of the standard deviation from a grouped distribution follows the same steps as the calculation from an ungrouped series. The necessary figures are presented in Table 5-5.

The basic formula for calculating the standard deviation from a frequency distribution is

$$\sigma = \sqrt{\frac{\Sigma fd^2}{N}}$$

Arithmetically, however, the simplest way to calculate the standard deviation is to extend the short-cut method used to calculate the arithmetic mean. This method, explained in the preceding chapter, involved adding or subtracting deviations from an assumed mean. This procedure gave the actual mean from which the sum of the deviations is zero.

The formulas for the short-cut method of calculating the arithmetic mean from a frequency distribution and that for calculating the standard deviation are quite similar:

$$\bar{X} = A + \frac{fd_s}{N} i \qquad \sigma = i \sqrt{\frac{\Sigma fd_s^2}{N} - \left[\frac{\Sigma fd_s}{N}\right]^2}$$

Notice that fd_s/N appears in both formulas. This portion of the arithmetic-mean formula served to correct the assumed mean for existing deviations. Its function is the same in the standard-deviation formula except that, because the deviations are now squared, this correction must be squared. Because the two formulas are so similar only one more column is needed in the example in Table 5-5 to provide all of the necessary data for calculation of the standard deviation. This column, fd_s^2, is necessary to square the deviations. It is found by multiplying the deviations, d_s, times the existing fd_s column. Algebraically this has no effect on the frequencies used to get the fd_s values but affects only the deviations. This column represents the products of the frequencies times the squared deviations. The total of this column will always be a positive number because squaring the deviations makes all the values in the column positive.

With the use of the values found in the example, we find that

$$\sigma = i \sqrt{\Sigma fd_s^2/N - [\Sigma fd_s/N]^2} = \$20 \sqrt{1320/500 - [-150/500]^2}$$
$$= \$20 \sqrt{2.64 - .30^2} = \$20 \sqrt{2.64 - .09}$$
$$= \$20 \sqrt{2.55} = \$20 \times 1.60 = \$32$$

Notice again that the standard deviation, \$32, in this problem is larger than the average deviation of \$27 because of the increased emphasis placed on extreme deviations.

Relative Dispersion

It is often necessary to compare two or more distributions. Quite often a comparison is desired of the degree to which the items in these distributions are dispersed around their individual means. Either the average or the standard deviation can be used for such a purpose, but the comparison must, of course, be consistent throughout—that is, if the measure of relative dispersion used in one distribution is based on the average deviation, measures of relative dispersion calculated for other distributions for purposes of comparison must also be based on the average deviation.

Coefficient of Variation. The measure used to convert measures of dispersion to relative measures is the coefficient of variation. Both the average and standard deviations are stated in terms of the mean of the distribution from which they are calculated. The function of the coefficient of variation is to convert these measures into percentages of their own means for purposes of comparison. The formula for the coefficient of variation is

$$V_\sigma = \frac{\sigma}{\bar{X}} \times 100$$

if the standard deviation is used, and

$$V_{A.D.} = \frac{A.D.}{\bar{X}} \times 100$$

if the average deviation is used. If it is necessary to use the coefficient of variation further algebraically, it must be based on the standard deviation. If, however, its calculation is strictly for purposes of comparison, if the calculation of the standard deviation involves more work than seems practical in a particular project, or if the answer is to be presented to a group unfamiliar with statistical measures, then the coefficient of variation can and should be based on the average deviation.

With the use of the information from the Rocket Company example, the coefficient of variation based on the average deviation is

$$V_{A.D.} = \$27/104 \times 100 = 26$$

The coefficient of variation based on the standard deviation is

$$V_\sigma = \$32/104 \times 100 = 31$$

If another company calculated a coefficient of variation based on the average deviation, and it came to some figure such as 14 compared to the 26 derived in this example, it would be possible to say that relative dispersion around the arithmetic mean is greater in the company used in our example, and vice versa—in the other company wages are more concentrated around the mean wage.

SKEWNESS

Skewness is lack of symmetry. Any measure of skewness indicates the difference between the manner in which items are distributed in a particular distribution compared with a normal distribution. If, for example, skewness is positive, the frequencies in the distribution are spread out over a greater range of values on the high-value end of the curve (the right-hand side) than they are on the low-value end. If the curve is normal, the spread will be the same on both sides of the center point and the mean, median, and mode will all be the same value. Examples of a normal curve, a positively skewed curve, and a negatively skewed curve are given in Figure 5-1.

FIGURE 5-1.   Negative, Normal, and Positive Curves

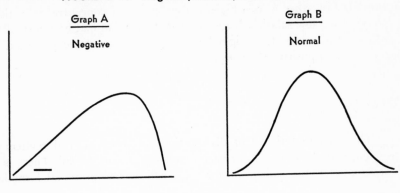

Graph A

Negative

Graph B

Normal

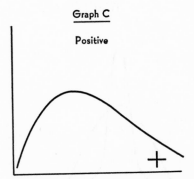

Graph C

Positive

Calculation of Skewness

In practice, skewness is rarely calculated in business and economic series. Because the most popular formula is relatively simple and because the general idea of skewness is an important concept, the formula will be explained briefly. A formula commonly used is

$$Sk = \frac{3(\bar{X} - Me)}{\sigma}$$

This formula is popular because it does not require that the mode be calculated. In series where the mode is difficult to determine because of the lack of a clearly evident most common value, this formula has a definite advantage. The formula can be illustrated by using the Rocket Company example. The arithmetic mean for the example has been calculated as $104, and the standard deviation as $32. The median is $106.40.

$$Sk = [3(\$104 - \$106.40)]/32 = -\$7.2/\$32 = -.22$$

This answer indicates that the distribution of wages in the Rocket Company is not perfectly symmetrical but is skewed negatively toward the lower values. In other words, high salaries are more concentrated in this factory than are low salaries. Notice that if the median had been a smaller value than the mean, the original subtraction would have produced a plus answer and positive skewness.

KURTOSIS

Three characteristics of distributions of data—central tendency, dispersion, and skewness—have been described in some detail. There is a fourth characteristic—called *kurtosis*—for which computational formulas

FIGURE 5–2

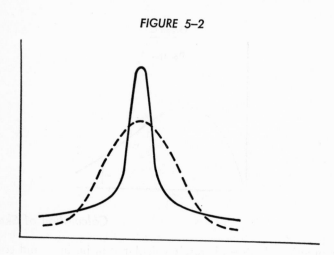

FIGURE 5–3

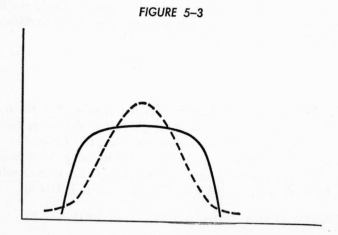

have also been derived. Although these formulas will not be presented, the characteristic itself will be described.

Kurtosis refers to the "peakedness" of the distribution. Three types of kurtosis are distinguished, the frame of reference being the "normal curve" (see footnote 2 and Chapters 2 and 6), which is called "mesokurtic." Briefly, if a curve has a narrower central portion and higher tails than the normal curve has, it is called "leptokurtic" (Figure 5–2). If a curve has a broader central portion and lower tails than a normal curve has, it is called "platykurtic" (Figure 5–3).

SUGGESTED READINGS

Chou, Y. C. *Applied Business and Economic Statistics.* New York: Holt, Rinehart and Winston, Inc., 1963, chap. 7.

Griffin, J. I. *Statistics, Methods and Applications.* New York: Holt, Rinehart and Winston, Inc., 1962, chap. 6.

Lewis, E. V. *Statistical Analysis, Ideas and Methods.* Princeton, N.J.: D. Van Nostrand Company, Inc., 1963, chap. 4.

Neter, J., and W. Wasserman. *Fundamental Statistics for Business and Economics.* Boston: Allyn and Bacon, Inc., chap. 7.

QUESTIONS

1. What is the purpose of the coefficient of variation?

2. State clearly why the quartile is called a positional measure of dispersion and the average deviation a calculated measure.

3. The sum of the deviations from the arithmetic mean is zero and yet the average deviation from the arithmetic mean is not necessarily zero. Explain.

4. What is the meaning of (a) the range, (b) the first and third quartiles, (c) the average deviation.

5. State clearly, numbering each step, how to calculate the following measures from ungrouped data: (a) average deviation, (b) standard deviation.

6. (a) What is the meaning of the average deviation and why is it at times more usable than the standard deviation?

    (b) Why is the standard deviation used more often than the average deviation?

7. "If the frequency distribution is normal, the average deviation and the standard deviation are identical." Is this statement true or false? State clearly why.

8. In a recent study, it was found that the average per capita consumption of milk in one of the Middle Atlantic states is .453 quarts per day and the standard deviation is .00432 quarts. Explain clearly the relation between these figures.

9. Each of two factories has a median wage of $45. In factory A the difference between the first and second quartiles is $10 and the difference between the second and third quartiles is $5. In factory B the difference between the first and second quartiles is $5 and the difference between the second and third quartiles is $10. On the basis of the information available, which factory seems to be the more attractive place in which to work?

10. Suppose that the median length of service in the army and navy is 24 months, and that in the army the difference between the first and second quartiles is 8 months and the difference between the second and third quartiles is 4 months, whereas in the navy the difference between the first and second quartiles is 4 months and the difference between the second and third quartiles is 8 months. Which branch of service would be more attractive to a person who dislikes military service?

11. What is the relation between the $\bar{X}$, Me, and Mo in (a) a normal curve, (b) a negatively skewed curve, (c) a positively skewed curve.

12. (a) If the frequency distribution is normal, the same percentage of the items will fall within a range of plus and minus 1 average deviation from the mean or median as will fall within a range of plus and minus 1 standard deviation. Discuss carefully the reason for the truth or falsity of this statement.

   (b) What percentage of the frequencies is located within the interquartile range in a normal distribution?

   (c) What percentage of the frequencies is located within the interquartile range in a distribution that has a high positive skewness?

13. An average is a measure representing a distribution. Why is there an interest in any further statistical measure to describe a distribution?

PROBLEMS

1. (a) Determine the measures of dispersion listed below for the wheat yields on 130 farms: (1) average deviation, (2) standard deviation, (3) quartiles, (4) range.

WHEAT YIELDS ON 130 FARMS

Bushels of wheat	No. of farms
8.5 but under 10.5	5
10.5 but under 12.5	10
12.5 but under 14.5	20
14.5 but under 16.5	25
16.5 but under 18.5	30
18.5 but under 20.5	21
20.5 but under 22.5	19
	130

(b) Assuming that your purpose is to report the degree of dispersion to the general public in a press release, which of these measures would you use? Would your answer be altered if the measure of dispersion were also to be used in making further computations?

2. (a) Using the following data, calculate the average and standard deviations.

Sale number	Amount
1	$1.50
2	2.25
3	3.00
4	2.20
5	1.25
6	1.70
7	2.10

(b) Which of these measures most clearly depicts the dispersion of the series? What factors would govern your choice in this instance?

3. (a) Given an arithmetic mean of $85, a mode of $95, and a median of $88, draw a curve representing the distribution from which these measures were calculated. Place the measures in their proper relative positions under the curve, and label the curve as being positively or negatively skewed.

(b) What would be the relation of these three measures in a normal distribution?

4. Calculate the coefficient of skewness for the distribution of grades in elementary statistics.

GRADE DISTRIBUTION IN STATISTICS I
(September through November 1964)

Percentage	No. of students
40 but under 50	28
50 but under 60	15
60 but under 70	19
70 but under 80	6
80 but under 90	1
90 but under 100	1
	70

5. If the record of amounts spent by you on various evenings gives a coefficient of variation of 50 percent and a standard deviation of $4, what was your average expenditure?

6. The measurements of 1500 women at Shliply College from 1960 through 1965 were recorded. These records show that the mean height

of these women was 65.25 inches and the standard deviation of their heights was 3.14 inches. The mean weight of these women was 125.75 pounds with a standard deviation of 18.75 pounds. Did these women have greater variation in their height or in their weight?

7. (a) Using the following frequency distribution, calculate (1) range, (2) average deviation, (3) quartile deviation, (4) standard deviation.

WAGES FOUND IN A SAMPLE OF 400 FACTORY WORKERS
(Utica, New York—December 1964)

Weekly wage (dollars)	No. of workers
45 but under 55	42
55 but under 65	68
65 but under 75	90
75 but under 85	115
85 but under 95	50
95 but under 105	15
105 but under 115	15
115 but under 125	5
	400

(b) Which measure of dispersion would be most useful for (1) a social worker, (2) an actuary, (3) a public relations man for industry, (4) a spokesman for organized labor.

8. Calculate the following measures of dispersion for the frequency distribution below: (a) range, (b) average deviation, (c) quartile deviation, (d) standard deviation, (e) coefficient of variation, (f) skewness.

DISTRIBUTION OF WAGES OF FEMALE EMPLOYEES
IN THE LONGBRANCH INN
(November 1964)

Weekly wage (dollars)	No. of employees
30 through 34.99	3
35 through 39.99	9
40 through 44.99	15
45 through 49.99	27
50 through 54.99	18
55 through 59.99	12
60 through 64.99	9
65 through 69.99	7

9. Using the following distribution, calculate the standard deviation.

WEEKLY SALES IN A SAMPLE OF 300 GROCERY STORES
(January 12–17, 1964)

Average weekly sales (dollars)	No. of stores
5000 but under 5500	22
5500 but under 6000	33
6000 but under 6500	35
6500 but under 7000	45
7000 but under 7500	73
7500 but under 8000	47
8000 but under 8500	28
8500 but under 9000	17
	300

10. The modal grade in class A is 83, the mean grade is 74, and the median grade is 77. In class B, the modal grade is 71, the mean 80, and the median 77.
   (a) Draw a curve representing each class. Place the measures in their proper relative positions on the horizontal axis.
   (b) Would it be possible to have more than one half of the students in class A receive less than the mean grade? Explain.
   (c) Would it be possible to have more than one half of the students in class B receive less than the mean grade? Explain.
   (d) If the measure is to be presented to a local school committee to aid in describing the distribution of grades, would you recommend using the average or the standard deviation?
   (e) If the standard deviations were calculated for each of these classes, how could the two standard deviations be compared when, as stated, the mean is different in each class?

11. Using the following frequency distribution, calculate (a) range, (b) quartiles, (c) average deviation from the median, (d) standard deviation.

AVERAGE MONTHLY TEXTBOOK SALES MADE BY
TWO HUNDRED PUBLISHERS' REPRESENTATIVES
(1964)

Sales per month (dollars)	No. of representatives
500 but under 900	20
900 but under 1300	30
1300 but under 1700	50
1700 but under 2100	40
2100 but under 2500	35
2500 but under 2900	25
	200

12. A study of 45,948 divorces taking place between 1900 and 1910 shows that the average length of the marriage before divorce was 20.68 years, with a standard deviation of 6.42 years. Comparable figures for the 4865 divorces in the same state in 1958 give an average duration of marriage of 18.36 years and a standard deviation of 6.10 years. Had marriages become more, or less, variable in their duration?

13. A group of 100 selected Radcliffe students average 65 inches in height with a coefficient of variation of 6.6 percent. What was the standard deviation in their heights?

14. Calculate the semi-interquartile range, average deviation, and standard deviation for the following distribution:

	No. of stores making these sales
Daily sales (dollars)	
10 but under 20	15
20 but under 30	35
30 but under 40	45
40 but under 50	20
50 but under 60	10
	125

15. A random sample of 101 weekly personal incomes in City A yields the following results: $\bar{X} = 100$, $\sigma = 30$. A random sample of weekly personal incomes in City B for the same period yields the following results:

	No. of persons in this class
Income (dollars)	
40 but under 50	7
50 but under 60	9
60 but under 70	10
70 but under 80	30
80 but under 90	20
90 but under 100	6

(a) In which city is the distribution of incomes more variable (demonstrate the basis of your answer verbally and arithmetically).

(b) Calculate skewness.

(c) Is the distribution positively or negatively skewed? What do these terms mean?

16. A sample of the scores obtained on entrance exams by 100 students at ABC College was taken. X represents the score on a single exam, $\Sigma fX = 4,200$, $\Sigma fX^2 = 120,000$, $\Sigma f(X - \bar{X})^2 = 16,900$, the lower limit of the modal class = 38, $d_1 = 3$, $d_2 = 9$, $i = 12$.

(a) Calculate $\bar{X}$, the mode, and the standard deviation.

(b) Sketch the graph of this distribution, in as much detail as possible from the data given, indicating (1) whether skewness is positive or negative, (2) the approximate position of the median, (3) why you placed the median where you did.

(c) Another college—namely, XYZ College—administered the same examination to 80 students, obtaining $\bar{X} = 50$ and $\sigma = 10$. In which college is the dispersion greater? Why?

Part Three

STATISTICAL INFERENCE

CHAPTER SIX

Probability,
the Normal Curve,
and Sampling Theory

Up to this point, most of the statistics introduced in this book has been descriptive in nature. For example, the frequency distribution, whether presented graphically or as a table, permits quantitative information to be organized in a concise but clear and complete form. In this sense, the frequency distribution performs a descriptive function. Similarly, the measures of central tendency, dispersion, and skewness that have been discussed permit the key characteristics of quantitative information to be adequately summarized and described. Although descriptive statistics is extremely important, it represents just one part of the general field of statistics. The other segment of the field can be called analytical statistics. The next few chapters will be almost entirely concerned with this very important area of statistics.

Analytic statistics, as the term implies, is concerned with analyzing, as opposed to purely describing, a set of data. Because analytical statistics reflects the concepts and techniques of "statistical inference," it can be best illustrated by defining this latter term. Statistical inference refers to the set of procedures whereby certain data, representing just a part or segment or sample of a larger mass of data, are analyzed. Conclusions pertaining to the complete mass of data are then formulated, the formulation being based on this analysis. In other words, inferences concerning the entire mass of data are made from the results of partial or incomplete or sample data alone.

Analytical statistics is based, ultimately, on the concept of probability. The reason is that probability, together with the concept of a "normal" curve, is the basis of sampling theory, and sampling theory is the foundation for the various techniques of statistical inference that have so many important applications in business and economics. This chapter will discuss probability, the normal curve and sampling theory. The next two chapters will deal with their application.

PROBABILITY

Each of the possible events that a person can observe in a lifetime can be placed into either one of two categories. The first represents all events that *are absolutely certain to happen*. Three examples of events belonging to this category are the *eventual* death of a person's next door neighbor, the *eventual* downward flight of a baseball batted into the air, and the drawing of *either* a spade, heart, diamond, or club in a single draw from a full deck of ordinary playing cards.

The second category is made up of all the events that *may or may not occur* at any one point in time or over any specified interval of time. The death of a person's next door neighbor tomorrow, or next week, or within a 10-year period, and a batted baseball landing in the centerfield bleachers, or landing safely, or landing in such a way that it puts the base runner out, are examples of events belonging to this category. The drawing of a spade in a single draw from a full deck of ordinary playing cards is another example. It is this second category of events that makes life in general interesting, and that has resulted in the development of the body of knowledge referred to as "probability theory" or "statistical inference."

It is commonplace to associate events, such as those specified above, with a certain *probability*. For example, any insurance company can quote you the probability that your next door neighbor will die tomorrow, next week, or within 10 years. In situations iike these, the probability depends, mainly, on your neighbor's age. This probability is what determines, in large part, the premium you must pay on your own life insurance. With respect to the baseball example, any "grandstand handicapper" will "quote you odds" on the next batter hitting a home run, hitting safely, or hitting into an out. The probability, in this example, depends on such factors as the batter's batting average, his record over the past week, and the particular pitcher on the mound. Finally, any "card shark" will tell you your "chances" of drawing a spade.

Probability, then, is a concept that refers to the likelihood that a specified event may happen, recognizing at all times that some events are more likely than others. From the purely statistical point of view, however, more rigorous definitions are required, namely, those that associate a numerical value with the probability of a given event. Such definitions can be formulated. These definitions are, in fact, the basis of many important applications of statistical techniques in business and economics.

Terminology

However, before actually defining probability, certain terms and concepts will be introduced. Their use will greatly facilitate the entire discussion of probability. Assume that an "experiment" or "trial" takes place. Good examples of such experiments are the drawing of a single card from a deck of 52 playing cards or the tossing of a pair of dice. The result of this experiment will be termed its "outcome." For example, the outcome of the experiments mentioned above could be an ace of hearts or a two-spot and a six-spot. Each possible outcome will have certain distinguishing "characteristics." As an illustration, each outcome in the card example can be characterized by its suit, denomination, or color; in the dice example, a given outcome can be characterized by whether its total is an even number or a number less than 10. An "event" refers to an outcome, or set of outcomes, that possesses a particular characteristic or set of characteristics. For example, the event, a spade, refers only to the set of outcomes that represents the suit spades; the event, an even number, refers only to dice totals that are even numbers.

Outcomes are "mutually exclusive" if the occurrence of any one of them makes impossible the simultaneous occurrence of any of the others. Outcomes are "equally likely" if there is no physical reason, inherent in the experiment, that would make one particular outcome occur more frequently than any other. For example, assume that an experiment consists of a single draw of one card from a brand new ordinary deck of 52 playing cards. There are 52 possible outcomes, and they are mutually exclusive and equally likely. They are mutually exclusive because if the resulting outcome is, say, a two of spades, this makes impossible the simultaneous occurrence of any of the other 51 outcomes. They are equally likely because each outcome is represented by a separate piece of cardboard possessing physical properties identical to those of the other cardboards (for example, each card is of the same size, shape, and texture). Each piece of cardboard, and accordingly each outcome, therefore has an equal chance of being selected.

In addition to the above terminology, the reader should be perfectly clear about the manner in which probabilities are expressed. As will be demonstrated below, probabilities are numbers that lie between 0 and 1. That is, they are expressed as fractions, ratios, decimals, or percentages. For example, the probability of a particular event may be calculated as $\frac{1}{4}$. The same probability could also be expressed as .25, or 25 percent, or as 1 chance in 4.

In what follows the reader should bear in mind the terminology—namely, "experiment," "trial," "outcome," "characteristic," "event," "mutually exclusive," and "equally likely"—introduced in this section. He should also remember how probabilities are expressed.

Probability Situations

Three different types of probability situations can be distinguished. They will be designated as *predetermined, incomplete-experiment,* and *complete-experiment* situations. Briefly, the first type is one in which the various probabilities can be determined before the performance of experiments. The second is one in which the probabilities can be determined only after a certain number of experiments has been performed, the number of experiments performed being less than the total number possible. The third is like the second, except that the number of experiments performed is equal to the total number possible.

The probability definitions applicable to these situations, though basically the same, are formulated in a slightly different manner in order to make clear the special circumstances associated with each situation. All business and economic probability applications can be placed into one of these three probability situations. The situations will now be fully described.

Predetermined Situations

The predetermined situations[1] are different from the other probability situations because the total number of all possible outcomes is fixed and known prior to the performance of any experiments or trials. Similarly, the number of outcomes that have the particular characteristic associated with the event in question is fixed and known beforehand. Finally, all of the outcomes are mutually exclusive and equally likely. *In situations of this kind, the probability that an event occurs will be defined as the ratio of* (1) *the number of outcomes in an experiment that have the characteristic associated with the event to* (2) *the total number of possible outcomes in the experiment.* The probability of a given event can be determined, therefore, without the necessity of performing an experiment.

For example, if an experiment consists of picking, at random, a single card from a deck of playing cards, it is obvious that the total number of possible outcomes is exactly 52. If an event represents the occurrence of a spade, it is obvious that the number of outcomes having this characteristic is exactly 13. If we apply the probability definition given above, the probability of obtaining a spade in a single draw is $13/52 = 1/4 = .25$. That is, there is 1 chance in 4, or a one-fourth probability, or a .25 probability, or 25-percent probability, that a spade will be drawn. This is not to say that every four draws, each draw being from a reshuffled and com-

---

[1] This situation could alternatively be termed "classical" because, historically, it was the situation assumed by the early classical writers in their work on the mathematics of probability. As these writers were quick to see, the situation is the one typically associated with games of chance. In many texts, the probabilities associated with this type of probability situation are termed a priori probabilities.

plete deck, will result in exactly 1 spade appearing. The correct interpretation is that over a long-run period, that is, after many hundreds of draws have been completed, the proportion of cards that are spades will approach the ratio of 1 to 4.

The reader should be able to show that the probability of drawing a picture card is $12/52 = 3/13 = .231 = 23$ percent, that the probability of drawing a card having a denomination of 7 or less (ace being low) is $28/52 = 7/13 = .538 = 54$ percent, and that the probability of drawing an ace of hearts is $1/52 = .019 = 2$ percent. Similarly, the reader should verify that the probability of tossing a pair of dice and coming up with a seven is $6/36 = 1/6 = .167 = 16$ percent, and that the probability of coming up with a seven or eleven is $8/36 = 2/9 = 22$ percent. The proper approach to the derivation of this last, rather troublesome, probability is first to specify the different possible outcomes. The total number of possible outcomes is given below, where D_1 represents the face showing on the first die, and D_2 the face showing on the second die:

D_1	D_2	D_1	D_2	D_1	D_2	D_1	D_2	D_1	D_2	D_1	D_2
1	1	2	1	3	1	4	1	5	1	6	1
1	2	2	2	3	2	4	2	5	2	6	2
1	3	2	3	3	3	4	3	5	3	6	3
1	4	2	4	3	4	4	4	5	4	6	4
1	5	2	5	3	5	4	5	5	5	6	5
1	6	2	6	3	6	4	6	5	6	6	6

The total number of possible outcomes is seen to be 36, the number of outcomes totaling seven to be 6, the number totaling eleven to be 2, and the number totaling either seven or eleven to be 8.

Incomplete-Experiment Situations

The second type of probability situation is one in which the probability ratio associated with a given event is not ascertainable before experiments are performed. Rather, the probability ratio is determinate only after a relatively long period has elapsed in which many experiments or trials have occurred under identical conditions. *In this type of situation, the probability that an event may occur is defined as the ratio of (1) the number of experiments in which the specified event occurred to (2) the total number of experiments performed.* The two basic assumptions underlying this definition are that (1) a relatively large number of experiments is performed under identical conditions, and (2) as the total number of experiments is increased, the probability ratio approaches a given value. This is called an incomplete-experiment situation because the total number of experiments actually performed is always less than the total number that could be performed.

The determination of insurance premiums is an example of the probability definition applied in this type of situation. An insurance company might discover that of 100,000 men who were 45 years of age in 1950, only 95,000 are still alive in 1960, 10 years later. Assuming that the same type of conditions prevail today (and are expected to prevail for the next 10 years) that prevailed in the 1950–1960 period, the probability that a 45-year-old man will be alive 10 years from now could be stated as 95,000/100,000 = 19/20 = .95 = 95 percent.[2] This probability follows because (1) since 100,000 men were studied over a 10-year period, there were 100,000 experiments; and (2) the specified event, being alive, occurred in 95,000 of these experiments.

In this example, a single experiment is viewed as the study of whether one man of 45 years of age was still alive after 10 years had elapsed. Thus each experiment has just two possible outcomes—a dead man or a live man. However, the outcomes are not "equally likely," as in predetermined situations. The basic probability assumption in this situation is that as the number of experiments increases (that is, as the size of the groups studied increases) the ratio of the number of men alive to the total number of men in the particular size group studied converges on a single value; or, to express it differently, the ratio settles down and approaches a given value. Presumably, this unique ratio would be very closely approximated after as many as 100,000 experiments have been completed. The following tables illustrate this basic assumption, which has been verified in many actual situations:

Table 6-1.   THE NUMBER OF MEN ALIVE IN THE FIRST 100, 200, . . . 100,000 EXPERIMENTS

	No. of experiments							
	100	200	500	1,000	2,000	10,000	50,000	100,000
Men alive	99	180	455	920	1,920	9,400	47,500	95,000

It can be seen that as the number of experiments (that is, as the group size) increases from 100 through 100,000 the ratio of the number of men alive to the total number of men studied converges on 95 percent, this ratio being actually obtained after 50,000 experiments.

It should be noted that the definition applicable in these situations is entirely consistent with the definition that is applicable in predetermined situations. For example, assume that a single experiment consists of drawing a single card from a reshuffled full deck. As the number of experiments is indefinitely increased, the ratio of (1) the number of experiments in which

[2] This ratio is then utilized in determining the premiums each 45-year-old man must be assessed so that he will pay his fair share of the payments due for his age group.

Table 6-2. PERCENTAGE OF MEN ALIVE IN FIRST 100, 200, . . . 100,000
EXPERIMENTS

	No. of experiments							
	100	200	500	1,000	2,000	10,000	50,000	100,000
Percentage of men alive	99	90	91	92	96	94	95	95

a spade occurs to (2) the total number of experiments will approach the ratio 1 to 4. This is the ratio that would be obtained by employing the predetermined definition directly. In fact, the definition given in predetermined situations is really a special instance of the more general definition given in this section. This fact is a blessing, because whenever a problem can be framed within a predetermined situation, the probability ratio in question can be ascertained without performing an extensive, and probably expensive, series of experiments.

Complete-Experiment Situations

In the third type of probability situation, the probability that an event may occur is defined as the ratio of (1) *the number of experiments in which the specified event occurred to* (2) *the total number of experiments performed.* This definition is identical to that formulated in the previous section; however, the two basic underlying assumptions are different. Here, it is assumed that (1) there is only a finite number of experiments that can possibly be performed, and (2) this finite number being known, a corresponding number of experiments is made. This is called a complete-experiment situation because the actual number of experiments performed is always equal to the total number of experiments possible.

A complete-experiment situation can be thought of as a mixture of the first two types. The explanation is that the number of outcomes possessing a particular characteristic is not obvious beforehand—rather, it can be determined only by experimentation. This problem is a characteristic of the second, and not of the first, type of situation. However, once determined, the probability ratio is fixed and known, and need not be regarded as approaching a given value.[3] This certainly is a characteristic of the first, and not of the second, type of situation.

[3] In incomplete-experiment situations, the probability ratio must be thought of as approaching a value, because the number of experiments that can possibly be performed is infinite, or at least too great to be practically attempted. However, the complete-experiment definition, like the predetermined definition, can be considered a special instance of the more general definition that applies in incomplete-experiment situations. The complete-experiment situation can be thought of as one in which the total number of possible experiments is performed so that the probability ratio derived actually attains the given value, rather than just approaching it. In this way, the definition is entirely consistent with the more general incomplete-experiment definition.

An example will illustrate this third type of situation—the complete-experiment situation. Assume that a plant employs 1,000 workers, and that 600 of them earned between $70 and $90 last week. What is the probability that if, today, a worker is randomly selected he will have earned between $70 and $90 last week? Because 600 of the 1000 workers possess this characteristic, the probability is, if we apply the complete-experiment probability definition, 600/1000, or 60 percent. In the present instance, a single experiment would consist of examining one worker's pay-roll record for last week; if there are 1,000 workers in the plant, only 1,000 experiments are possible, and the probability ratio obtained is the *unique* ratio for last week. Similarly, the probability that a worker selected at random may have earned less than $70 *or* more than $90 last week is 40 percent. What is the probability of a worker's having earned more than $90? You can't tell, exactly. But you can say that it is 40 percent or less.

Probability Situations and Their Applications

As already indicated, the first type of probability situation is representative of most gambling or game-of-chance situations. Later chapters will show, further, that many of industry's quality-control applications are also quite representative of predetermined situations. As indicated above, the second type of probability situation is representative of all insurance situations. The second part of this chapter, which deals with the "normal" distribution, as well as the following chapter, will illustrate how applicable the third probability situation is in business and economics.

Range and Limits of the Probability Ratio

The range of the probability ratio, as well as its upper and lower limits, can be determined from the following example. Assume that an experiment consists of the random drawing of a single card from a full normal deck of playing cards. The probability that the card will be a spade is the ratio of (1) the number of outcomes that are spades, 13, to (2) the total number of possible outcomes, 52. This is $13/52 = 1/4$. The probability that the card will be a spade or a diamond is the ratio of (1) the number of outcomes that are either spades or diamonds, 26, to (2) the total number of outcomes, 52. This is $26/52 = 1/2$. The probability that the card will be a spade or diamond or heart or club is the ratio of (1) the number of outcomes that are either spades or diamonds or hearts or clubs, 52, to (2) the total number of possible outcomes, 52. This is $52/52 = 1$.

But this last event represents an absolutely certain event; that is, there is no question that the card selected will be a spade, diamond, heart, or club. Therefore the probability of an event that is certain to occur is always 1.

One is also the upper limit of the probability ratio. It is the upper limit because, to enable the ratio to be greater than 1, the number of outcomes that have a certain characteristic would, in the present instance, have to be greater than 52, but this is clearly impossible, because the total number of possible outcomes is only 52.

What is the probability of selecting a card that has a denomination of six? It is the ratio of (1) the number of outcomes that are sixes, 4, to (2) the total number of possible outcomes, 52. This is $4/52 = 1/13$. What is the probability of selecting a card that has a denomination of seventeen? It is the ratio of (1) the number of outcomes that are seventeen, 0, to (2) the total number of possible outcomes, 52. This is $0/52 = 0$.

But the last event represents a clearly impossible event. Therefore the probability of an impossible event is always 0.

Zero is also the lower limit of the probability ratio. It is the lower limit because, if the ratio is less than 0, there would have to be a negative number of outcomes possessing a certain characteristic, but this situation clearly makes no sense.

It can be concluded, then, that the definition of probability given in this chapter and employed throughout the remainder of the book implies that (1) the probability of an impossible event is 0, (2) the probability of a certain event is 1, and (3) the probability of an event that is neither impossible nor certain is a ratio greater than 0 but less than 1.[4]

The probability concepts, definitions, and properties introduced in this chapter will be employed throughout the remainder of this text. Furthermore, several important probability theorems will be discussed in Chapter 8. These theorems will not be treated at this point because the definition of probability is, by itself, of central importance in many business and economic applications, and deserves expansion. These applications, which relate in particular to the concept of statistical inference, will be discussed in the next two chapters and throughout much of the remainder of this book. The present chapter, however, must continue to lay the groundwork for these applications. One of the most important of these foundation stones is the "normal" curve and its basic properties.

[4] This statement does not, of course, mean that a *precise* and appropriate ratio can always be determined for the probability of every possible event that will occur in life. What can be said is that, though the precise probability ratio (which will be designated by the letter p) for any given event (for example, the invasion of West Germany by the Soviet Union)may be unknown, the ratio, whatever it is, must satisfy the following mathematical condition: $0 \leq p \leq 1$. One last point. This section demonstrated how the range and limits of the probability ratio can be derived by employing an illustration that was representative of a predetermined situation. The reader should be able to verify quickly these conclusions for any of the other types of probability situations.

THE NORMAL CURVE

The normal curve occupies a central position in analytical statistics. Together with the concept of probability, it serves as the basis of much of the sampling theory that will be developed later in this chapter. For this reason, an understanding of the normal curve is fundamental to an understanding of the various applications of statistical inference.

The normal curve is a bell-shaped symmetrical curve that has exactly the same number of frequencies and the same range of values on both sides of the arithmetic mean, its center and highest point.[5] As this description implies, the curve, which is portrayed in Figure 6-1, is exactly

FIGURE 6–1

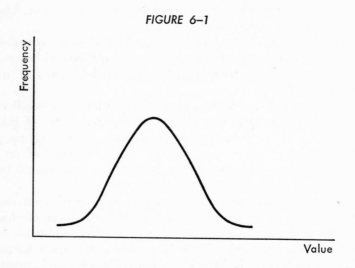

alike on both sides of the center; if the page on which it is printed were to be folded in the center of the curve, the two sides would exactly coincide. It must also be pointed out that the normal curve in a strict sense describes an infinite series of events. The ends of the curve are asymptotic in that they always approach but never touch the horizontal axis. Obviously, it is impossible to have an infinite series in the ordinary course of business, education, and the like, but the fact that most series employed in practice are finite does not injure the normal-curve concept to any great degree.

Admittedly, the previous paragraph is not a very exact description. A much more precise definition may be obtained by stating that the

[5] All three—the arithmetic mean, median, and mode associated with a normal curve— have the same value, namely, that lying directly beneath the peak of the curve.

normal curve is similar to that of the expanded binomial,[6] or, still better, by presenting the exact formula for the curve.[7] Yet this increase in preciseness may be of more harm than use. It is unnecessary to become thoroughly confused by either the binomial or the mathematics of the normal curve equation. An explanation of each may be found in a legion of sources. For the purpose of this text the important idea is to grasp the picture of the curve itself and to understand that it is capable of mathematical derivation.

If the idea is accepted that the curve is derived from a formula, it is relatively easy to understand that if it is mathematically produced it can be completely dissected and analyzed and any of its characteristics measured. In this way the Table of Areas has been obtained (see text discussion, pages 145–148, and Appendix Table IV).

The Normal Curve in Business

The normal curve is rarely directly observed in business and social statistics. It is as difficult to find an instance in which sales in a company follow a normal curve as it is to find a country in which incomes are distributed in this fashion. The explanation is that in order to generalize from it, data must be homogeneous—and even then care must be taken not to overgeneralize. The "Law of Normality," that items will be distributed in the shape of a normal curve, applies only to specific types of data—that is, certain types of "errors." These "errors," chance fluctuations in random sampling, are almost always normally distributed.

Thus the normal curve is extremely important, not because many distributions of business and economic data closely approximate it, but because probability and sampling theory and application depend on it.

The Normal Curve and the Standard Deviation

It was pointed out, in the previous chapter, that the standard deviation and the normal curve have a unique and extremely important relation. This relation, which will be described in this and the following sections, has a direct bearing on several types of probability applications in business and is the basis of all sampling and statistical-inference techniques. The former situation will be discussed in this chapter, and the latter situation will be the entire subject matter of the next two chapters.

$$[6]\ (q + p)^N = q^N + Nq^{N-1}p + \frac{N(N - 1)}{1 \times 2} q^{N-2}p^2 + \frac{N(N - 1)(N - 2)}{1 \times 2 \times 3} q^{N-3}p^3$$
$$+ \cdots + p^N$$

$$y = \frac{N}{\sigma \sqrt{2\pi}} e^{-\frac{x^2}{2\sigma^2}}$$

It can be proven mathematically that the standard deviation can be employed to divide the normal curve into segments. By using such a technique, it is found that a distance of 1 standard deviation on either side of the arithmetic mean of a normal curve would include about 34 percent of the frequencies in the distribution, and consequently ±1 standard deviation from the mean will include 68 percent of the frequencies. Similarly, ±2 standard deviation from the mean will include 95 percent of the frequencies, and ±3 will include 99+ percent of the items in the distribution. This division is pictured in Figure 6-2.

FIGURE 6–2

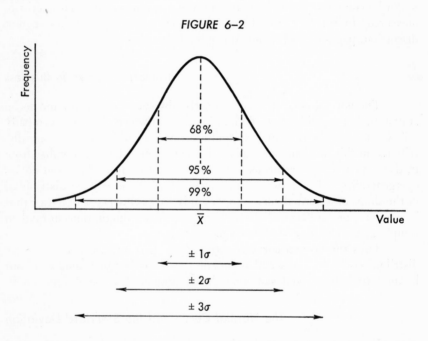

In terms of the Rocket Company example of the previous chapter, if the distribution of wages were perfectly normal, definite statements could be made by using the arithmetic mean of $104, the standard deviation of $32, and the number of workers, 500. Under these conditions, 68 percent of the workers, 340 men, would receive wages within a range of ±1 standard deviation from the mean wage—within a range of $32 on both sides of the mean. Sixty-eight percent of these workers would then receive a wage between $136 ($104 + $32) and $72 ($104 − $32). Ninety-five percent of these workers, 475 men, would receive a wage within 2 standard deviations of the mean—between $168 and $40. Ninety-nine plus percent, 495 men, would receive a wage within 3 standard deviations of the mean—between $200 and $8. Graphically these relations would appear as illustrated in Figure 6-3.

This "segmentizing" characteristic of the standard deviation is invaluable in normal-curve analysis, quality control, and other sampling designs. Complete tables, described in the next section, have been derived that permit the area under a normal curve to be divided into any number of standard deviations.

FIGURE 6–3

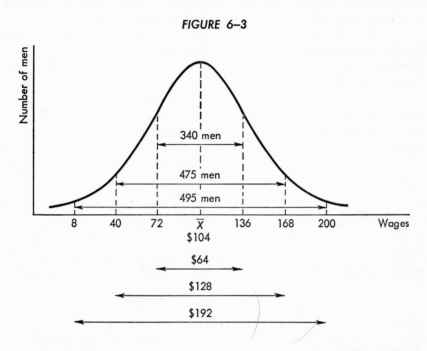

The Table of Areas

The Table of Areas under a normal curve (Appendix Table IV) has been mathematically constructed so that the percentage of the area under any normal curve between the mean and a value any number of standard deviations away can be determined. For example, if the mean of a normal curve is 80 and if the standard deviation is 10, a value of 64 is 1.6 standard deviations away from the mean of 80. It is 1.6 standard deviations away because the actual difference between 80 and 64 is 16, and this, on division by the value of one standard deviation, is 1.6. By locating 1.6 in the extreme left-hand column of Appendix Table IV and reading the body of the table under the column headed by .00, one can readily determine that 44.52 percent of the area under a normal curve lies between the mean and a value 1.6 standard deviations away. If the number of standard deviations had been 1.62—that is, if the second decimal place had been 2 instead of 0—the body of the table would have been read under the column headed by .02. Then the percentage of the area under the curve would be 44.74.

A simple problem should help to clarify further the method of using the Table of Areas. Suppose that a company manufacturing electric lights finds from previous experience that its lights have an average life of 520 hours, with a standard deviation of 146 hours. If this experience applies to lights being currently manufactured, and if we assume that the life of the bulbs follows a normal distribution, a great deal can be deduced concerning 8000 lights that might be sold to one customer.

This customer might be interested in the number of bulbs wearing out during particular intervals. Such information might be of assistance in planning maintenance allowances for purchasing replacement bulbs. The number of bulbs that will wear out can be found for any interval. As an example, the number wearing out between 200 and 300 hours will be found. First it is necessary to find x, the actual difference between the arithmetic mean and each point selected. It can be found by subtraction, thus:

$$
\begin{array}{cc}
520 & 520 \\
-200 & -300 \\
\hline
320 & 220
\end{array}
$$

Now that the actual differences have been found, it is necessary to convert these figures into standard deviations so that they may be located in the Table of Areas. This is the operation designated at the top of the left column of the table as x/σ. In this example the calculation would be

$$320/146 = 2.19 \qquad 220/146 = 1.51$$

These answers indicate that 200 hours is 320 hours less than the mean length of life and that this difference equals 2.19 standard deviations— that is, 200 hours represents a point that is 2.19 standard deviations away from the mean. Similarly, 300 hours is 220 hours less, and this equals 1.51 standard deviations.

These values may now be located in the table. On looking them up in the table it is found that .4857 corresponds to 2.19, and .4345 to 1.51.

These figures indicate that the area between 200 hours and the arithmetic mean includes about 48.5 percent of the total area under the curve and that the area between 300 hours and the arithmetic mean includes about 43 percent of the total area under the curve.

Now, if 200 hours is about 48.5 percent of the area away from the center of the normal curve on one side and 300 hours is about 43 percent away on the same side, the area between the two figures is obviously found by subtraction, thus:

$$
\begin{array}{r}
.4857 \\
-.4345 \\
\hline
.0512
\end{array}
$$

In other words, about 5 percent of the total area under the curve is between 200 hours and 300 hours. Figure 6-4 illustrates this. The crosshatched plus the lined sections represent .4857 or 48.57 percent of the area; the crosshatched section represents 43.45 percent of the area; and the lined section, 5.12 percent.

If the entire area represents 8000 lights, the number of lights wearing out between 200 and 300 hours can be found by multiplying

FIGURE 6–4

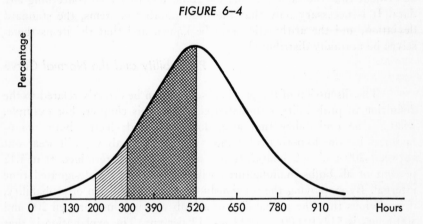

the total number by the percentage of the area under the curve between 200 and 300:

$$\begin{array}{r} 8000 \\ \times\ .0512 \\ \hline 409.6 \end{array}$$

Of the total 8000 lights, 409.6 or, rounding off, 410 bulbs can be expected to expire between 200 and 300 hours of life.

Other questions might be asked. For example, how many bulbs could be expected to last longer than 600 hours? The arithmetic mean is the center of the curve; thus, with an arithmetic mean of 520 hours, half of the lights—4000 bulbs—will lie in the area containing the lengths of life less than the average. The real problem is to find out what number of lights is between the arithmetic mean of 520 hours and the limit in question, 600 hours. The difference between these two figures is 80 hours. By dividing this difference by the standard deviation of 146 hours, it is found that the difference of 80 hours is about .55 standard deviations. If we look this figure up in the Table of Areas, it is found that .2088, or about 21 percent, of the area under the curve is between the center of the curve and .55 standard deviations on one side of the center. By multiplication (.2088 × 8000 bulbs) it is found that 1670.4 light bulbs are between the arithmetic mean of 520 hours and the limit of 600 hours. Now, 4000 bulbs have worn out before, and including, the center of the curve, and another 1670.4 between the center and the limit of 600 hours. Of 8000 bulbs, there are then only 2329.6 bulbs that are expected to last longer than 600 hours. It should now be obvious that with this technique, and with the assumptions made at the beginning of the problem, many important facts can be discovered concerning these bulbs.

Although this example concerns electric light bulbs, it should also be evident that the same information could be discovered concerning any data. It is necessary only that the total number of items, the standard deviation, and the arithmetic mean be known and that the items themselves be normally distributed.

Probability and the Normal Curve

The discussion of the previous section can be directly related to the definition of probability formulated earlier in this chapter. For example, what is the probability that a randomly selected electric bulb, manufactured by the hypothetical company mentioned above, will wear out between 200 and 300 hours? It has already been determined that 5.12 percent of all bulbs manufactured will wear out in the designated time interval. By employing the previously developed definition of probability, it is obvious that the probability of a bulb wearing out between 200 and 300 hours is $512/10,000 = .0512 = 5.12$ percent. The explanation is that in 512 of every 10,000 experiments[8] the event, a bulb wearing out between 200 and 300 hours, occurs. Similarly, the reader should be able to verify that the probability of a single bulb, selected randomly from a production lot, lasting longer than 600 hours is 29 percent.[9]

The following sections will show how sampling theory is based on the relations, developed so far in this chapter, between probability, the normal curve, the arithmetic mean, and the standard deviation.

SAMPLING THEORY

Much of the statistical information used in economics and business is gathered by means of sampling. It was pointed out in Chapter 1 that not only is it often impossible, either physically or because of limitations imposed by time or pecuniary considerations, to take a census of all the items in the statistical universe, but it is also usually unnecessary. The results of a properly taken sample, if subjected to rigorous analysis, will

[8] A single experiment consists of testing a single light bulb and recording when it wears out. If 10,000 light bulbs were tested, 10,000 experiments were performed.

[9] As long as the specified mean and standard deviation, as well as the assumption of a normal distribution, apply, this example can be viewed as a complete-experiment situation. This statement can be made because the probability ratios obtained can be regarded as unique, and not as approaching a limit.

ordinarily enable the investigator to arrive at generalizations that are valid for the entire population.[10] For example, wage data taken from a carefully selected group of 2000 American workers might well be representative of the wage patterns prevailing throughout the entire country. The entire operation of the various public-opinion polling services, such as Gallup and Roper, are based on this principle.

The acceptance of sampling is indeed widespread. In his study of American women,[11] Dr. Kinsey took a sample of the female population. His purpose was to gather data that might be used to generalize concerning the sex habits of all American women. Most critics believe that the group of women who comprised the sample was not typical of American women in general—in other words, that Dr. Kinsey's sample did not accurately represent the universe from which it was taken. They believe that the sample might have represented the population more accurately had greater care been taken in selecting it.[12] This is not the place to analyze any particular study, but there are two important points worth mentioning in connection with the Kinsey Report. First is the fact that, although the particular sample used in Dr. Kinsey's investigation has often been criticized, there has never been any serious claim that sampling itself was an improper method to use. This fact indicates the degree to which the sampling method, compared with the census, has won the approval of statisticians. The second point is that, to be completely usable statistically, a sample must be properly collected so that it accurately represents the universe from which it is taken. The remainder of this chapter will be concerned with the development of the sampling theory underlying applications such as those just indicated.

Learning about the Population from a Sample

Assume that a sample has been correctly taken and that from it measures such as the arithmetic mean have been calculated. A question immediately arises concerning the relations between these measures computed from the sample and the same measures for the entire universe. Are the sample measures accurate estimates of the universe measures, or are they merely rough approximations? This question must be answered before the statistician can proceed to use the sample measures in the conduct of his investigation. Obviously, some measure of reliability is

[10] As defined in Chapter 1, a *population* or *universe* refers to all the items or elements in a group under study. A sample refers to some subgroup, or some portion or segment, of the population or universe.

[11] Alfred C. Kinsey and Associates, *Sexual Behavior in the Human Female* (New York: E. P. Dutton & Co., Inc., 1954).

[12] William G. Cochran, Frederick Mosteller, and John W. Tukey, with the assistance of W. O. Jenkins, *Statistical Problems of the Kinsey Report* (Washington, D.C.: The American Statistical Association, 1954).

needed. Although the discussion in this text will concern itself only with the reliability of the arithmetic mean calculated from a sample, the same principles are used in determining the reliability of other measures (for example, the standard deviation) calculated from a sample. How can any estimate of the arithmetic mean of an entire universe be made on the basis of the arithmetic mean calculated from a small group of items taken from that universe? Fortunately, there is a definite relation between measures, such as the arithmetic mean, calculated from samples and those calculated from the universe.

Simple Random Sampling

Throughout the following discussion it is assumed that the samples have been collected by employing the principles of "simple random sampling." This term applies to any technique ensuring that every item and every combination of items in the universe has an equal chance of being included in the sample. Thus, if a sample of 10 balls is drawn from a universe composed of red and black balls that are homogeneous except for color, every ball in the universe must have exactly the same chance of being a part of the sample. Similarly, every possible combination of 10 balls must also have this same opportunity. It should be evident that these conditions cannot be met if haphazard sampling methods are employed, but can be realized only as a result of careful planning.

If all the items in the universe can be numbered, a random sample may be obtained in two ways. The numbers corresponding to the items can be enclosed in capsules and placed in a globe from which a group may be drawn at random. The items corresponding to the numbers selected in this manner compose the random sample. Whenever a capsule is drawn for inclusion in the sample it must be replaced before the next drawing takes place. If this were not done, the nature of the universe would be altered somewhat. Although this variation is of little importance if the size of the population is large, with smaller populations it assumes some significance. The same results can be obtained by the use of the table of random numbers that is found in Appendix B (see Table II). The numbers in this table have themselves been selected at random. A starting point should be selected at random, perhaps by placing a pencil on the page while the eyes are closed. The digits in the number so located identify the first item in the sample. Additional numbers are obtained by moving in any direction in the table. This procedure will result in a random sample because the random numbers and their position in the table are themselves the result of chance selection.[13]

[13] Unfortunately, it is often impossible or impractical to identify and number each item in the universe. In these circumstances, methods must be developed that will approximate the conditions of random sampling. If directories are available, the practice of selecting page numbers and items on pages at random is usually followed. In so doing, as a matter of convenience,

A Simple Experiment

The major results of sampling theory can be demonstrated by employing a highly simplified example. The same conclusions can also be reached by utilizing a more realistic example. However, the advantage of realism is more than offset by the disadvantage of greatly increased complexity and tediousness. For this reason, the simplified example will be employed in what follows.

Assume that the knowledge of the arithmetic mean of a certain population is desired. Assume, further, that there are only 4 items in this population. This is the simplification referred to in the preceding paragraph. The same results can be illustrated with a population composed of any number of items. The population could represent, for example, the 4 families living on Lake Street, and the information desired could be the average yearly income of these families.[14] In this type of simplified situation, it would be entirely feasible to determine the income for each family in the population and to calculate directly the arithmetic mean for the population. The calculation is illustrated in Table 6-3.

Assume, however, that samples, each composed of exactly 2 items, are taken from this population. A sample of this size greatly simplifies the analysis, which is perfectly valid for a sample of any size. Because the concepts developed in this chapter are based on the principles of simple random sampling, each sample is taken in the following manner:[15]

1. Each of the four incomes is recorded on one of four disks, each disk being an exact duplicate of the other.
2. The disks are placed in a bowl and thoroughly shaken.
3. While blindfolded, a person selects one disk.

---

rules are often adopted that alter the chances of the inclusion of items or combinations of items in the sample. For instance, when directories are employed, the rule might call for the drawing of only one item from any individual page, thus precluding the incorporation in the sample of combinations composed in total or in part of more than one item on any one page. Similarly, if the sampling procedure called for taking every tenth item on a list, combinations of items not separated by nine spaces could not become part of the sample. Obviously, in these and similar situations all possible combinations of items do not have equal chances of selection, even though the sampling method is random. Such samples are called "restricted" random samples. Discussions relating to the application of sampling designs of this nature can be found in various texts published by John Wiley & Sons, Inc., New York, such as W. G. Cochran, *Sampling Techniques*, 1953; W. E. Deming, *Some Theory of Sampling*, 1950; M. H. Hansen, W. N. Hurwitz, and W. G. Madow, *Sample Survey Methods and Theory* (2 vols.), 1953.

[14] The incomes of the four families living on Lake Street, then, make up the entire group under study (they are the population). This information may be desired, for example, because the city, which wishes to convert the property on Lake Street into a main highway, is attempting to evaluate the relative hardship that would be imposed on the families concerned as a result of relocation.

[15] Alternatively, the method employed could be one that utilized the Table of Random Numbers.

4. The number on this disk is recorded by a second person.

5. The disk is placed back in the bowl.

6. The disks are again thoroughly shaken.

7. Again, the blindfolded person selects a single disk, the number on which is again recorded.

One complete sample of 2 items has been taken, and in this way any number of samples of size 2 can be taken.[16]

The sampling process just described meets the requirements of simple random sampling. Regardless of which sample (1st or 80th) is being taken, or of which item in the sample (first or second) is being selected, each of the four values in the population has the same chance of being chosen. Furthermore, each combination of 2 items also has the same

Table 6-3.   YEARLY INCOME OF FAMILIES LIVING ON LAKE STREET
(1964)

	Yearly income (thousands of dollars)
Family	
Black	6
Jones	2
Smith	14
White	10
Total	32
Arithmetic mean ($\Sigma X/N$)	8

chance of being selected. The explanation is that a given item is always being selected from a population of four values, each value being represented by an equal number of items, and that there is no physical reason, inherent in the sampling process, why any item or group of items is more likely then any other to be included or excluded.

The Sampling Distribution of the Mean

The experiment described above depicts a procedure whereby any number of samples, of a fixed size, can be selected according to the prin-

[16] In effect, the original population of four items has been transformed, by the sampling method employed, into an *infinite* population composed, however, of just four different values. Each of these values is represented by an equal number of items, so that the population mean is still 8. The population has been transformed into an infinite population because the sampling process is such that no matter how large the sample becomes, the number of items in the population cannot be exhausted. If items were *not* replaced after they were selected, the population would be *finite* and the maximum sample size would be 4—that is, a sample of 4 would exhaust or use up all the items in the population.

ciples of simple random sampling. This procedure, and the simplified universe to which it is applied, will serve as the basic structure from which all the sampling theory employed in this text will be derived.

It is quite evident that different samples can result from the above experiment. For example, one sample may be made up of the two values 6 and 2, and another sample may consist of the values 2 and 14, or 14 and 10, or some other combination. It is extremely important, at this point, to know all of the *different* possible samples that could result from this experiment.

Table 6-4 shows that exactly 16 *different* samples of size 2 can possibly be taken from this population. D_1 designates the value on the first disk selected, and D_2 designates the value on the second disk. The table was derived in the following way. The first disk selected could have been a 6. The second disk could have been either a 2, 6, 10, or 14, giving rise to the 4 different samples shown in the first two columns. If the first disk

Table 6-4.   DIFFERENT POSSIBLE SAMPLES OF SIZE TWO

D_1	D_2	D_1	D_2	D_1	D_2	D_1	D_2
6	2	2	2	14	2	10	2
6	6	2	6	14	6	10	6
6	10	2	10	14	10	10	10
6	14	2	14	14	14	10	14

had been a 2, the second disk could have been a 2, 6, 10, or 14, giving rise to the 4 different samples shown in columns 3 and 4. The other samples, shown in columns 5 and 6, and 7 and 8, were obtained similarly. Thus, though literally hundreds of samples could be selected in this experiment, only 16 *different* possible samples could result. As this statement implies, many of the hundreds of samples taken would be identical. Table 6-5 shows the arithmetic mean calculated for each of the samples of Table 6-4.

As can be seen from Table 6-5, if an experiment consists of selecting a single sample of 2 items and calculating this sample's mean, each experiment has 16 possible outcomes. Of these, 1 has a value of two, 2 have a value of four, 3 a value of six, 4 a value of eight, 3 a value of ten, 2 a value of twelve, and 1 has a value of fourteen. As just demonstrated, the total number of possible outcomes as well as the number possessing certain characteristics, is fixed and known prior to the performance of any experiments. Furthermore, these 16 outcomes are mutually exclusive and equally likely. (These two terms were defined on page 135.) Each of the 16 sample means is equally likely because each of the two components of each possible sample is obtained by selecting at random a disk that is a physical duplicate of the other disks, there always being exactly 4 disks from which to choose.[17] The circumstances of this example therefore coincide with those of the predetermined situations discussed on pages 136–137.

In situations such as these, the probability that an event will occur was defined as the ratio of (1) the number of outcomes in an experiment that have the characteristic associated with the event to (2) the total number of possible outcomes in the experiment. If we apply this definition to the present example, the probability of obtaining a sample mean of

Table 6-5. SAMPLE MEANS OF ALL POSSIBLE SAMPLES OF SIZE TWO

(a)
Means values corresponding to samples of Table 8-2

4	2	8	6
6	4	10	8
8	6	12	10
10	8	14	12

(b)
Frequency array of sample means

Value	No. of times occurring
2	1
4	2
6	3
8	4
10	3
12	2
14	1
	16

2 is $\frac{1}{16}$. This is calculated as the ratio of the number of outcomes having a value of 2 (1) to the total number of possible outcomes (16). The probability of obtaining a value of 4 is $\frac{2}{16}$. This is calculated as the ratio of the number of outcomes that have a value of 4 (2) to the total number of possible outcomes (16). In a similar fashion, the probability of obtaining a sample mean with a value of 6, 8, 10, 12, or 14 is, respectively, $\frac{3}{16}$, $\frac{4}{16}$, $\frac{3}{16}$, $\frac{2}{16}$, and $\frac{1}{16}$. Table 6-6 summarizes these results.

The probabilities just derived are directly related to an extremely

[17] The multiplication theorem of Chapter 8 will show, also, that the probability of obtaining any of the sample means of Table 6-5 is $\frac{1}{16}$.

important frequency distribution referred to as the *sampling distribution of the mean*. It is defined as the *frequency distribution (expressed either in relative or absolute terms) of the means of an extremely large number of samples, each sample being of the same size*[18] *and selected at random from a given population.*[19] This distribution can be illustrated with respect to the simple experiment introduced above.

As Table 6-6 shows, the probability of obtaining a sample mean of 2 is $\frac{1}{16}$. That is, there is 1 chance in 16 of obtaining a mean of 2. If an extremely large number, say 16 million, of samples is taken, it would be expected that "approximately" $\frac{1}{16}$, or one million, of them would have a mean of 2. The word "approximately" is inserted because, as indicated in the section on probability, the probability ratio is interpreted as the ratio that will be approached in the long run as the number of experiments becomes larger and larger. However, for as many as 16 million experiments

Table 6-6. PROBABILITY OF OBTAINING A GIVEN SAMPLE MEAN

Sample mean	Probability
2	1/16
4	2/16
6	3/16
8	4/16
10	3/16
12	2/16
14	1/16

it would be expected that the ratio, in this example, would be only negligibly different from $\frac{1}{16}$. Because the probability of obtaining a sample mean of four is $\frac{2}{16}$, approximately $\frac{2}{16}$, or 2 million, of the samples would have a mean of 4. The ratios and absolute numbers for these, as well as the other possible sample means, are arranged in Table 6-7. The first two columns represent the sampling distribution of the mean for this experiment because they depict the frequency distribution, expressed in *relative* terms, of the means of an extremely large number of samples, each sample being of the same size and selected at random from a given population. The first and third columns also represent the sampling distribution of

---

[18] The sampling distribution of the mean for the same population will differ, in certain respects, as the sample size differs. In particular, the sampling distribution will become less dispersed as the sample size increases, and it will resemble a normal curve more and more as the sample size increases. More of this later.

[19] An alternative, and mathematically more precise, way of phrasing this definition is to state that the sampling distribution of the mean is the frequency distribution (absolute or relative) of sample means that is approached as the number of samples taken becomes indefinitely large.

the mean for this experiment because they depict the frequency distribution, expressed in *absolute* terms, of the means of an extremely large number of samples, each sample being of the same size and selected at

Table 6-7.   SAMPLING DISTRIBUTION OF THE MEAN CONSTRUCTED
(For Sixteen Million Samples of Size Two)

Sample mean	Ratio of no. of times the specified mean occurred to total number of sample means	No. of times the specified mean occurred (millions)
2	1/16	1
4	2/16	2
6	3/16	3
8	4/16	4
10	3/16	3
12	2/16	2
14	1/16	1
Total	16/16 = 1	16

FIGURE 6–5

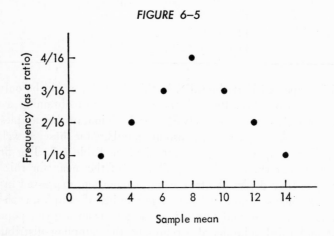

random from a given population. Figures 6-5 and 6-6 illustrate these distributions graphically.

The sampling distribution of the mean is of central importance in sampling theory. In the next three sections, three of its most significant attributes—namely, its arithmetic mean, pattern of distribution or shape, and standard deviation—will be examined.

FIGURE 6-6

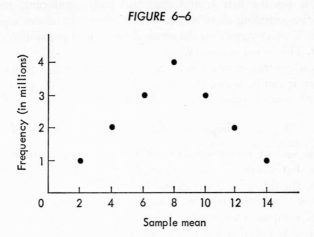

Sample mean

Mean of the Sampling Distribution of the Mean

All the business and economic applications of statistical inference discussed in the next chapter are based on the sampling distribution of the mean and its three major attributes. In this section, one of these, the arithmetic mean, will be studied.

Assume that an extremely large number, let us say 16 million, of samples of size 2 are taken from the population of Table 6-3, and that the sample mean for each of these samples is calculated. From the previous section, it is apparent that $\frac{1}{16}$ or 1 million of these means will have a value of 2, $\frac{2}{16}$ or 2 million a value of 4, $\frac{3}{16}$ or 3 million a value of 10, $\frac{2}{16}$ or 2 million a value of 12, and $\frac{1}{16}$ or 1 million a value of 14. The first and third columns of Table 6-7 show this.

The arithmetic mean of these sample means is determined by dividing the sum of the values of all the sample means by the number of means. Let the Greek letter for capital m, which is designated by the symbol μ, represent this arithmetic mean. Its value, in the present example, is calculated as follows:

$$\mu = [(1 \text{ million} \times 2) + (2 \text{ million} \times 4) + (3 \text{ million} \times 6)$$
$$+ (4 \text{ million} \times 8) + (3 \text{ million} \times 10) + (2 \text{ million} \times 12)$$
$$+ (1 \text{ million} \times 14)] \div 16 \text{ million}$$

$$= \frac{\begin{array}{c} 2 \text{ million} + 8 \text{ million} + 18 \text{ million} + 32 \text{ million} \\ + 30 \text{ million} + 24 \text{ million} + 14 \text{ million} \end{array}}{16 \text{ million}}$$

$$= \frac{128 \text{ million}}{16 \text{ million}} = 8$$

Now for the first remarkable, and truly significant, result. The mean of the sampling distribution derived from the above equations is 8, and this is exactly equal to the mean of the parent population derived in Table 6-3. This is not a coincidence.

As a general result, which can be mathematically proved for any population, it can be stated that *the arithmetic mean of the sampling distribution of the mean is equal to the population mean.*

Shape of the Sampling Distribution of the Mean

The second major attribute of the sampling distribution of the mean, its shape, will be examined in this section. Before beginning the discussion, the following point should be emphasized. Any given sampling distribution is constructed from selecting at random an extremely large number of samples, each sample being of the *same* size. As this implies, each original population has many sampling distributions, each of which corresponds to a fixed sample size. As an illustration, 16 million samples, each composed of 2 items, can be selected and the sampling distribution of the mean constructed. Similarly, 16 million samples, each composed of 4 (or any other number) items, can be selected and the sampling distribution constructed. Although each of these distributions will have the same arithmetic mean—equal to the population mean—the shape of each *can* differ and the dispersion of each will differ.

With respect to the shape of the sampling distribution of the mean, it can be proved mathematically that *if the original population is distributed normally, the sampling distribution of the mean will also form a normal curve.* This holds regardless of the sample size employed in constructing the distribution. Even more important, it can be mathematically proved that *even if the original population is not distributed normally, the sampling distribution of the mean approaches the shape of the normal curve as the sample size becomes larger.* This latter point is important enough to repeat: even if the parent population does not form a normal curve, as is true in most business and economic situations, the sampling distribution of the mean approaches normality as the sample size grows larger.[20] Furthermore, the sampling distribution of the mean corresponding to a non-normal parent population very closely approaches the normal curve even for relatively small sample sizes.

This observation can be rather dramatically illustrated with reference to the population of Table 6-3. Here the parent population does not even closely resemble a normal curve. As illustrated in Figure 6-7, the population of Table 6-3 forms a rectangular[21] distribution. Yet the sam-

[20] This truly significant result follows from the mathematics of the crucial "central limit theorem" of statistics.

[21] A rectangular distribution can be defined as one in which each of the possible values is represented by an equal number of items.

pling distribution of the mean constructed from a sample size of 2 (see Figures 6-5 and 6-6) certainly exhibits a tendency toward normalcy. It is triangular in shape rather than rectangular, as is the original population.

FIGURE 6–7

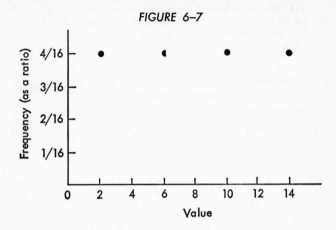

FIGURE 6–8.   *Sampling Distribution of the Mean for a Sample Size of Three*

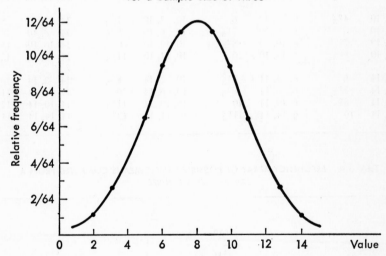

Furthermore, the sampling distribution constructed from a sample size of only 3 resembles very closely a normal curve, as Figure 6-8 shows.[22] If the

[22] This sampling distribution was constructed in a manner similar to that corresponding to a sample size of 2. All the possible outcomes for each experiment were determined by enumerating all the possible combinations of 3 items that could be selected at random, each item being replaced after each draw. The enumeration was accomplished by adding, separately, each of the four values of Table 6-3 to each of the 16 outcomes of Table 6-4 (Table 6-8). There are 64 different possible outcomes. These outcomes can be checked as follows: there are 4

different possibilities for the first item selected, for each of these possibilities there are 4 different possibilities for the second item selected, and for each of these 16 possibilities, there are 4 possibilities for the third item selected—$4 \times 4 \times 4 = 64$. Table 6-8 also shows the sample means calculated for each of the 64 possible samples. Table 6-9 indicates that 1, 3, 6, 10, 12, 12, 10, 6, 3, and 1 of these means have the values, respectively, of 2, $3\frac{1}{3}$, $4\frac{2}{3}$, 6, $7\frac{1}{3}$, $8\frac{2}{3}$, 10, $11\frac{1}{3}$, $12\frac{2}{3}$ and 14. By employing, as before, the predetermined probability definition, the probabilities of these values are found to be, respectively, $\frac{1}{64}$, $\frac{3}{64}$, $\frac{6}{64}$, $\frac{10}{64}$, $\frac{12}{64}$, $\frac{12}{64}$, $\frac{10}{64}$, $\frac{6}{64}$, $\frac{3}{64}$ and $\frac{1}{64}$.

Table 6-8. ALL-INCLUSIVE LIST OF DIFFERENT POSSIBLE SAMPLES OF SIZE THREE, WITH CORRESPONDING MEANS

Sample	$\bar{X}$	Sample	$\bar{X}$	Sample	$\bar{X}$	Sample	$\bar{X}$
2, 2, 2	2	6, 2, 2	$3\frac{1}{3}$	10, 2, 2	$4\frac{2}{3}$	14, 2, 2	6
2, 6, 2	$3\frac{1}{3}$	6, 6, 2	$4\frac{2}{3}$	10, 6, 2	6	14, 6, 2	$7\frac{1}{3}$
2, 10, 2	$4\frac{2}{3}$	6, 10, 2	6	10, 10, 2	$7\frac{1}{3}$	14, 10, 2	$8\frac{1}{3}$
2, 14, 2	6	6, 14, 2	$7\frac{1}{3}$	10, 14, 2	$8\frac{2}{3}$	14, 14, 2	10
2, 2, 6	$3\frac{1}{3}$	6, 2, 6	$4\frac{2}{3}$	10, 2, 6	6	14, 2, 6	$7\frac{1}{3}$
2, 6, 6	$4\frac{2}{3}$	6, 6, 6	6	10, 6, 6	$7\frac{1}{3}$	14, 6, 6	$8\frac{2}{3}$
2, 10, 6	6	6, 10, 6	$7\frac{1}{3}$	10, 10, 6	$8\frac{2}{3}$	14, 10, 6	10
2, 14, 6	$7\frac{1}{3}$	6, 14, 6	$8\frac{2}{3}$	10, 14, 6	10	14, 14, 6	$11\frac{1}{3}$
2, 2, 10	$4\frac{2}{3}$	6, 2, 10	6	10, 2, 10	$7\frac{1}{3}$	14, 2, 10	$8\frac{2}{3}$
2, 6, 10	6	6, 6, 10	$7\frac{1}{3}$	10, 6, 10	$8\frac{2}{3}$	14, 6, 10	10
2, 10, 10	$7\frac{1}{3}$	6, 10, 10	$8\frac{2}{3}$	10, 10, 10	10	14, 10, 10	$11\frac{1}{3}$
2, 14, 10	$8\frac{2}{3}$	6, 14, 10	10	10, 14, 10	$11\frac{1}{3}$	14, 14, 10	$12\frac{2}{3}$
2, 2, 14	6	6, 2, 14	$7\frac{1}{3}$	10, 2, 14	$8\frac{2}{3}$	14, 2, 14	10
2, 6, 14	$7\frac{1}{3}$	6, 6, 14	$8\frac{2}{3}$	10, 6, 14	10	13, 6, 14	$11\frac{1}{3}$
2, 10, 14	$8\frac{2}{3}$	6, 10, 14	10	10, 10, 14	$11\frac{1}{3}$	14, 10, 14	$12\frac{2}{3}$
2, 14, 14	10	6, 14, 14	$11\frac{1}{3}$	10, 14, 14	$12\frac{2}{3}$	14, 14, 14	14

Table 6-9. FREQUENCY ARRAY OF POSSIBLE SAMPLE MEANS COMPUTED FROM A SAMPLE SIZE OF THREE

Mean	No.
2	1
$3\frac{1}{3}$	3
$4\frac{2}{3}$	6
6	10
$7\frac{1}{3}$	12
$8\frac{2}{3}$	12
10	10
$11\frac{1}{3}$	6
$12\frac{2}{3}$	3
14	1
	64

sample size were increased to 5 or 6,[23] the gaps between the plotted points of Figure 6-8 would be narrowed considerably, and the curve would resemble, more and more, the normal curve.

The following conclusions, then, can be made. If the original population is normal or close to normal, the sampling distribution of the mean will be normal, regardless of the sample size. Even if the original population deviates significantly from normal, the sampling distribution of the mean approaches the normal curve as the sample size increases. The samples that are employed in practice are typically of such a size that the corresponding sampling distribution of the mean is distributed normally. For these reasons, the following discussions will assume that the sampling distribution of the mean follows a normal curve.

The alert reader may now see an extremely important concept beginning to take shape. A pattern is being traced out, one that will soon tie together the previous discussions of probability, areas under the normal curve, the arithmetic mean, and the basic principles of sampling theory. But first, the third important attribute of the sampling distribution must be treated.

Standard Deviation of the Sampling Distribution of the Mean

The standard deviation is the final major attribute of the sampling distribution of the mean that will be examined. This, like the standard deviation of any distribution, measures the amount of dispersion in the distribution. Furthermore, if the distribution approximates a normal curve, many interesting facts can be learned about the manner in which the individual items are distributed. This idea is fundamental to all sampling theory.

The standard deviation of the sampling distribution, because it is so important, is given a special name and a special symbol. This particular standard deviation is called the standard error of the mean. Its symbol is $\sigma_{\bar{x}}$.

It can be mathematically proved that $\sigma_{\bar{x}}$ can be calculated from the formula $\sigma_{\bar{x}} = \sigma/\sqrt{n}$ where σ is the standard deviation of the original population and n is the sample size. As will be demonstrated below, the validity of this formula can be proved by referring to the original population of Table 6-3 and the sampling distribution of Figures 6-5 and 6-6, which corresponds to a sample size of 2.

Table 6-10 shows that the population standard deviation is 4.472. If we apply the above formula,

$$\sigma_{\bar{x}} = \sigma/\sqrt{n} = 4.472/\sqrt{2} = 4.472/1.414 = 3.162$$

[23] This distribution is quite possible, even though there are only 4 different values in the original population, because the immediate replacement of each item selected makes the population infinite for all practical purposes.

This result can be checked with respect to the sampling distribution of Figures 6-5 and 6-6. The standard error of the mean, as already indicated, is a measure of the amount of dispersion in the sampling distribution of the mean. Because the individual items in this distribution are sample means, the standard error of the mean measures the extent to which an extremely large number of sample means clusters around the mean of all the sample means. This measure can be calculated by employing the usual formula for the standard deviation: $\sigma = \sqrt{[\Sigma(X - \bar{X})^2]/N}$. In the present context, X, the value of an individual item, refers to the value of a sample mean because the individual items in the sampling distribution of the

Table 6-10.   CALCULATION OF POPULATION STANDARD DEVIATION

	Yearly income X	$X - \mu$	$(X - \mu)^2$
Family			
Black	6	−2	4
Jones	2	−6	36
Smith	14	6	36
White	10	2	4
Total	32	0	80

$$\mu = \frac{\Sigma X}{N} = \frac{32}{4} = 8$$

$$\sigma = \sqrt{[\Sigma(X - \mu)^2]/N} = \sqrt{80/4} = \sqrt{20} = 4.472$$

mean are sample means. In addition, $\bar{X}$, the value of the mean of the entire distribution, refers to the value of μ because μ is the mean of the sampling distribution of the mean. Therefore the standard error of the mean can be calculated from

$$\sigma_{\bar{X}} = \sqrt{[\Sigma(\bar{X} - \mu)^2]/N}$$

where $\bar{X}$ denotes the mean of an individual sample and μ the mean of the population (which equals the mean of the sampling distribution of the mean).

The example utilized throughout this part of the chapter dealing with sampling theory will be introduced again. If 16 million samples of size 2 were selected at random from the population of Table 6-3 and their means calculated, the different possible values, together with the number of times each occurred, would be given by the first and third columns of

Table 6-7. Using this table, the standard error of the mean is calculated, in Table 6-11, in the same manner that any standard deviation can be calculated. It can be seen that the standard error calculated by this method is exactly equal to the standard error calculated, above, by the formula $\sigma_{\bar{x}} = \sigma/\sqrt{n}$. The validity of this formula has, in this way, been verified.

In practice, the standard error of the mean is always calculated by the formula $\sigma_{\bar{x}} = \sigma/\sqrt{n}$. The reason for this method is obvious. If it were necessary to take an extremely large number (for example, 16 million) of

Table 6-11. CALCULATION OF THE STANDARD ERROR OF THE MEAN DIRECTLY FROM THE SAMPLING DISTRIBUTION
(Based on n = 2, Sixteen Million Samples, and the Original Population of Table 6-3)

Value of sample mean $\bar{X}$	$(\bar{X} - \mu)$	$(\bar{X} - \mu)^2$	No. of times each sample mean occurred (in millions) f	(in millions) $f(\bar{X} - \mu)^2$
2	−6	36	1	36
4	−4	16	2	32
6	−2	4	3	12
8	0	0	4	0
10	2	4	3	12
12	4	16	2	32
14	6	36	1	36

$$\sigma_{\bar{x}} = \sqrt{\frac{\Sigma f(\bar{X} - \mu)^2}{N}} = \sqrt{\frac{160 \text{ million}}{16 \text{ million}}} = \sqrt{10} = 3.162$$

samples in order to determine the standard error of the mean, sampling, in general, would be too time-consuming, costly, and impractical. If the formula verified above is applied, it is necessary only to know the standard deviation of the population and the sample size. The determination of the sample size is, of course, no problem. If a sample of 100 items is taken, $n = 100$. The standard deviation of the population is a different matter. Usually it is unknown. Fortunately, however, it can be very closely estimated from the results of a single sample or from past experience. Therefore the formula given in this section becomes very practical. This very important point will be fully discussed in the next chapter, which deals with applications. The present chapter is concerned mainly with developing the necessary theory.[24]

An additional observation, one that will prove useful in the next chapter, will be made at this point. The formula by which the standard error of the mean is calculated—namely, $\sigma_{\bar{x}} = \sigma/\sqrt{n}$—indicates that the value of $\sigma_{\bar{x}}$ varies directly as σ, the standard deviation of the population. That is, the higher the value of σ, the higher will be the value of $\sigma_{\bar{x}}$. The standard error, however, varies inversely with respect to sample size. That is, the higher the value of n, the lower the value of $\sigma_{\bar{x}}$. In most situations, σ cannot be controlled. n, however, can generally be controlled, at least within certain limits. As this statement implies, the value of $\sigma_{\bar{x}}$ can be controlled—that is, made higher or lower—by controlling the sample size. The larger the sample size, the lower is $\sigma_{\bar{x}}$, and therefore the lower the amount of dispersion in the sampling distribution. This important principle is utilized in the next chapter, which is concerned with the application of the theory developed in this chapter.

SUMMARY

The concept of probability was examined in the first part of this chapter. Three types of probability situations were distinguished. These were designated as predetermined, incomplete-experiment, and complete-experiment situations. The probability definition applicable to each was carefully formulated, and the general properties of the "probability ratio" were derived.

The concept of the normal curve was discussed in the second part of this chapter. In particular, the relation between the area under a normal curve and the arithmetic mean and standard deviation of the normal curve was indicated. It was pointed out that by employing the table of areas, the percentage of the area under a normal curve between the mean and a value any number of standard deviations away can be determined.

Finally, the notion of statistical inference was introduced. The major results of statistical theory were then demonstrated. The demonstration necessarily centered around the concept of the sampling distribution of the mean. This concept is defined as the frequency distribution

[24] It should be pointed out that the formula, $\sigma_{\bar{x}} = \sigma/\sqrt{n}$, applies specifically to infinite populations. It can be used safely for finite populations, however, whenever the ratio of the number of items in the sample to the number in the finite population is less than 5 percent. The ratio is usually less than 5 percent in situations that arise in practice. If the ratio happens to be 5 percent or greater, the value obtained by employing the above formula should be multiplied by a correction factor, $\sqrt{(N-n)/(N-1)}$. N refers to the number of items in the finite population, and n refers to the number of items in the sample. This correction factor is usually called the "finite multiplier."

of an extremely large number of sample means, each of the same size and selected from the same parent population. The mean of the sampling distribution, designated by the symbol μ, is equal to the mean of the universe. The shape of the sampling distribution is normal for most, if not all, applications that arise in business and economics. The standard deviation of the sampling distribution, which is termed the standard error of the mean and designated by the symbol $\sigma_{\bar{x}}$, can be calculated from the formula $\sigma_{\bar{x}} = \sigma/\sqrt{n}$.

The concepts of probability and the normal curve were introduced at the outset of this chapter because it would not have been possible to demonstrate the major results of sampling theory without using these concepts as tools in the analysis. The next two chapters will show how these results can be productively employed in practice. These applications, moreover, will continually draw on the concepts of probability and the normal curve. In this way, the three parts of this chapter—namely, probability, the normal curve, and sampling theory—are an integrated body of knowledge; they serve as the foundation stones of the basic applications of statistical inference in business and economics.

SUGGESTED READINGS

Bryant, E. C. *Statistical Analysis*. New York: McGraw-Hill Book Company, Inc., 1960, chap. 4.

Ekeblad, F. A. *The Statistical Method in Business*. New York: John Wiley & Sons, Inc., 1962, chap. 7.

Huntsberger, D. V. *Elements of Statistical Inference*. Boston: Allyn and Bacon, Inc., 1961, chap. 5.

QUESTIONS

1. Distinguish between the three types of probability situations described in the text, and give several examples of each.
2. Using the probability definitions given in this chapter, show that it is impossible for the probability of a given event to be greater than 1 or less than 0.
3. Describe the general characteristics of the normal curve.
4. The column at the extreme left of the Table of Areas under the Normal Curve is identified by x/σ. Explain the meaning of this fraction.
5. What are the conditions of simple random sampling?
6. How could you reduce the value of $\sigma_{\bar{x}}$?
7. Would a sample mean which came from a distribution with $\sigma_{\bar{x}} = 2$ be more representative, on the average, of the population mean than a sample which came from a distribution with $\sigma_{\bar{x}} = 8$? Explain.

8. Describe the three most important attributes of the sampling distribution of $\bar{x}$.

1. Calculate the probability of drawing a jack (no specific suit) from a pack of playing cards.
2. If the distribution of the length of life of Brand A flashlight batteries is perfectly normal, the average length of life of these batteries is 120 hours, and the standard deviation is 36 hours, how many of 160 batteries would (a) have a length of life between 85 and 135 hours, (b) wear out before 48 hours, (c) last longer than 130 hours, (d) have a length of life between 48 and 84 hours?
3. In a particular game you will win $5 if you throw either a 3 or an 8 with a pair of dice. Calculate the probability of winning $5.
4. The Nutmakers Inc. company has been manufacturing nuts for many years. Their sole product has been a .75-inch nut, and the individual items have been distributed normally around this point. They have just completed 10,000 nuts having a standard deviation of .012 inches. The government plans to use these nuts in jet planes and requests certain specific information.
   (a) The largest 2500 of these nuts will be larger than what size?
   (b) The middle quarter of these nuts in terms of size will be between what two dimensions?
   (c) How many of the nuts will be larger than .726 inches?
5. The average test grade in a particular class is 79. The standard deviation is 5. If the class is distributed normally, how many students in a class of 200 did *not* receive a grade between 75 and 85?
6. Calculate the probability of throwing a 10 on the first throw of a pair of dice.
7. It has been found that any student who gets less than 45 on a statistics test usually fails the course and that grades are normally distributed.
   (a) If, on the latest test, the average grade is 55 and the standard deviation 5, what percent of the class will probably fail statistics?
   (b) What percent of the class will probably receive an "A", assuming that to do so requires a grade of 90 or better?
8. The Bright Company finds that its fluorescent tubes usually have an average life of 12 months, with a standard deviation of 2 months, and that the lives of the tubes are distributed normally. Assume that 100,000 have just been produced.
   (a) How many will probably need replacing between 5 and 6 months after installation?

    (b) How many will last longer than 15 months?

    (c) How many will have a life between 9 and 13 months?

    (d) How many will wear out before the end of the eighth month?

    (e) What is the probability of a tube lasting longer than 17 months?

    (f) The 20 percent of the tubes with the longest life will last longer than how many months?

    (g) The middle third of the bulbs, in terms of length of life, will wear out between what two dates?

9. The Confederate Electric tube company has found from experience that their receiving tubes have an average usable life of 5.6 years with a standard deviation of .75 years. Assume that this information is applicable to present tube production and that the usable life of receiving tubes follows a normal distribution. Eight hundred receiving tubes have been produced this week.

    (a) How many will have to be replaced during the fifth year?

    (b) How many will wear out before the seventh year?

    (c) How many will last longer than 6 years?

    (d) How many will have a life between 4.5 and 6.5 years?

10. Three students take different tests. Adam gets a score of 79, Bud 91, and Carl 22. The average grades on the three tests were 92, 96, and 30, respectively. The standard deviations were 8, 3, and 8. Assuming that the grades on each test were normally distributed, state the position of each student in his particular class. (For example, Bud's score in another group of class tests was such that only 4 percent of the students taking the test received a grade lower than his.)

11. Imagine a bubble-gum machine similar to that found in many stores. The balls of gum are of various colors and the purchaser wins a prize if, on inserting a penny, he receives a white ball. The machine contains a total of 500 balls. How many of the balls must be white to give the purchaser 1 chance in 20 of winning a prize?

12. A well-known gambling device, frequently known as a "one-armed bandit," consistently attracts customers. The machine consists of three wheels on which are pictures of various objects such as oranges, pears, and so forth. When a coin is inserted in the machine and the handle of the device pulled downward, the three wheels spin, each supposedly spinning independently of the other two. If all three wheels stop so that a particular combination appears, the customer wins the jackpot. Assuming that each wheel presents the same set of two different pictures, what is the probability that the same picture will appear on all three wheels at the same time?

13. Assume that the following distribution is typical of the wages of all rocket workers and that the universe is normal.

WEEKLY WAGES PAID TO WORKERS IN ALL
UNDERGROUND ROCKET COMPANY PLANTS
(1965)

	No. of workers
Wages (dollars)	
40 but under 60	360
60 but under 80	420
80 but under 100	510
100 but under 120	660
120 but under 140	570
140 but under 160	480
	3000

(a) The union requests that in a new wage contract the minimum wage shall be $62. What percentage of all rocket workers would benefit from this minimum?

(b) Using the Table of Areas, calculate the number of workers in this company that would fall in each class interval if the 3000 workers were distributed normally.

(c) Workers receiving more than $150 per week are assumed to be highly skilled. What percentage of the workers in this industry are highly skilled?

(d) It is suggested that all workers receiving between $105 and $115 per week form a separate union to be known as the "Union of Average Workers." What percentage of the industry's workers would belong?

14. A random sample of 82 items is drawn from a universe of high-grade bonds known to be distributed in an approximately normal fashion. The arithmetic mean of the sample is $200, and the standard deviation is $10.

(a) The middle 60 percent of the items in the sample lie between what limits?

(b) How many items in this sample have a value of $190 or more?

(c) How many items in this sample lie between $176 and $217?

(d) What is the possibility that the mean of the universe is $211 or more?

15. The average test grade in a particular class is 73. The standard deviation is 5. If the grades in the class are distributed normally, how many students in a class of 100 did *not* receive a grade between 65 and 75?

16. Assume that the bulb-manufacturing industry is extremely competitive. A particular bulb manufacturer wants very much to obtain a large order (of 150,000 bulbs) from a particular customer. The manufacturer knows that the lowest bidder will obtain the order, and that all his competitors are submitting bids. The manufacturer also knows that this customer follows a policy of giving a bonus of 50 cents for

each bulb that is shown to last longer than 600 hours; the customer follows this policy because of the great savings he makes from not having to stop production every few hours in order to replace bulbs. The bulb manufacturer can produce the 150,000 bulbs for a total cost of $15,000. To this he must add a minimum profit of $5,000. The bulb manufacturer decides to treat the total bonus ($.50 times each bulb lasting more than 600 hours) he will receive later as a reduction in his current costs. He knows that the length of life of his bulbs is normally distributed, and that his bulbs have an average length of life of 470 hours and a standard deviation of 100 hours. What is the most competitive (that is, the lowest) price (per bulb) the bulb manufacturer can charge?

17. One fourth of the items in an extremely large population have a value of 2, $\frac{1}{2}$ a value of 4, and $\frac{1}{4}$ a value of 6. Employing the probability definition applicable in predetermined situations, show that
   (a) The means of the sampling distributions of the mean, corresponding to sample sizes of 2 and 3, both equal the mean of the population.
   (b) The standard errors of the mean, corresponding to sample sizes of 2 and 3, both equal $\sigma/\sqrt{n}$.
   (c) The shape of the sampling distribution more closely resembles that of the normal curve as n increases from 2 to 3.
   [*Hint:* Consider an experiment in which a single disk is selected, with replacement, from a box containing 4 disks, 1 of which has a value of 2, 2 a value of 4, and 1 a value of 6. Number each disk from 1 to 4.]

18. One fourth of the items in an infinite population have a value of 1, one fourth a value of 3, one fourth a value of 5, and one fourth a value of 7. Employing the predetermined definition of probability, show that
   (a) The mean of the sampling distribution corresponding to a sample size of 2 equals the mean of the universe.
   (b) The standard error of the mean, corresponding to a sample size of 2, equals $\sigma/\sqrt{n}$.
   (c) The shape of the sampling distribution more closely resembles that of the normal curve as n increases from 2 to 3.

19. Assume that a finite population contains 4 items, each item having a different value. These values are 1, 3, 5, and 7. Assume that a sample of size 2 is taken *without* replacement. Show that
   (a) The mean of the sampling distribution equals the mean of the universe.
   (b) The standard error of the mean for this sampling distribution can be determined by taking the product of the formula for an infinite population and the finite multiplier; that is, show that, in this case, $\sigma_{\bar{x}} = (\sigma/\sqrt{n})\sqrt{(N-n)/(N-1)}$. (See footnote 24.)

CHAPTER SEVEN

Sampling Applications:
Confidence Intervals
and Tests of Significance

The previous chapter laid the groundwork for the subject matter of the present chapter. The concepts of probability and the normal curve were introduced and then utilized to develop the sampling theory that underlies the sampling applications to be discussed now. All these applications can be grouped under two main headings: *confidence intervals* and *tests of significance*. These terms will be carefully defined in the following pages. It is most interesting to note that these applications are generally relevant not only to the fields of business and economics but to the other social sciences and to all the physical and engineering sciences.

CONFIDENCE INTERVALS

The first group of applications that will be discussed comes under the heading of confidence intervals. The following example will introduce this concept.

Assume that a researcher is seeking to determine the mean of a certain population. The researcher takes a random sample of 100 items from the population and discovers that the sample mean is 80. From this fact he might conclude that the population mean is "around 80." How willing would you, as a corporation executive or as chairman of a committee of economists, be to accept this estimate as the basis of a policy recommendation?

The answer, of course, depends on the nature of the problem being considered. The estimate, by itself, provides you with more information than you had previously and, for this reason alone, is useful. However, the inevitable question that arises is, "How reliable is this estimate?" or "How close, in reality, is this sample mean to the population mean?" or "What is the likelihood that this estimate is within 5, or 10, or 20 of the population mean?" These questions point up the weakness in relying on the single estimate of 80. One of the truly remarkable attributes of the entire concept of statistical inference is that it provides a means of successfully dealing with questions such as those posed above.

As these questions imply, what is in fact desired is a probability statement relating to the estimate of 80. For example, "There are 95 chances of 100 that the population mean is 80" or "There is a 95-percent probability that the population mean is 80" or "There is a 95-percent probability that the population mean is ±5 of 80 (that is, between 75 and 85)." Although the third statement quoted is not as precise as the first and second, it can be just as useful. It is not possible to make statements such as the first and second quoted here. However, the technique of statistical inference makes it entirely possible to formulate probability statements analogous to the third one quoted above. This is a truly important result.

The third probability statement quoted above is an illustration of a confidence interval. *A confidence interval indicates the probability that the population mean[1] lies within a specified range of values.* Again, the statement, "There is a 95-percent probability that the population mean lies within plus and minus 5 of 80 (that is, between 75 and 85)," is an illustration of this concept. The low and high values in this range are termed *confidence limits.* In the above example, 75 is the lower confidence limit, and 85 is the upper confidence limit. The difference between the lower and upper limits is termed the *size* or *width* of the confidence interval. In the foregoing example, the size of the confidence interval is 10 (85 − 75 = 10). Finally, the probability associated with a confidence interval is termed the *confidence level.* In the example given here the confidence level is 95 percent.

Determination of a Confidence Interval

Now that the concept of a confidence interval has been defined, the really crucial consideration is, "How can it be determined?" That is, how can one calculate the probability that the population mean is located within a specified range of values? The sampling theory developed in the previous chapter, together with the discussion relating to probability and areas under a normal curve, provides the answer.

Assume that a sample is randomly drawn from a given population and that the sample mean is calculated. This sample mean is just one of an

---

[1] Or any other estimate of a population parameter.

extremely large number that could have been selected. As has been previously indicated, the distribution of this extremely large number of possible sample means is referred to as the sampling distribution of the mean. From the results of the previous chapter, the reader should recall that the sampling distribution of the mean will exactly follow a normal distribution, regardless of sample size, if the original distribution is normal, and that it will very closely resemble a normal curve, for sufficiently large sample sizes, even if the original population is not normal. Furthermore, the mean of the sampling distribution is equal to the mean of the population, and its standard deviation, termed the standard error of the mean, can be calculated from the relation $\sigma_{\bar{x}} = \sigma/\sqrt{n}$.

The reader should now recall the results of the previous chapter relating to areas under a normal curve. It will be remembered, for example, that 95 percent of the area under a normal curve lies within ± 1.96 standard deviations of the mean of the normal curve. Now the reader should consider the results of the previous chapter relating to probability—particularly the probability definition that is pertinent in complete-experiment situations. This definition indicates, for example, that if a certain event occurs in 95 percent of all possible experiments, the probability that the event may occur in any single experiment is 95 percent. Therefore, because 95 percent of all possible values under a normal curve lie within plus and minus 1.96 standard deviations of the mean, the probability that any single value, selected at random, will lie within ± 1.96 standard deviations of the mean is 95 percent.

All the important results summarized in the previous two paragraphs can now be synthesized. Throughout this synthesis the reader should be able to recognize the importance of the concept of probability, which was utilized in defining the sampling distribution of the mean, and which will now be employed in constructing confidence intervals.

Because the sampling distribution of the mean follows a normal curve, and because the mean of the sampling distribution equals the population mean, 95 percent of all possible sample means will lie within plus and minus 1.96 standard deviations (that is, 1.96 standard errors) of the population mean. This statement implies that there is a 95-percent probability that any single sample mean, selected randomly, will lie within plus and minus 1.96 standard errors of the population mean.

In the example cited earlier, a random sample of 100 items was selected, the sample mean being 80. The mean of the population from which this sample is drawn is unknown; therefore it must be estimated on the basis of this single sample. Assume, however, that the standard deviation of the original population, σ, is known to be 30. The standard error of the sampling distribution of which this single sample is a member can then be calculated exactly. It is $\sigma_{\bar{x}} = \sigma/\sqrt{n} = 30/\sqrt{100} = 3$. Because

1 standard error equals 3, 1.96 standard errors will equal 5.88 (1.96 × 3 = 5.88). Thus 95 percent of all possible sample means, calculated from samples of size 100, will lie within plus and minus 5.88 of the population mean. Again, for emphasis, although the value of the population mean itself is not known exactly, it is known that 95 percent of all possible sample means that could be calculated from samples of size 100 will lie within plus and minus 5.88 of the population mean. This implies that there is a 95-percent probability that any single sample mean will lie within plus and minus 5.88 of the population mean. Such knowledge is highly valuable. From it the confidence interval can be calculated directly.

In the example cited in this section, the sample mean is 80. It was concluded in the previous paragraph that there is a 95-percent probability that any single sample mean will lie within plus and minus 5.88 of the population mean. The implication is that there is a 95-percent probability that the population mean lies within the interval 80 ± 5.88 = 74.12–85.88. That is, there is a 95-percent probability that the population mean is some value between 74.12 and 85.88. In this example, the confidence interval is 74.12–85.88, the confidence limits are 74.12 and 85.88, the size or width of the confidence interval is 85.88 − 74.12 = 11.76, and the confidence level is 95 percent.

Interpretation of the Confidence Interval

The concept of the confidence interval therefore enables the researcher to construct a range of values and to determine the probability that the population mean lies within this range. In the present illustration, the researcher can state that he is 95-percent confident that the population mean is some value between 74.12 and 85.88. Or, to express this idea differently, he is 95-percent confident that the population mean lies within ± 1.96 standard errors of the sample mean of 80. He is 95-percent confident because 95 percent of all the confidence intervals that could possibly be constructed, on the basis of all the possible samples that could possibly have been drawn, will include the population mean within their limits. This is true despite the fact that, because the different possible sample means can take on different values, the confidence limits based on one sample will be different from those based on another.

To illustrate this point, assume that the population mean is known to be 83. Then 95 percent of all possible sample means, calculated from samples of a fixed size, will lie within plus and minus 1.96 standard errors of 83. That is to say, 95 percent of all possible sample means will lie within ± 5.88 of 83, or between the values 77.12 and 88.88. Figure 7-1 illustrates this. The vertical line is constructed at a value of $\mu = 83$. Twenty samples are taken, and their means are indicated by the points plotted along the horizontal axis. As was just pointed out, it would be expected that 95 per cent of them, that is, 19, would lie between 77.12 and 88.88. This is shown to be the situation.

In Figure 7-2, a 95-percent confidence interval has been constructed for each sample mean. These intervals are shown by the series of horizontal arrows appearing above the horizontal axis. The center of each arrow corresponds to one of the sample means plotted along the horizontal axis. The ends of each arrow are determined by adding and subtracting 5.88 to the sample mean to which the center of the arrow corresponds. As can be seen, although the size of each of the 20 confidence intervals is the same, the

FIGURE 7-1

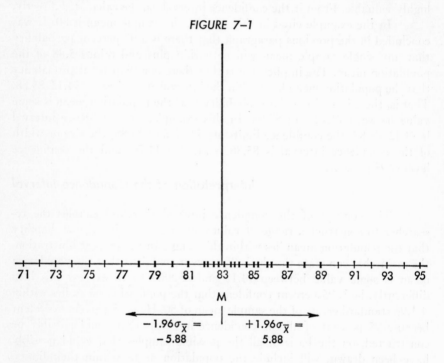

confidence limits are different. But the major point is that 95 percent of these confidence intervals include the population mean within their limits. *Thus, if a single sample is taken, and a 95-percent confidence interval is constructed from it, there is a 95-percent probability that this confidence interval includes the value of the population mean.*

Table 7-1 is an alternative presentation of the results of Figures 7-1 and 7-2. The first column shows the 20 different sample means, and the second column shows the 20 confidence intervals constructed on the basis of these means. The third column emphasizes the fact that, although the confidence limits are different for each confidence interval, the size of each interval is the same, each interval being constructed by adding and subtracting 5.88 to each sample mean. The last column indicates that 19 of the

20 confidence intervals include the value of the population mean. Again, the implication is a 95-percent probability that any one interval includes the population mean.

The preceding discussion presents the first really important application of probability and sampling theory. Because a confidence interval

FIGURE 7–2

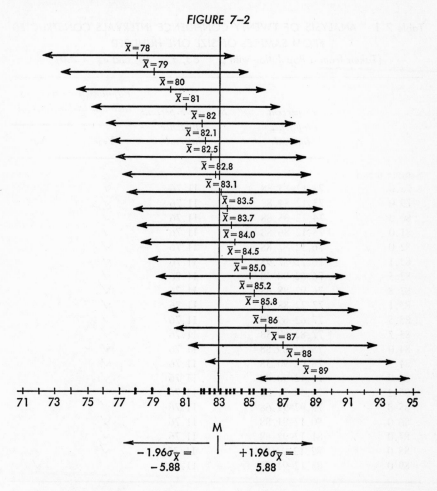

can be constructed on the basis of just a single sample, the population mean can be estimated within a certain range of values and with a specified degree or level of confidence on the basis of just a single sample. Thus realistic and meaningful conclusions relating to an entire population can be made on the basis of the results of a typically small segment or sample of the population. This statement, of course, is a definition of the term "statistical inference." The saving in time and money made possible by this technique is obvious. Not quite so obvious is the fact that, with the use of this technique, problems which once were not even tackled because of the impossibility of taking a census are now being solved every day.

But the analysis is not yet complete. The careful reader should now be raising questions such as "How high can the confidence level be raised?" and "How can the size of the confidence interval be reduced so that a

Table 7-1.   ANALYSIS OF TWENTY CONFIDENCE INTERVALS CONSTRUCTED
FROM SAMPLES OF SIZE ONE HUNDRED
(Taken from a Population with $\mu = 83$, $\sigma = 30$, and $\sigma_{\bar{x}} = 3.0$)

	95-percent confidence interval	Size of 95-percent confidence interval	Population mean = 83 included within interval	
			Yes	*No*
Sample mean				
78.0	72.12–83.88	11.76	✓	
79.0	73.12–84.88	11.76	✓	
80.0	74.12–85.88	11.76	✓	
81.0	75.12–86.88	11.76	✓	
82.0	76.12–87.88	11.76	✓	
82.1	76.22–87.98	11.76	✓	
82.5	76.62–88.38	11.76	✓	
82.8	76.92–88.68	11.76	✓	
83.1	77.22–88.98	11.76	✓	
83.5	77.62–89.38	11.76	✓	
83.7	77.82–89.58	11.76	✓	
84.0	78.12–89.88	11.76	✓	
84.5	78.62–90.38	11.76	✓	
85.0	79.12–90.88	11.76	✓	
85.2	79.32–91.08	11.76	✓	
85.8	79.92–91.68	11.76	✓	
86.0	80.12–91.88	11.76	✓	
87.0	81.12–92.88	11.76	✓	
88.0	82.12–93.88	11.76	✓	
89.0	83.12–94.88	11.76		✓

closer estimate of the population mean can be made?" It turns out that these two questions are very closely related. They will be answered in the following sections.

Possible Confidence Levels

The first question posed above will be dealt with first. The answer to it is that the confidence level can be any number greater than 0 but less than 1. However, the confidence level is actually a probability—specifically, the probability that the population mean lies within a certain range of values. Because the confidence level can never reach a value of 1, this probability can never reach a value of 1. But a probability of 1 implies absolute certainty. In other words, a range of values, within which the population mean is *absolutely certain* to lie, can never be constructed from the results of a single sample. The reason for this statement will become evident as the discussion of this section progresses. It will be explicitly treated at the end of this section.

However, a confidence interval corresponding to any confidence level less than 1—for example, .9999—can be constructed. Thus, employing .9999 as an illustration, a researcher can construct a confidence interval, and he can have 99.99-percent confidence that the population mean lies within this interval. That is, he can be 99.99-percent certain that the population mean lies within this interval. The confidence interval corresponding to a level of .9999, as well as the interval corresponding to any other level, is constructed in the same way that the 95-percent interval discussed earlier was constructed.

The construction is made in the following manner. The Table of Areas indicates that 49.99519 percent of the area under a normal curve lies within a distance of 3.4 standard deviations on one side of the mean of a normal curve. That is, 99.99038 percent of the area will lie within plus and minus 3.4 standard deviations of the mean. With respect to the present problem, it can be said that 99.99038 percent $\cong$[2] 99.99 percent of all possible sample means will lie within ± 3.4 standard errors of the population mean. Because one standard error, in the example used throughout this section on confidence intervals, equals 3.0, 3.4 standard errors equals 10.2 ($3.0 \times 3.4 = 10.2$). Thus 99.99 percent of all possible sample means lie within ± 10.2 of the population mean.

Because 99.99 percent of all possible samples lie within ± 10.2 of the population mean, there is a 99.99-percent probability that any sample mean computed from a single sample will lie within ± 10.2 of the population mean. If the sample mean is 80, the researcher is 99.99-percent confident that the population mean is a value between 69.8 and 90.2 (that is, 80 ± 10.2).

There are four steps involved in determining the confidence interval relating to any specified confidence level:

1. Divide the confidence level by 2.

2. Look this value up in the body of the Table of Areas in order to determine the number of standard deviations that separate this value from the mean of the normal curve. This number is located in the leftmost column of the table.

[2] The symbol $\cong$ means "approximately equal to" rather than "exactly equal to."

3. Multiply the number of standard deviations by the value of the standard error of the mean.

4. Add and subtract this value to the mean of the sample.

As an additional example, assume that the 60-percent confidence interval is to be constructed for the sample employed throughout this section. First, .60 is divided by 2. Second, this value, .30, is looked up in the body of the Table of Areas. The closest value to it is seen to be .2995, which corresponds to .84 standard deviations. Third, this number is multiplied by the value of the standard error: .84 × 3.0 = 2.52. Fourth, this value is added to, and subtracted from, the sample mean: 80 ± 2.52 = 77.48–82.52. The 60-percent confidence interval is thus equal to 77.48–82.52. That is, the researcher can be 60-percent confident, because there is a 60-percent probability, that the population mean is some value between 77.48 and 82.52.

At the beginning of this section it was pointed out that the confidence level could be any value greater than 0 but less than 1. The method, just discussed, of constructing confidence intervals should indicate why an interval corresponding to a confidence level of 1, or absolute certainty, can never be constructed. Because the normal curve represents an infinite distribution of values—in particular, because the tails of the curve always approach, but never quite touch, the horizontal axis—it is never possible to include 100 percent of the area under this curve within any finite number of standard deviations of the mean. That is, ±2 standard deviations will include 95.44 percent of the area on both sides of the mean; ±3 deviations will include 99.73 percent; ±4 deviations will include 99.99366 percent; and ±5 deviations will include 99.99994266 percent. But no matter how many standard deviations are added and subtracted, exactly 100 percent of the area can never be included. This fact implies that no range can ever be determined within which *all* possible sample means must lie. Therefore it is not possible to construct a 100-percent confidence interval.

Relation between the Confidence Level and the Size of the Confidence Interval

An attentive reader might now ask why anyone would consider constructing any confidence interval other than one corresponding to a .999⋯9 confidence level. Such an interval is *almost* absolutely certain to include the population mean. The probability would be .999⋯9. The really observant reader should be able to provide the answer. It relates to the *size* of the confidence interval.

The sizes of the three confidence intervals constructed in this section are presented in Table 7-2. It is quite apparent that as the confidence level rises the limits of the confidence interval grow farther apart—that is, as the confidence level rises, the size of the confidence interval increases.

This relation is a perfectly general result. *It is possible to construct, from a single sample, a confidence interval of any size.* This is the answer to the first question posed at the end of the second-to-the-last section. *However, for a fixed sample size, as the size of the confidence interval is decreased, the confidence level falls,* or, alternatively, *as the confidence level is increased, the size of the confidence interval increases.* For this reason, confidence levels less than .999···9 are usually employed. For a fixed sample size, the level of confidence placed in estimates based on sample results can be increased only by simultaneously increasing the size of the confidence interval. The researcher must be careful not to select a confidence level that is so high that the resulting confidence interval is too wide to be employed as the basis of any policy recommendations.

For example, assume that information concerning the average weekly wage of factory workers in the Northwest is desired. A sample is taken, and the 99.999-percent confidence interval is constructed. Assume

Table 7-2.   COMPARISON OF SIZES OF DIFFERENT CONFIDENCE INTERVALS
(Based on $\bar{X} = 80$, n = 100, $\sigma_{\bar{x}} = 3.0$)

Confidence level (in percentages)	Confidence interval	Size of confidence interval
60	77.48–82.52	5.04
95	74.12–85.88	11.76
99.99	69.80–90.20	20.40

this interval turns out to be $15–$350. The information, as presented, is really meaningless because everyone knew that the population mean was within this range before the sample was taken. What people want to know is whether the average is closer to $90 or to $100.

The foregoing statement implies that the information may be of value only if the population mean can be estimated within, for example, $10. However, it might turn out that the only confidence level that will permit an interval with a size of only $10 is 20 percent. This level is clearly too low to be meaningful. In effect, it states that there is only 1 chance in 5 that the population mean is within the specified $10 interval.

In summary, a confidence interval of any *size, or* a confidence interval corresponding to any confidence *level* greater than 0 but less than 1, can be constructed from a single sample. But for a fixed sample size it is not *necessarily* possible to achieve both the *desired* confidence level and *desired* interval size. The reason is that, for a fixed sample size, the confidence level can be increased only by increasing the size of the interval, and the interval can be reduced only by reducing the confidence level.

This fact makes it conceivable that no really useful conclusions can be derived from a given sample. Can anything be done to ensure that this type of stalemate does not occur? That is, can anything be done to make certain that the sample results are compatible with (1) a confidence interval of meaningful size *and* (2) an acceptable confidence level? The answer, which is in the affirmative, involves a knowledge of the relation between sample size and confidence intervals. Attention is focused on this relation in the following sections.

The Standard Error of the Mean and Confidence Intervals

For any specified confidence level the size of the confidence interval depends on the value of the standard error of the mean. For example, assume that the 95-percent confidence interval is to be constructed on the basis of a sample mean of 80. If the standard error of the mean is, for example, 3, the 95-percent confidence interval is $80 \pm 1.96 \times 3 = 80 \pm 5.88 = 74.12\text{--}85.88$. The size of this interval is 11.76 ($85.88 - 74.12 = 11.76$). If, however, the standard error is larger than 3, the 95-percent confidence interval will be wider. For example, assume that the standard error equals 5. Then the 95-percent confidence interval equals $80 \pm 1.96 \times 5 = 80 \pm 9.80 = 70.20\text{--}89.80$. Its size is 19.6 ($89.8 - 70.2 = 19.6$). In general, then, for any given confidence level, the greater the standard error of the mean, the greater the size of the confidence interval.

Similarly, for any specified size of confidence interval, the height of the confidence level depends on the standard error of the mean. For example, assume that a confidence interval of size 4 is to be constructed on the basis of a sample mean of 80. Because of the way confidence intervals are constructed, the mean value must fall in the middle of the interval. Therefore, if the size of the interval is to be 4, the upper confidence limit must be 82 and the lower limit 78. In other words, 2 must be added to, and subtracted from, the sample mean of 80.

But the value 2 is the result of multiplying the value for the standard error of the mean by the *number* of standard deviations corresponding to a specified confidence level. For example, assume that $\sigma_{\bar{x}} = 3$. Let Y represent the *number* of standard deviations that must be multiplied by the value of the standard error. Because the result of this product must equal 2 in order to satisfy the specified confidence interval of 4, Y must equal .67: $3Y = 2$, $Y = .67$. By looking up .67 in the leftmost column of the Table of Areas, we see that 24.86 percent of the area under a normal curve lies between the mean and a value that is .67 standard deviations away from the mean. Thus plus and minus .67 standard deviations would include 49.72 percent of the area under a normal curve (24.86 percent on each side of the mean). This means that 49.72 percent of all possible sample means will lie within ±.67 standard errors of the population mean. Therefore the probability that a single sample mean will have a value within $\pm.67$ standard errors of the mean, or, in the present example, a value between 78 and 82, is 49.72 percent. The confidence level corresponding to a size interval of 4, when the standard error is 3, is therefore 49.72 percent.

If the standard error were larger than 3, say 5, the confidence level corresponding to a size interval of 4 would be lower. In this instance, it would be 31.08 percent, because the following relation must now be satisfied: $5Y = 2$, $Y = .4$. As .4 corresponds to 15.54 percent of the area under a normal curve on one side of the mean, the relevant confidence level is 31.08 percent (15.54 percent on each side of the mean).

In general, then, for a fixed confidence level, the greater the standard error of the mean, the wider the size of the confidence interval; for a fixed size of confidence interval, the greater the standard error of the mean, the lower the confidence level. Because the size of the standard error determines the size of the confidence interval and the height of the confidence level, these two vital factors can be controlled if the size of the standard error can be controlled. Furthermore, a relatively small standard error is usually desirable, because this corresponds *both* to a relatively high confidence level and a relatively narrow confidence interval. The factors affecting the size of the standard error, and therefore the size and level of the confidence interval, will be considered next.

Sample Size and Confidence Intervals

The variables affecting the size of the standard error can be ascertained by examining the formula by which it is computed: $\sigma_{\bar{x}} = \sigma/\sqrt{n}$. The formula indicates that the standard error is directly related to the standard deviation of the population and inversely related to the square root of the sample size; in other words, the larger the standard deviation of the population, the larger the standard error of the mean, and the larger the sample size, the smaller the standard error of the mean. This relation was pointed out in Chapter 6.

As indicated then, usually little can be done to control the standard deviation of the population. That is to say, if the size of the standard error of the mean is to be controlled, it must be controlled by controlling the sample size. This can usually be accomplished. That a large sample size reduces the size of the standard error is one reason for desiring a large sample size. This statement does not imply, however, that the largest possible sample size should always be taken. Large samples cost more money than do small samples. It's cheaper to interview 100 people, or to examine 100 tax returns, than it is to interview and examine, respectively, 10,000 people or 10,000 tax returns. Similarly, if a sample consists of observations on the breaking strength of steel bars, because the sampling process is a destructive one (the breaking point cannot be determined until the bar breaks), a sample of 100 is cheaper than a sample of 10,000.

An *efficient* sample size can therefore be defined as one that allows the construction of a confidence interval of the desired size *and* level at the lowest possible cost. This definition implies that an efficient sample size is the smallest possible sample that will permit the desired requirements of *both* the interval size and level to be satisfied. An example will illustrate how such a sample size can be determined.

Assume that the U.S. Department of Commerce wants to learn the mean weekly income of factory workers in New England. For the purposes to which it wishes to put this information, a 95-percent confidence interval is deemed sufficient. The Department, further, wants the confidence interval to be no larger than $6. Because the interval is to be $6, a value of $3 must be added to, and subtracted from, the sample mean. But this value is obtained by multiplying the standard error of the mean by the number of standard deviations corresponding to the specified confidence level.

In this example, the confidence level is 95 percent. Therefore the number by which the standard error must be multiplied is 1.96, because 95 percent of the area under a normal curve lies within ± 1.96 standard deviations of the mean. Thus the following relation, from which the standard error can be determined, holds:

$$1.96 \, \sigma_{\bar{x}} = \$3, \, \sigma_{\bar{x}} = \$1.53$$

A standard error of the mean of $1.53 will result in a confidence interval with a width of $6 and a confidence level of 95 percent. For example, if a sample were taken and the sample mean were $90, the 95-percent confidence level would be $90 \pm 1.96 \times \$1.53 = \$90 \pm \$3 = \$87–\$93$.

Now that the required value of the standard error of the mean has been determined, the required sample size must be discovered. That is, what sample size will result in a standard error of $1.53? Assume that the population standard deviation is known to be $15. The required sample size can be evaluated by algebraically solving the following relation:

$$\sigma_{\bar{x}} = \sigma/\sqrt{n}, \, \$1.53 = \$15.00/\sqrt{n}$$

The equation is best solved by first squaring both sides of the last equation:

$$(1.53)^2 = (15.00)^2/(\sqrt{n})^2$$
$$2.3409 = 225.00/n$$
$$2.3409n = 225.00, \, n = 96.1$$

Thus, if a sample size of 96 is selected, the standard error of the mean will equal $1.53. For example, if $n = 96$,

$$\sigma_{\bar{x}} = 15/\sqrt{96} = 15/9.798 = 1.53$$

In effect, because a sample size of 96 will result in a standard error of $1.53 (if we assume that the population standard deviation is 15), a sample size of 96 will permit the construction of a 95-percent confidence interval with a size of $6.

The steps involved in determining the smallest possible sample size that will enable a confidence interval, of specified width and specified level, to be constructed can be summarized as follows:

1. Divide the specified size of the confidence interval by 2.

2. Determine, from the Table of Areas, the number of standard deviations that correspond to the specified confidence level.

3. Divide the answer in step 1 by the answer in step 2. This quotient is the value that the standard error of the mean must equal in order to permit the simultaneous occurrence of the specified confidence level and the specified size of interval.

4. Square the answer obtained in step 3.

5. Square the standard deviation of the population.

6. Divide the answer obtained in step 5 by that of step 4. This quotient is the value that the sample size must reach if the standard error determined in step 3 is to be obtained.

The important, and often overlooked, conclusion of this section is that by proper selection of sample size an adequate confidence level *and* interval size can always be simultaneously obtained. This statement implies that the most *efficient* sample size should always be considered *before* the sample is actually taken. In some instances it may become apparent that the most efficient size will be too costly in terms of time and money. If this problem is encountered, the money and effort that would have been needlessly expended can be saved and devoted to alternative uses. Thus it is not always correct for a researcher to assume that if he takes the largest possible sample consistent with his limited resources he will necessarily obtain meaningful results. Furthermore, even if meaningful results are obtained by expending all of one's resources, a smaller sample size might still have yielded satisfactory results, and at a lower cost. The moral of all this is that before a researcher goes about taking samples, he should

1. Specify the desired confidence level

2. Specify the size interval that will be meaningful

3. Determine the minimum sample size that will enable both of the above conditions to be met

Summary

It has been pointed out that a confidence interval is one of the two most important concepts underlying most applications of statistical inference. It can be of great practical importance in situations relating to business, economics, and other social, engineering, and physical sciences. To show the value of the confidence interval, the major results of earlier discussions relating to the arithmetic mean and standard deviation, probability, areas under the normal curve, and sampling theory were synthesized and integrated. A chain of concepts begun in Chapter 3, or perhaps even in Chapter 1 where the nature of statistical theory and application was introduced, has been completed. Though the additional links to be forged in later discussions will add to the length of this chain, the ends of the chain have been joined, and in a sense the chain itself has been completed at this point.

In defining a confidence interval it was necessary to define also the three distinguishing characteristics of any confidence interval. These characteristics are (1) the confidence level, (2) the confidence limits, and (3) the size or width of a confidence interval. The reader should be very clear on all these definitions.

The latter part of this discussion of confidence intervals has been concerned mainly with the necessary details of its application. That is, after the concept was defined and interpreted, its determination in actual practice was discussed. This procedure involved a knowledge of the close relation between the two key practical aspects of a confidence interval—namely, its size and confidence level. It was learned that this relation depends on the standard error of the mean, which in turn depends on the size of the sample.

The student can gain additional insight into the many situations in which the concept of confidence intervals has important application by conscientiously working out the problems at the end of this chapter. Other applications will be explicitly treated later in this chapter and in the following chapter.

The next section of the present chapter will examine the second basic concept underlying the application of the techniques of statistical inference. This is the concept of a *test of significance*.

TESTS OF SIGNIFICANCE

The second group of sampling applications that will be discussed comes, as noted at the outset of this chapter, under the heading of tests of significance. It is often referred to also by the terms "hypothesis testing" and "decision making." These last two terms are perhaps more descriptive of the general concept. An outline of the procedure typically followed will illustrate this. According to this procedure, a "hypothesis" is formulated, its credibility is "tested," and a "decision" is "made" as a result of the test. The words in quotation marks call for some clarification.

For the present purpose, a hypothesis may be defined as a statement that may or may not be true. The person who formulates the hypothesis, that is, makes the statement, never really knows whether or not the hypothesis (statement) is true. A sample is taken, and the hypothesis is tested by determining the probability of obtaining this particular sample if the hypothesis is in fact true. The probability is evaluated by utilizing the sampling theory developed in the previous chapter. If the probability is very low, the sample results are said to discredit the hypothesis, and a decision is made to reject the hypothesis. On the other hand, if the probability is very high, the sample results are said to be consistent with the hypothesis, and a decision is made to accept the hypothesis.

Throughout the foregoing paragraph, reference was made to the probability of obtaining a particular sample result. This probability is evaluated by utilizing the sampling theory developed in the previous chapter. The aspect of sampling theory particularly relevant for this purpose was not explicitly presented in the earlier discussion, although it was implied throughout. This fundamental aspect of sampling theory, which will be treated below, is called sampling variation.

Sampling Variation

The example employed in the previous chapter will be utilized here to illustrate sampling variation. An infinite population composed of an equal number of each of the four values—6, 2, 14, 10—is assumed. The mean of this population is 8. Tables 6-4 and 6-5 show the different possible samples of size 2, together with their sample means, that could be randomly selected from this population. Only $\frac{1}{4}$ of these sample means have a value equal to the population mean. $\frac{3}{4}$ of all possible sample means have a value that is different from the population mean. As this remark implies, it is much more likely that the mean of a single randomly selected sample will differ from the population mean than that it will equal the population mean. In fact, it could actually be impossible for the sample mean to have a value equal to the population mean. See Table 6-8, which shows this. All possible sample means, computed from samples of size three, are arrayed. As can be seen, none of these sample means has a value of 8. It is to be expected, then, that the mean of a sample will differ from the mean of the population from which it is drawn. Furthermore, the value of a particular sample mean, calculated from items selected at random, will depend solely on the play of chance. This is what is meant by sampling variation.

It should be emphasized, however, that the greater the difference between the sample mean and the population mean, the smaller the probability that the sample was drawn from the specified population. As Table 6-9 shows, there is a 100-percent probability of obtaining a sample mean that differs, in either direction, from the population mean of 8 by as much as $\frac{2}{3}$ or more; that is, there is a 100-percent probability of obtaining a mean that has a value equal to $7\frac{1}{3}$ or less or $8\frac{2}{3}$ or more. There is a $40/64 = 62.5$-percent probability of obtaining a mean that differs by as much as 2 or more, and a 0-percent probability of obtaining a mean that differs by more than 6.

As will be demonstrated in some detail below, this last aspect of sampling variation is the basis of the hypothesis testing described at the outset of the section. As a further introduction to this discussion, assume that the following experiment takes place. A person is confronted with two boxes. He is told that one box contains four physically identical disks having the values, respectively, 6, 2, 14, and 10. He is not told which of the two boxes this is. He is told that the second box contains a different number of disks, the disks having individual values and a mean value that are different from those of the first box. The person is then asked to

1. Select one disk from one of the boxes.
2. Record its value and replace it in the box.
3. Select a second disk from the same box.
4. Record its value and replace it in the box.
5. Select a third disk from the same box.
6. Record its value.
7. Calculate the mean of these three values.
8. On the basis of this sample result, state whether he would accept the hypothesis that the box from which he has been selecting is the one containing the four values, 6, 2, 14, and 10. Or, what amounts to the same thing, state whether he would accept the hypothesis that the box from which he has been selecting has a mean of 8. When a problem is formulated in this way, the value, 8, is called the hypothetical mean.

Assume the sample mean, calculated in this way, is 15. This mean differs from the hypothetical mean, 8, by 7. As Table 6-9 shows, it is impossible to obtain a sample mean of 15, or a sample mean that differs from the hypothetical mean by as much as 7, from the specified population. Obviously, the hypothesis would be rejected. The sample result is definitely inconsistent with the hypothesis. Assume that the sample mean is $7\frac{1}{3}$. This differs from the hypothetical sample mean of 8 by $\frac{2}{3}$. If the hypothesis is true, 100 percent of all possible sample means will differ from the population mean by as much as $\frac{2}{3}$ or more. Therefore there is a 100-percent probability that a sample, of size 3, drawn from the specified population, will have a mean which will differ from the specified population mean by as much as $\frac{2}{3}$ or more. This sample result is clearly consistent with the hypothesis. It should be emphasized that this result does not prove the hypothesis to be true; it merely is not inconsistent with the hypothesis.

Assume, finally, that the sample mean is 2. This mean differs from the hypothetical mean, 8, by 6. As Table 6-9 shows, such a sample result is not impossible if the hypothesis is true. Some people might say that because the result is not impossible if the hypothesis is true, the sample result is not inconsistent with the hypothesis. However, there is a probability of only $\frac{2}{64}$ or 3.1 percent that such a sample result would occur if the hypothesis is true. Most people, in this situation, would argue that because the probability of obtaining such a result is so small if the hypothesis is true, the hypothesis should be rejected. Although such a sample result is not impossible, the odds against its occurring are so great that most people would rather not gamble on it.

The basic principle just introduced will be further developed and refined in the sections immediately following. It will be seen that these principles can be forged into a very important decision-making tool. The practical application of this tool requires an understanding of such concepts as a *significant difference*, a *significance level*, *regions of acceptance and rejection*, *one-tailed and two-tailed tests*, and *type I and type II errors*. The following sections deal with these concepts. The discussion will be facilitated by centering it around a type of problem quite often faced by the typical firm.

A Significant Difference

The firm, referred to immediately above, requires metal rods for the manufacture of its basic product. It operates a special rodding department that produces the rods within the basic manufacturing plant. The rods must have a breaking strength of 140 pounds per square inch. If rods are produced with a lesser breaking strength, the firm's fully manufactured product will be of lower quality than desired, and consumer good will and future sales will be damaged. If rods are produced with a higher breaking strength, the firm's fully manufactured product will be of higher quality than necessary, and costs will be unnecessarily high.

The problem facing the firm is this. How can it best check the quality of the metal rods actually produced? The particular attribute of the rods that needs checking is of a nature to make an inspection of each and every rod impossible. The only way to determine the breaking strength of a given rod is to apply pressure and observe the point at which the rod breaks. But if this procedure is applied to every rod produced, no rods will be available for the manufacture of the basic product. Even if the attribute being checked did not imply the destruction of the rod—as in checking, for example, length or weight—the checking of each and every rod might be too expensive to be considered. The sampling and probability theory already developed provide a means of satisfactorily meeting these types of problem.

A sample of, let us say, 64 rods is randomly selected from a production lot composed of several thousand rods. The breaking strength of the 64 rods is tested, and a decision is made whether to accept or reject the entire production lot. The decision is based on the following rationale.

The mean breaking strength of the 64 rods in the sample is calculated and found to be 120 pounds per square inch. The fact that this sample mean is 20 pounds less than the desired mean of 140 pounds does not necessarily indicate that the population, from which the sample was randomly selected, has a mean different from 140 pounds per square inch. As illustrated in the preceding section, it is very unlikely, because of sampling variation, that the mean of a single sample will equal the mean of the population. Of course, it is also unlikely that a given sample mean will differ very much from the population mean. The relevant question, then, is whether a difference of 20 pounds is *significant?* A significant difference, as employed in this context, can be defined as *a difference that is too great to be attributable solely to sampling variation*. If this difference is too great to be attributed to the play of chance inherent in sampling variation, it must be attributable to the fact that the true population mean is not equal to 140.

This question of significance can be answered by following the procedure outlined earlier. First, a hypothesis is formulated. It can be stated, most simply, as follows: "The population mean is 140 pounds per square inch."[3] Next, the probability of obtaining the given sample, if the hypothesis is true, is determined. Because the difference between the sample mean and the population mean is 20, the relevant question is, "What is the probability of obtaining a sample mean that differs from the population mean by as much as 20?"

It has been determined, from earlier discussions, that if many samples of size 64 are taken, and if a frequency distribution is constructed from the resulting sample means, the sampling distribution of the mean will be approximately normally distributed, its mean will be the same as the mean of the universe, and its standard deviation can be calculated from the formula $\sigma_{\bar{x}} = \sigma/\sqrt{n}$. The sample mean of 120 pounds is just one of many that *could* have been selected from a population with a mean of 140 pounds. Of course, it is not known that this sample actually did come from a population with a mean of 140. The problem, in fact, is to determine the probability that it *could* have come from such a population.

Assume that, from past experience, the standard deviation of the original population, σ, is known to be 32 pounds per square inch. That is, the nature of the production process is such that, regardless of the actual value of the population mean, the population standard deviation is fixed and known. The standard error of the mean can then be calculated as $\sigma_{\bar{x}} = \sigma/\sqrt{n} = 32/\sqrt{64} = 4$. It can be determined, from the Table of Areas under a Normal Curve, that 68 percent of all possible sample means will lie within plus and minus 1 standard error of the population mean,

---

[3] Alternatively, it could be stated that "there is no significant difference between the sample mean and the population mean." A hypothesis formulated in this way is referred to as a "null" hypothesis.

that 95 percent will lie within plus and minus 1.96 standard errors, that 99 percent will lie within ±2.58 standard errors, and that very nearly 100 percent of all possible sample means will lie within ±5 standard errors. In this problem, because 1 standard error of the mean has a value of 4 pounds per square inch, 20 pounds would represent 5 standard errors. Therefore, if the sample mean of 120 is actually selected from a population with a mean of 140, the difference would represent 5 standard errors. Because virtually all sample means will lie within 5 standard errors of the population mean, it would be almost impossible for a single sample mean to be as much as 5 standard errors away from the mean. The probability would be less than 1 in a million.

The results of this sample certainly do not tend to support the hypothesis. The probability of obtaining a sample mean that differs from the population mean by 20 or more is, in this instance, so small that the difference would be considered significant. That is, the probability of obtaining a sample mean that differs from the population mean by 20 or more is so small that few men would attribute the result to the forces of chance and sampling variation. Most men would conclude that the population from which this sample was drawn has a mean breaking strength that is not equal to 140 pounds. The entire production lot would be rejected on the basis of this single sample. If this is a particularly expensive decision to make, a second sample might be taken. At the very least, it can be concluded that the production lot in question would not be utilized at this point.

The Significance Level

Assume, now, that the sample of 64 items has a mean of 136 instead of 120. The difference between the sample mean and the population mean is now 4 pounds per square inch. This figure represents a difference equivalent to 1 standard error. Because 68 percent of all possible sample means will lie *within* ±1 standard error of the population mean, 32 percent will have a value that is 1 standard error or more *away* from the population mean. In other words, 32 percent of all possible sample means will have a value that is 1 standard error or more below, or 1 standard error or more above, the population mean. Therefore the probability of obtaining a single sample mean differing from the population mean by as much as, or more than, 1 standard error is 32 percent. That is to say, if the population mean were 140, there is approximately 1 chance in 3 of coming up with a sample mean differing from the population mean by 4 or more pounds per square inch. Expressed still another way, there is a 32-percent probability that a sample mean will have a value of 136 or less, or 144 or more, if the population mean is actually 140.

Is this difference significant? That is, is this sample result inconsistent with the hypothesis? The answer depends on whether a person views the occurrence of an event that has a probability of 32 percent as being too rare to be attributable to sampling variation alone. This view depends not only on a person's gambling instincts but also on the consequences of being wrong. This last point will be treated later. Right now, certain rules of thumb will be indicated. In practice, any difference between the sample mean and the hypothetical mean that has a 5 percent or less probability of resulting, if the hypothesis is true, is generally considered significant. Such a difference would lead to a rejection of the hypothesis. In the example given above, the hypothesis would therefore be accepted, because 32 percent is a good deal higher than 5 percent. It should be pointed out, however, that this 5-percent rule is not a rigid one. In some situations, a 1-percent rule, or some other rule, is deemed more appropriate.

Before the drawing of a sample, the investigator will typically specify, on the basis of criteria that will be treated in a later section, the probability at which he will reject a hypothesis. For example, assume that he specifies 5 percent. This figure implies that if the difference between the sample mean and the hypothetical mean is such that it would occur only 5 percent or less than 5 percent of the time, the hypothesis would be rejected. Alternatively, assume that the investigator specifies a 1-percent probability. This specification implies that if the difference between the sample mean and the hypothetical mean is such that it would occur only 1 percent, or less than 1 percent, of the time, the hypothesis would be rejected. The probability specified by the investigator is termed the *significance level* of the statistical test.

The flexibility permitted in determining the significance level brings up the following point. Whether an observed difference is significant depends on the significance level selected. For example, if the standard error of the mean is 4, then a difference of 9 between the sample mean and the hypothetical mean would be rejected at a 5-percent significance level but not at a 1-percent significance level. The reason is that there is approximately a 2-percent probability of obtaining a difference as large as 9. This probability is calculated as follows. A difference of 9 represents 2.25 standard errors. The Table of Areas shows that 97.56 percent of all possible sample means will lie within ± 2.25 standard errors of the population mean. Thus apparently only 2.44 percent will have a value that differs from the population mean as much as, or more than, 2.25 standard errors. Because a probability of 2.44 percent lies above a 1-percent significance level but not above a 5-percent level, the hypothesis would be rejected at the 5-percent significance level but not at the 1-percent level.

A final related point, and one that was made in a different form in an earlier section, is that the greater the difference between the sample mean and the hypothetical mean, the smaller the probability that the sample could have been drawn from a population having the specified hypothetical mean. In the above example, there is a 5-percent probability of getting a difference as large as, or larger than, 1.96 standard errors; because 1 standard error equals 4, there is a 5-percent probability of getting a difference as large as, or larger than, $1.96 \times 4 = 7.84$. However, there is only a 2.44-percent chance of getting the larger difference of $2.25\sigma_{\bar{x}} = 2.25 \times 4 = 9.00$, and only a 1-percent chance of getting the still larger difference of $2.58\sigma_{\bar{x}} = 2.58 \times 4 = 10.32$. This point leads to the concept of areas or regions of acceptance and rejection.

Areas of Acceptance and Rejection

Assume, as in earlier illustrations relating to the breaking strength of metal rods, that the standard error of the mean equals 4, and that the hypothetical mean is 140 pounds per square inch. Assume that a sample is randomly selected and that the hypothesis will be tested at the 5-percent significance level. Up to now, the hypothesis has been tested by computing the sample mean, calculating the difference between the sample mean and the hypothetical mean, and determining the probability of such a difference if the hypothesis is, in fact, true. If many samples are taken over a period of time, and such is quite often true in quality-control experiments, the difference between the sample and hypothetical mean, as well as the probability of this difference, would have to be calculated each and every time. An alternative procedure for testing the hypothesis makes necessary only one initial calculation. This procedure is based on the concept of areas or regions of acceptance and rejection.

An area of acceptance can be defined as a range of values such that if the sample mean falls in this range, the hypothesis is accepted. An area of rejection can be defined as a range of values such that, if the sample mean falls in this range, the hypothesis is rejected. These areas are constructed in the following manner.

If the significance level is 5 percent, any difference between the sample mean and hypothetical mean that is equal to, or greater than, 1.96 standard errors will be considered significant, and the hypothesis will be rejected. Such a difference will be considered significant, at the 5-percent significance level, because only 5 percent of all possible sample means will differ from the hypothetical mean by as much as, or more than, 1.96 standard errors, if the hypothesis is true. This statement implies that there are only 5 chances in a 100, or 1 in 20, of obtaining such a sample if the true mean of the population actually equaled the hypothetical mean.

The hypothetical mean, in the present example, is 140, and the standard error of the mean is 4. Therefore any sample mean having a value of 132.16 or less, or 147.84 or more, will be rejected. The explanation is that the difference—namely, 7.84 or more—between the hypothetical mean of 140 and the sample means indicated represents a difference of at least 1.96 standard errors $(1.96\sigma_{\bar{x}} = 1.96 \times 4 = 7.84)$. Such differences will occur only 5 percent of the time, if the hypothesis is true. The two regions of rejection, in this example, are represented by the range of values equal to and less than 132.16, and equal to and greater than 147.84. The region of acceptance is represented by the values lying between 132.16 and 147.84.

Figure 7-3 shows this distribution. Each tail, representing a region of rejection, of the sampling distribution of the mean contains $2\frac{1}{2}$ percent of the total area under the curve. If a sample mean has a value equal to or greater than 147.84, or equal to or less than 132.16, the hypothesis will be rejected. Sample means other than these will lead to an acceptance of the hypothesis.

In general, the values separating the regions of rejection from the region of acceptance are determined by

1. Dividing the specified significance level by 2
2. Subtracting the answer obtained in step 1 from 50 percent
3. Determining, from the Table of Areas, the number of standard errors corresponding to this percentage
4. Multiplying the value obtained in step 3 by the value of 1 standard error
5. Adding and subtracting the value obtained in step 4 to and from, respectively, the hypothetical population mean

For example, the values corresponding to a 5-percent significance level are determined, in the present example, as follows:

1. 5 percent $\div$ 2 = $2\frac{1}{2}$ percent
2. 50 percent $-$ $2\frac{1}{2}$ percent = $47\frac{1}{2}$ percent
3. $47\frac{1}{2}$ percent corresponds to 1.96 standard errors
4. $1.96 \, \sigma_{\bar{x}} = 1.96 \times 4 = 7.84$
5. $140 \pm 7.84 = 132.16$ and 147.84

It should be pointed out also that as the significance level is lowered the area of rejection also becomes smaller, and the area of acceptance becomes larger. For example, if a 1-percent significance level is selected, the regions of rejection will be the ranges of values equal to or less than 129.68 $(140 - 2.58 \times 4 = 129.68)$ and equal to or greater than 150.32 $(140 + 2.58 \times 4 = 150.32)$. These regions are smaller than those corresponding to a 5-percent significance level. The region of acceptance for a 1-percent level—namely, values greater than 129.68 and less than 150.32— is greater than that for a 5-percent level. Figure 7-4 shows these regions for the 1-percent significance level.

FIGURE 7–3

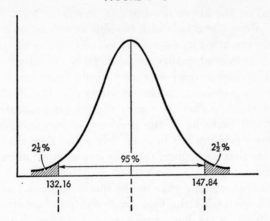

FIGURE 7–4

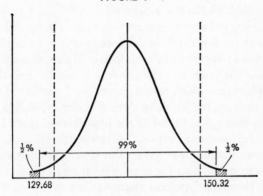

FIGURE 7–5

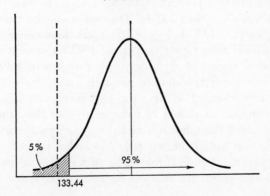

One-Tailed versus Two-Tailed Tests

Throughout the above illustrations, it was assumed that the firm was concerned about metal rods with too high as well as too low a breaking point. The firm produced its own rods; as indicated at the outset of this discussion, rods of inferior quality would mean loss of future sales, whereas rods of a quality higher than necessary would mean unnecessarily high costs. Whenever a problem is concerned with values that are higher as well as lower than the hypothetical mean, the relevant statistical test is a *two-tailed* test. All examples of the previous sections involved two-tailed tests. Whenever a problem is concerned only with values that are lower, or only with values that are higher, than the hypothetical mean, a *one-tailed* test is in order.

For example, assume that in the quality-control problem utilized throughout this discussion the firm decides to purchase its requirements of metal rods from an outside supplier at a fixed price. Because the price to the firm is now fixed, the firm will worry only about rods with too low a breaking point. Rods of higher quality than necessary no longer imply higher costs to the firm. In this situation, a one-tailed test is in order. The regions of rejection and acceptance are determined in the following manner.

Assume that a 5-percent significance level is to be employed. Because only sample means lower than 140 will be considered, the region of rejection should represent the range of values that is below 140 and that represents values of sample means which would occur only 5 percent of the time if the hypothesis is true. As the Table of Areas illustrates, only 5 percent of all possible sample means will be below the hypothetical mean by as much as, or more than, 1.64 standard errors. Therefore there is a 5-percent probability that a given sample mean has a value that is as much as, or more than, 1.64 standard errors less than the hypothetical mean. Because one standard error equals 4, there is a 5-percent chance that a randomly selected sample mean has a value equal to or less than 133.44 ($1.64 \times 4 = 6.56$, $140 - 6.56 = 133.44$), if the hypothesis is true. The region of rejection, for a one-tailed test and a 5-percent significance level, is therefore a range of values equal to or less than 133.44. The region of acceptance is the range of values higher than 133.44. Figure 7-5 shows these ranges.

The general rules formulated (page 192) for determining the value that separates a region of rejection from a region of acceptance apply directly to regions corresponding to two-tailed tests. For a one-tailed test, rule 1 should be changed so that the significance level is divided by 1 instead of 2, and rule 5 should be changed so that the value obtained in rule 4 is subtracted from, but not added to, the hypothetical mean if the region of rejection lies in the left tail, and added to, but not subtracted from, the hypothetical mean if the region of rejection lies in the right tail.

Up to this point, the reasons for and consequences of selecting a particular significance level have not been considered. These will now be discussed. This discussion necessarily involves the concepts of type I and type II errors.

Type I and Type II Errors

Assume that it has been decided to employ a 5-percent significance level. This is interpreted, as indicated above, in the following manner. If the difference between the sample mean and the hypothetical mean is so great that there is only a 5-percent (or less) probability of its occurring if the hypothesis is true, the hypothesis is rejected. It is rejected, not because such a difference is impossible, but because such a result is very unlikely if the hypothesis is true. Usually an investigator would not gamble on a long shot of 5 in 100. He would conclude, rather, that the sample results are inconsistent with the hypothesis and that therefore the hypothesis should be rejected. In other words, the sample results are too different from those indicated by the hypothesis to be accounted for by the variation inherent in random sampling.

Type I Errors.   By now, the following points are evident and, in fact, are probably bothering the reader. Assume that a 5-percent significance level is employed. If the hypothesis is actually true, 5 percent of all possible sample means will lie in the region of rejection. If the hypothesis is actually true, the results of the statistical test will still lead to a rejection of the hypothesis 5 percent of the time. If the hypothesis is actually true, a *wrong* decision will be reached 5 percent of the time. However, this amount of error is unavoidable. Whenever inferences regarding an entire universe are drawn from the results of a single sample, this type of error is always present. Fortunately, as will be shown, the probability of its occurring can be controlled. An error of this kind is given a special name. Whenever a true hypothesis is rejected—that is, whenever a hypothesis is rejected when, in fact, it should be accepted—a *type I* error has occurred.

It should be apparent that the probability of making a type I error is equal to the significance level. This fact implies that the lower the significance level, the lower the probability of making a type I error. For example, if the significance level is 1 percent instead of 5 percent, a true hypothesis will be rejected 1 percent instead of 5 percent of the time, and a type I error will occur only 1 percent instead of 5 percent of the time. If this is the situation, why isn't the significance level reduced to a very tiny fraction, such as, for example, .0001 percent? The answer is that, for a fixed sample size, the smaller the probability of a type I error, the greater the probability of a *type II* error. These two types of errors must then be balanced against each other in terms of the economic consequences of each.

Type II Errors.   A type II error is the second basic type of probability error that can occur in hypothesis testing and management decision making based on statistical inference. *A type II error occurs whenever a false hypothesis is accepted*. An example will clarify this concept.

Assume that $n = 64$, $\sigma_{\bar{x}} = 4$, the hypothetical mean is 140, a two-tailed test is called for, and the significance level is 5 percent. This is the same metal-rods example introduced earlier. The regions of rejection are represented by values of 132.16 or less and 147.84 or more (page 191). The region of acceptance is therefore made up of the range of values between 132.16 and 147.84. Assume, now, that the hypothesis is actually false and that the true mean is actually 130. The investigator, who must draw inferences on the basis of a single sample, is, of course, unaware of this. What is the probability that this false hypothesis will be incorrectly accepted? The answer involves determining the probability that a sample mean, drawn from a population with a mean of 130, will fall within the acceptance region, which is made up of values between 132.16 and 147.84. This is a simple problem of calculating the area under a normal curve between the values of 132.16 and 147.84, the mean and standard error of this curve being, respectively, 130 and 4. Figure 7-6 shows this to be 29 percent.

This figure was derived in the ordinary way. The difference between 130 and 132.16, which is 2.16, represents .54 standard errors (2.16 ÷ 4 = .54). The Table of Areas indicates that 21 percent of the area under a normal curve will lie between the mean and a value .54 standard errors away. The difference between 130 and 147.84, which is 17.84, represents 4.46 standard errors. Approximately 50 percent of the area under a normal curve lies between the mean and a value 4.46 standard errors away. Because 50 percent of the area lies between 147.84 and 130, and 21 percent between 132.16 and 130, 29 percent must lie between 132.16 and 147.84. As this region is the region of acceptance, the probability of accepting the hypothesis that the true mean is 140, when, in fact, the true mean is 130, is 29 percent. The probability of making a type II error is, in this instance, 29 percent.

It is important to be able to evaluate a type II error. For example, assume that although the firm desires each metal rod to have a breaking strength of 140 pounds per square inch, the firm is not overly concerned if the actual breaking strength is at least greater than 120. But if the actual breaking strength is 120 or less, assume that physical injury can result to persons utilizing the final product. Here the firm has a moral responsibility to its customers, as well as the possibility of a very damaging lawsuit. The firm, then, would be particularly concerned about the probability of its accepting a false hypothesis when the true mean is really 120 or less. If the actual population mean is 120, and if the significance level is 5 percent, the probability of making a type II error is almost 0 percent. This conclusion follows, if we use the same procedure employed above, because the lower limit of the acceptance region, 132.6, is 3.1 standard errors away

FIGURE 7-6

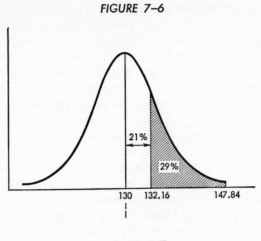

FIGURE 7-7

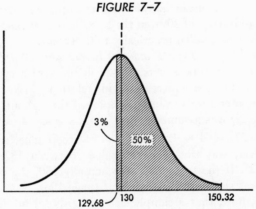

from 120, and the upper limit, 147.84, is 6.96 standard errors away. Thus it is practically impossible to obtain a sample mean in this acceptance region if the true mean is 120. The reader can verify that this conclusion holds, to an even greater extent, for any population mean less than 120. It is particularly important for a firm that is concerned with a population mean of 120 or less to understand the probability of making a type II error.

Relation between Type I and II Errors for Fixed Sample Size. Assume that the significance level, and therefore the probability of a type I error, is 1 percent. Assume, also, that $n = 64$, $\sigma_{\bar{x}} = 4$, the hypothetical mean is 140, a two-tailed test is called for, and that the actual mean is 130. The area of acceptance would be the range of values between 129.68 and 150.32 (page 192). Figure 7-7 shows that the probability of accepting the false hypothesis—that is, the probability of making a type II error—is 53 percent. But this example is exactly the same as a previous one (pages

195–197), except that the significance level here is 1 percent, whereas it was 5 percent in the earlier example. In this earlier example, the probability of a type II error was found to be 29 percent. Therefore it can be concluded that, for a fixed sample size, which implies a fixed standard error of the mean, the probability of a type I error cannot be reduced without simultaneously increasing the probability of a type II error. Similarly, it can be shown that for a fixed sample size the probability of a type II error cannot be decreased without simultaneously increasing the probability of a type I error.

Relation between Type II Error and Size of Difference between Hypothetical and Actual Mean. It has already been demonstrated that the greater the difference between the hypothetical and the actual population mean, the smaller the probability of a type II error. With a 5-percent significance level, when the actual mean was 130, representing a difference of 10 from the hypothetical mean, the probability of a type II error was seen to be 29 percent (pages 195–197). It was also seen (pages 196–197) that when the actual mean in the same example was decreased to 120, representing a difference of 20 from the hypothetical mean, the probability of a type II error had fallen practically to 0 percent.

Relation between Type I and II Errors and Sample Size. For a fixed probability of a type I error, the probability of a type II error will decrease as the sample size increases. This relation can be illustrated with reference to the metal-rods example employed throughout this discussion. In this example, it was assumed that $\sigma = 32$, $n = 64$, and that, therefore, $\sigma_{\bar{x}} = \sigma/\sqrt{n} = 32/\sqrt{64} = 4$. The region of acceptance, at the 5-percent significance level, was the range of values between 132.16 and 147.84 (pages 191–192). If the true mean was actually 130, the probability of a type II error was shown to be 29 percent (page 196).

Assume, now, that a sample size of 100 is taken, all other factors remaining unchanged. Then, $\sigma_{\bar{x}} = \sigma/\sqrt{n} = 32/\sqrt{100} = 3.2$. At the 5-percent significance level, the region of acceptance would be the range of values within $\pm 1.96 \ \sigma_{\bar{x}} = \pm 1.96 \times 3.2 = \pm 6.272$ of the hypothetical mean of 140. In other words, the region of acceptance is the range of values between 133.728 ($140 - 6.272 = 133.728$) and 146.272 ($140 + 6.272 = 146.272$). The reader can verify that, in this instance, if the true mean is actually 130, the probability of making a type II error is about 17 percent. This percentage is considerably lower than the 29-percent probability associated with a sample size of 64.

It has thus been demonstrated that for a fixed probability of a type I error the probability of a type II error will decrease as the sample size increases. As might well be expected, it can also be demonstrated that for a fixed probability of a type II error the probability of a type I error will decrease as the sample size increases. Further, it can be demonstrated that the probability of both types of errors can be simultaneously decreased as the sample size increases. As this statement implies, it is possible to determine a sample size that will hold both probabilities as low as you desire. Space will not be devoted to these demonstrations, although some of the problems at the end of the chapter illustrate them.

Summary. All the conclusions relating to type I and type II errors will now be listed:

1. For a fixed sample size, the probability of a type I error cannot be decreased without simultaneously increasing the probability of a type II error.

2. For a fixed sample size, the probability of a type II error cannot be decreased without simultaneously increasing the probability of a type I error.

3. The probability of a type II error is smaller the greater the difference between the hypothetical and actual population means.

4. For a fixed probability of a type I error, the probability of a type II error will decrease as the sample size increases.

5. For a fixed probability of a type II error, the probability of a type I error will decrease as the sample size increases.

6. The probabilities of both type I and II errors can *simultaneously* be made as small as desired provided only that the sample size can be increased sufficiently.

Conclusions 1, 3, and 4 have been demonstrated above. The student can demonstrate for himself the validity of the remaining conclusions by working through the problems at the end of the chapter.

This section has attempted to drive home two very important points. First, whenever the statistical-inference technique of hypothesis testing is employed in decision making, there is always the possibility of drawing an incorrect conclusion as the result of the occurrence of a type I or type II error. *Second, although this possibility is always present, the probability of its occurring can generally be evaluated and, more important, controlled.* With respect to control, the sample size is the determining variable.

The next section will deal with another general type of problem situation in which the principles of hypothesis testing are directly applicable and extremely useful. This situation relates to the significance of a difference between two sample means.

Significance of a Difference between Two Means

This section will carry a bit further the sampling theory developed in the previous chapter. The technique of a test of significance will then be employed to illustrate how the theory can be fruitfully applied in practice. Because this material is concerned with the relation between two populations and two sample means, it will be presented under the heading of the "significance of a difference between two means."

Assume that two different populations have identical means. Assume that an extremely large number of pairs of samples is randomly drawn, one sample in each pair coming from one population and one sample coming from the other. Assume that, although the size of samples taken from the two different populations may be different, the size of samples taken from the same population are the same. For example, 1 million samples, each of size 100, could be taken from the first population, and 1 million samples, each of size 45, could be taken from the second population. If, in each pair of samples, the sample mean coming from the first population is consistently subtracted from the sample mean coming from the second population, a distribution of differences will be generated. Some of these differences will be positive and some of them will be negative. It can be mathematically proved that the mean of this distribution of differences will be 0, and that the standard deviation of this distribution, which is called the *standard error of the difference* and designated by the symbol σ_D, can be calculated from the formula $\sigma_D = \sqrt{\sigma_1^2/n_1 + \sigma_2^2/n_2}$ In this formula, σ_1^2 designates the square of the standard deviation of the first population and σ_2^2 that of the second, and n_1 designates the sample size of the first population and n_2 that of the second population. Furthermore, if the original populations are normally distributed, the distribution of differences will be normally distributed for any sample size. Even if the original populations are not normally distributed, the distribution of differences will approach normality as the sample size increases. For the sample sizes generally employed in practice, the distribution of differences can usually be taken as normal.

These results can be a powerful tool in the kit of the decision maker. He knows that if two samples are drawn from populations with the same mean, the difference between the sample means will represent one of an extremely large number of possible differences that are distributed normally and have an arithmetic mean of 0. Furthermore, he knows how to determine the standard deviation of this distribution. These results enable him to formulate a hypothesis and employ a test of significance. These results and techniques will now be utilized to solve an important type of problem that often arises in practice.

The following hypothetical situation will be used to illustrate the type of problem that can be solved by the sampling theory just introduced. Assume that the firm discussed in the previous sections decides to purchase its entire requirements of metal rods from an outside supplier under a long-term contract. The firm has narrowed down its choice of suppliers to the two lowest bidders, which have submitted identical bids. Although the firm is completely indifferent to which of these two suppliers it finally selects, it must give all its business to just one of them in order to take advantage of rather substantial quantity discounts. Before flipping a coin to decide between the two, the firm decides to make one further check. Though each supplier has contractually agreed to meet the same minimum specifications, could the quality of one supplier's product possibly be higher than that of the other? The firm decides to compare the quality of each supplier's product. If there is, in fact, no significant difference between the quality of each supplier's product, the firm will flip a coin to decide between them.

In order to make this test, the firm asks each supplier to ship one week's requirements. The firm takes a random sample of 100 rods from supplier A and a random sample of 45 rods from supplier B. The mean breaking strength of the rods included in the sample taken from supplier A is 140 pounds per square inch, whereas the mean breaking strength of the rods included in the sample taken from supplier B is 145.

This evidence might, at first, make supplier B's product appear superior. However, earlier discussions relating to sampling variation pointed out that the mean of a particular sample will almost always be different from the mean of the population from which it was selected. In other words, in the above example, the sample means of 140 and 145 could possibly have come from populations with the same means. The relevant question, then, is whether the difference between these two sample means is significant? That is, is a difference as large as 5 (145 − 140 = 5) too large to be attributable to sampling variation alone? Or, putting it differently, what is the probability of obtaining a difference as large as 5 if the two sample means actually did come from populations with identical means? All these questions are based on the fact that if the two samples do come from populations with identical means, the difference of 5 between the sample means is the result purely of the play of chance or sampling variation that is always present in random sampling. Can such a chance factor account for the difference in this case? The sampling theory introduced above can provide the answer to this question and the others. The following hypothesis is formulated: "The two samples come from populations which have identical means." This hypothesis is tested in the following way.

It is known, from the above discussion, that if the two samples come from populations with the same means, the difference of 5 would be exactly 5 units away from the mean of a distribution of differences. The reason is that the mean of such a distribution is 0. It is also known that this distribution of differences is distributed normally. The crucial question is, then, "What is the probability of obtaining a difference as large as 5 between the mean of a normal distribution and one of the items in this distribution?" The answer depends on the standard deviation of this normal distribution. This particular standard deviation is called the standard error of the difference and is calculated from the formula $\sigma_D = \sqrt{\sigma_1^2/n_1 + \sigma_2^2/n_2}$.

Assume that the standard deviation of the original population from which supplier A's sample was taken is known to be 10 pounds per square inch. This deviation will be designated by σ_1. Assume that the standard deviation of the original population from which supplier B's sample was taken is known to be 6 pounds per square inch. This will be designated by σ_2. The size of supplier A's sample will be indicated by n_1 and that of supplier B's by n_2. The standard error of the difference can now be calculated from the formula $\sigma_D = \sqrt{\sigma_1^2/n_1 + \sigma_2^2/n_2} = \sqrt{(10)^2/100 + (6)^2/45} = \sqrt{1 + .8} = \sqrt{1.8} = 1.34$.

Because one standard deviation equals 1.34, a difference of 5 between the mean, 0, of the distribution of differences and one of the items in this distribution represents 3.7 ($5 \div 1.34 = 3.7$) standard deviations. That is, the difference of 5 is 3.7 standard deviations away from the mean of a normal curve. As the Table of Areas indicates, approximately 99.98 percent of the area under a normal curve will lie within ± 3.7 standard deviations of the mean. Thus there are only about 2 chances in 10,000, or a .02-percent probability, of obtaining a value that differs from the mean by as much as, or more than, 3.7 standard deviations. The difference of 5 is highly significant. It would be considered significant at any of the significance levels—for example, 5 percent, 1 percent, .1 percent—typically used in practice. It is therefore concluded that the two samples could not have come from populations with identical means. One of the populations has a mean that is higher than the other. Because the sample mean obtained from supplier B's shipment is higher than that obtained from supplier A's, it would appear that supplier B has the superior product. Accordingly, the long-term contract would be signed with supplier B.

SAMPLING APPLICATIONS:
UNKNOWN σ AND LARGE n

In all the sampling concepts and applications presented thus far in this chapter, it has been assumed that the standard deviation of the original population was known. This assumption was made to facilitate the direct application of the sampling theory developed in the previous chapter and to focus complete attention on the relevant probability and sampling concepts. Sometimes this assumption is valid in practice. Sometimes the standard deviation of the population, σ, is known as a result of a previous study. Usually, however, there are no prior studies from which such information can be reliably drawn. In these circumstances the only way to determine the *exact* value of σ is to take a complete census of the entire population and calculate it directly. Naturally, if a census is made, there is no need to apply sampling theory and techniques. The population mean can be determined exactly from the census data. In practice, σ is, for quite obvious reasons, not determined in this way. The reason for taking a sample in the first place is that it is either physically impossible or too costly and/or time-consuming to take a census. Furthermore, as pointed out in the previous chapter, it is often unnecessary to take a census; perfectly reliable and usable results can be obtained from a sample at a lower cost than can equivalent results obtained from a census. As this statement implies, σ must be *estimated* from the results of a single sample.

This fact does not appreciably alter any of the techniques introduced in this chapter. The reason is that for a "large" sample size— that is, for a large n—the estimated population standard deviation is a very close approximation to the actual population standard deviation. The difference between the estimated and actual standard deviations is generally so small that the conclusions derived, from confidence intervals or tests of hypotheses, are the same, for all practical purposes, whether the actual or estimated standard deviation is employed in the analysis. In the present context, a large sample is defined to be any sample that has 30 or more items. Methods for dealing with "small" (fewer than 30 items) samples will be examined in the next section.

The *estimated* standard deviation of the population is calculated from the formula $\hat{\sigma} = \sqrt{\Sigma(X - \bar{X})^2/(n - 1)}$. $\hat{\sigma}$ is the symbol that distinguishes the *estimated* standard deviation from the *actual* standard deviation that is represented by the symbol σ. X designates the value of an individual item in the *sample*, $\bar{X}$ the value of the *sample* mean, and n the number of items in the *sample*.[4] In the formula for the standard deviation

---

[4] The formula $\hat{\sigma} = \sqrt{\Sigma(X - \bar{X})^2/(n - 1)}$, which has $n - 1$ rather than just n in the denominator, is employed so that the estimated value of the population "variance," $\hat{\sigma}^2$, will be an "unbiased" estimate of the actual population "variance," σ^2. By definition, the "variance" of a population, σ^2, is the square of the standard deviation of the population, σ. An "unbiased" estimate is one for which the "expected value," or the value on the average, precisely equals the true value of the parameter being estimated. This concept can be illustrated with respect to the population of Table 6-3 and the sampling distribution of Table 6-7 and Figures 6-5 and 6-6. Table 7-3 shows the population variance estimated, according to the above formula, from each of an extremely large number, let us say 16 million, of samples that were randomly drawn. Each of the 16 *different* possible samples has the same probability of being drawn (namely, $\frac{1}{16}$). The first sample can be taken as an illustration of the calculation of $\hat{\sigma}^2$:

$$\bar{X} = \frac{6 + 2}{2} = 4, \Sigma(X - \bar{X})^2 = (6 - 4)^2 + (2 - 4)^2 = 8$$

and

$$\hat{\sigma}^2 = \Sigma(X - \bar{X})^2/(n - 1) = \frac{8}{2 - 1} = 8$$

It can be seen that the average (that is, the arithmetic mean) value of all these estimated of the *population*

$$\sigma = \sqrt{\Sigma(X - \mu)^2/N}$$

X represents the value of an individual item in the *population*, μ the value of the *population* mean, and N the number of items in the *population*.

Interest has centered, in this section, on the determination of the population standard deviation only because knowledge of this measure is necessary for the determination of the standard error of the mean. The standard error, remember, is calculated from the formula $\sigma_{\bar{x}} = \sigma/\sqrt{n}$. If the value of the population standard deviation employed in this formula is an estimate of the actual value, the value of the standard error of the mean derived from this formula is an estimate of the actual standard error. As pointed out above, if the sample size is 30 or more, the estimated standard deviation of the population will be very close to the actual

---

variances (that is, $(\Sigma\hat{\sigma}^2/\Sigma f = 20)$ precisely equals the actual population variance calculated in Table 6-10.

Table 7-3. VERIFICATION THAT $\hat{\sigma}^2 = \Sigma(X - \bar{X})^2/(n-1)$ IS AN UNBIASED ESTIMATE OF THE POPULATION VARIANCE
(Based on Sixteen Million Samples of Size Two from the Population of Table 6-3)

	Estimated variance $\hat{\sigma}^2 = \dfrac{\Sigma(X - \bar{X})^2}{n-1}$	No. of times sample occurred (millions) f	(Millions) $f\hat{\sigma}^2$
Different possible samples			
6, 2	8	1	8
6, 6	0	1	0
6, 10	8	1	8
6, 14	32	1	32
2, 2	0	1	0
2, 6	8	1	8
2, 10	32	1	32
2, 14	72	1	72
14, 2	72	1	72
14, 6	32	1	32
14, 10	8	1	8
14, 14	0	1	0
10, 2	32	1	32
10, 6	8	1	8
10, 10	0	1	0
10, 14	8	1	8
		16	320

$$\text{Average } \hat{\sigma}^2 = \frac{\Sigma f \hat{\sigma}^2}{\Sigma f} = \frac{320 \text{ million}}{16 \text{ million}} = 20$$

standard deviation. For this reason, if the sample size is 30 or more, the estimated standard error of the mean will be very close to the actual standard error. As also pointed out above, for these "large" samples, the estimated standard error will typically be so close to the actual standard error that conclusions, derived from confidence intervals or tests of significance, will be the same whether the actual or estimated standard error of the mean is employed in the analysis. An estimate of the standard error of the mean will be designated by the symbol $\hat{\sigma}_{\bar{X}}$, in contrast to the symbol, $\sigma_{\bar{X}}$, which is employed to designate the actual standard error. The formulas corresponding to these symbols are

$$\hat{\sigma}_{\bar{X}} = \hat{\sigma}/\sqrt{n}$$
$$\sigma_{\bar{X}} = \sigma/\sqrt{n}$$

remembering that $\hat{\sigma}_{\bar{x}}$ is a very close approximation to $\sigma_{\bar{x}}$ for "large" samples.[5]

As an illustration of the estimation of the standard error of the mean, assume that the first sample in Table 6-4, namely, 6 and 2, is selected at random from the population of Table 6-3. The standard error would be estimated by first determining $\hat{\sigma}$ and dividing the answer by $\sqrt{n}$. Now, $\hat{\sigma} = \sqrt{\Sigma(X - \bar{X})^2/(n - 1)}$. $\bar{X}$ for the first sample of Table 6-4 is $(6 + 2)/2 = 4$. Thus $\hat{\sigma} = \sqrt{[(6 - 4)^2 + (2 - 4)^2]/(2 - 1)} = \sqrt{8/1} = 2.8$. Therefore the estimated standard error of the mean would be $\hat{\sigma}_{\bar{x}} = \hat{\sigma}/\sqrt{n} = 2.8/\sqrt{2} = 2.8/1.4 = 2.0$. The true standard error, from Table 6-11, is 3.2. The reason for the relatively large difference between the estimated and actual standard error is attributable to the extremely small sample (2 items) employed here.

It must be stressed that the discussion presented in this section is extremely important, because it corresponds to the situation commonly met in practice. The important results of this discussion will now be summarized. If the actual population standard deviation, and therefore the actual standard error of the mean, is known, the applications relating to confidence intervals and tests of significance can be handled precisely as indicated in all the previous sections of this chapter. If, as is usually true, the actual population standard deviation, and therefore the actual standard error, is unknown, these applications must be handled as indicated in this section. In other words, whenever the population standard deviation is required in order to determine the standard error of the mean or in order to determine, as in the section on confidence intervals, the optimum sample size,[6] it must be estimated from a single sample. As long

[5] It can be proved mathematically that $\sigma_{\bar{x}}^2$ is an "unbiased" (see footnote 4) estimate of $\sigma_{\bar{x}}^2$. The reader can verify this by employing the technique used in footnote 4.

[6] In this instance, a "pilot" study—that is, a preliminary sample composed of 30 or 40 items—would be selected in order to obtain an estimate of the population standard deviation.

as the sample size is large—that is, greater than or equal to 30—an adequate estimate can be obtained. This estimate is calculated from the formula $\hat{\sigma} = \sqrt{\Sigma(X - \overline{X})^2/(n - 1)}$. In these situations, the analysis proceeds exactly as indicated in the previous sections of this chapter, except that $\hat{\sigma}$ is used instead of σ, $\hat{\sigma}_{\overline{x}} = \hat{\sigma}/\sqrt{n}$ is used instead of $\sigma_{\overline{x}} = \sigma/\sqrt{n}$, and $\hat{\sigma}_D = \sqrt{\hat{\sigma}_1^2/n_1 + \hat{\sigma}_2^2/n_2}$ is used instead of $\sigma_D = \sqrt{\sigma_1^2/n_1 = \sigma_2^2/n_2}$.

SAMPLING APPLICATIONS:
UNKNOWN σ, SMALL n, AND THE t DISTRIBUTION

The previous section discussed the application of sampling theory in situations in which the actual population standard deviation was unknown and the sample size, n, was large. This section is concerned with situations in which the actual population standard deviation is unknown and the sample size is "small." A small sample is defined to be one in which the number of items is less than 30. In these situations, the same procedures and techniques relevant when the population standard deviation is known can be employed, except that $\hat{\sigma}$ is used instead of σ; $\hat{\sigma}_{\overline{x}}$ is used instead of $\sigma_{\overline{x}}$; the t distribution is used instead of the normal distribution, and the original population must be normally distributed. That is to say, if n is small, if σ is unknown, and if the original population is not normally distributed, the sampling procedures discussed in this chapter are not valid.

It is necessary to substitute the t distribution, which will be examined below, for the normal distribution because, when the sample size is less than 30, the population standard deviation cannot be reliably estimated from the results of a single sample. In other words, for small samples, there is a high probability that any single estimate of the population standard deviation will differ appreciably from the actual population value. This means that the standard error of the mean and the standard error of the difference cannot be reliably estimated, and, without reasonably accurate knowledge of these measures, the procedures discussed so far in this chapter cannot be directly applied. However, if the original population is normally distributed, the t distribution can be employed to derive the same results obtainable from the large sample methods already discussed. It is not necessary to rely on the t distribution when dealing with large samples because, as the sample size increases, the probability of obtaining an appreciably inaccurate estimate of the population standard deviation decreases. When the sample size is as large as 30, the probability of obtaining an appreciable difference between the estimated and actual values of the population standard deviation is so small that it can be ignored.

t Distribution

The "t distribution" is the special name given to a particular distribution of values that, like the normal distribution, can be rigidly defined mathematically.[7] In general, it is a symmetrical curve that always approaches but never touches the horizontal axis. In these respects it is like the normal curve. It differs from the normal curve in that, for the small sample sizes being considered, its tails are higher. Like the normal curve, there is a table of areas that has been mathematically constructed to indicate the percentage of the area under a t distribution between any two values. Relevant portions of this table are presented in Appendix B (Table V). The manner in which this table is utilized can best be demonstrated by briefly discussing the theory underlying its construction.

Assume that an extremely large number of samples, of a fixed size, is selected at random from a normally distributed population. Assume that for each sample, the population mean, μ, is subtracted from the sample mean, $\bar{X}$, and that this difference, which may be positive or negative, is divided by the standard error of the mean *as estimated from each sample*. That is, assume that each difference, $\bar{X} - \mu$, is divided by the $\hat{\sigma}_{\bar{x}}$ corresponding to that sample. Let this final value be designated by the letter t. Because an extremely large number of samples is taken, an extremely large number of t values will be generated. It can be mathematically proved that the arithmetic mean of all these t values is zero, with positive and negative t values symmetrically distributed around the mean of zero. However, as with the normal curve, the greater the difference between the mean, zero, and any given t value, the smaller the probability that the given t value will occur. The t distribution, which is employed in the application of sampling techniques to small samples when the population standard deviation is unknown, is simply the frequency distribution, expressed in relative terms, of the t values just defined.

As indicated at the outset of this discussion, a t distribution is constructed by taking an extremely large number of samples, each of the same size. Though the t distribution is always symmetrical, the exact shape it takes depends on the particular sample size employed in constructing it. As this statement implies, the t distribution is really a whole family of curves, the exact shape of each curve depending on the sample size employed in constructing it. Because each curve is mathematically

[7] The t distribution is defined by the equation

$$y_c = \frac{y_m}{(1 + t^2/d)[(d + 1)/2]}$$

where y_c is an ordinate at a stated distance t from an origin at 0 on the t scale, y_m is the maximum ordinate at $t = 0$, and d is the number of degrees of freedom of t.

derived, the percentage of the area under each curve between any two t values can be determined, and a table, similar to the Table of Areas under a Normal Curve (Appendix Table IV), can be constructed for each curve. However, it would take a great number of pages to present each of these possible tables in detail. To save space, Appendix Table V has been constructed by taking the most important portions of each of these separate tables and condensing them into one table. Because, in the present context, interest centers on sample sizes of less than 30 and on t values that have a probability of 5 percent or less of occurring, these are the bench marks typically utilized in Appendix Table V.

This table is read as follows. The extreme left-hand column is headed by the words "degrees of freedom." The meaning of this mathematical concept will not be discussed in this chapter. At present, it is only necessary to know that each value in this column corresponds to a sample that is composed of one more item than the given value. For example, a value of 11 corresponds to a sample size of 12. Or, expressing this idea differently, a sample size of 12 corresponds to 11 degrees of freedom. The remaining columns indicate the probability of obtaining various t values. For example, the 4th column from the right indicates the t values, both positive and negative, which are so large that they would occur only 5 percent or less than 5 percent of the time. Naturally, t values that are higher than these would occur a smaller percentage of the time. The third and second columns from the right present the same information for the 2-percent and 1-percent probability levels, respectively. For example, if a sample of 10, representing 9 degrees of freedom, is taken, there is a 5-percent probability of obtaining a t value, either positive or negative, of 2.262 or higher, a 2-percent probability of obtaining a t value of 2.821 or higher, and a 1-percent probability of obtaining a t value of 3.250 or higher.

Confidence Intervals

To illustrate the direct application of this table, problems involving confidence intervals and tests of significance will now be discussed. Assume that the firm discussed throughout this chapter wishes to determine the mean breaking strength of metal rods purchased from a particular supplier. This knowledge can be obtained by constructing a 95-percent confidence interval. A sample of 15 rods is selected at random. It is believed that the population from which this sample is obtained is normally distributed. The mean of this sample is 150 pounds per square inch and $\Sigma(X - \bar{X})^2 = 3,360$. Therefore

$$\hat{\sigma} = \sqrt{\Sigma(X - \bar{X})^2/(n - 1)} = \sqrt{3,360/14} = \sqrt{240} = 15.5$$

and

$$\hat{\sigma}_{\bar{x}} = \hat{\sigma}/\sqrt{n} = 15.5/\sqrt{15} = 4.0$$

Appendix Table V indicates that with a sample size of 15, and, therefore, 14 degrees of freedom, there is only a 5-percent probability of obtaining a t value, positive or negative, that is equal to or greater than 2.145. Thus, there is a 95-percent chance that any t value selected at random will lie between -2.145 and $+2.145$. As noted in the previous sections, each t value is derived from the equation $t = (\bar{X} - \mu)/\hat{\sigma}_{\bar{x}}$, which, by algebraic manipulation, can be expressed as $\bar{X} - \mu = t\,\hat{\sigma}_{\bar{x}}$, $\mu = \bar{X} - t\hat{\sigma}_{\bar{x}}$. By substituting in this last equation the values obtained, above, for the upper and lower limits of t and for $\hat{\sigma}_{\bar{x}}$, the 95-percent confidence limits for the mean breaking strength of the metal rods can be obtained: $\mu = 150 - (-2.145)$ $(4) = 150 - (-8.6) = 158.6$, and $\mu = 150 - (2.145)(4) = 150 - (8.6)$ $= 141.4$. Thus you can be 95-percent confident that the true mean is between 141.4 and 158.6 pounds per square inch. The steps involved in constructing confidence intervals for situations requiring the use of the t distribution are listed below:

1. Calculate the sample mean.
2. Calculate $\hat{\sigma}_{\bar{x}}$.
3. Subtract the desired confidence level from 1.00, expressing this difference as a percentage.
4. Determine, from the Table of Areas under a t Distribution, the t value that corresponds to the percentage derived in step 3 and to the number of degrees of freedom relevant in the problem.
5. Multiply this t value by the value, obtained in step 2, of $\hat{\sigma}_{\bar{x}}$.
6. Add and subtract the product obtained in step 5 to and from, respectively, the value of the sample mean obtained in step 1. The two resulting values represent the specified confidence limits.

Tests of Significance

Assume, now, that you wish to test the hypothesis that the mean breaking strength of the metal rods is 170 pounds per square inch. The sample described above is taken. t is calculated from $t = (\bar{X} - \mu)/\hat{\sigma}_{\bar{x}}$, where μ represents the hypothetical mean of 170. This t value is $t = (150 - 170)/4 = -5.0$. Appendix Table V shows that, with 14 degrees of freedom, a t value, positive or negative, as high as 2.145 would occur only 5 percent of the time, a value as high as 2.624 only 2 percent of the time, and a value as high as 2.977 only 1 percent of the time. The t value obtained, 5.0, is certainly significant. The hypothesis is rejected.

As pointed out earlier, the application of sampling theory to small samples is justified only when the original population is normally distributed. Whenever this theory is to be applied to situations involving the significance of the difference between two means, it can be justified only by placing an additional restriction. In these situations, the standard deviations of the two original populations must be equal. Assume that these conditions are met. Assume, for example, that you want to determine whether the mean breaking strength of rods purchased from two different suppliers is significantly different, and that you have reason to believe that each of these parent populations is normally distributed with the same standard deviation. Two samples are taken. One is the sample described above. Assume that this sample comes from a lot shipped by supplier A. The other sample is composed of 20 rods drawn from a lot shipped by supplier B. The mean of this second sample is 160 and $\Sigma(X - \bar{X})^2 = 6,156$. The population standard deviation estimated from the first sample, which will be designated by the symbol $\hat{\sigma}_1$, has already been determined, above, to be 15.5. $\hat{\sigma}_2$, the population standard deviation estimated from the second sample, is equal to $\sqrt{\Sigma(X - \bar{X})^2/(n - 1)} = \sqrt{6,156/19} = \sqrt{324} = 18$.

Because the actual standard deviation of each of these populations is assumed to be the same, the standard deviation estimated from each of the two samples is an estimate of the same value. This statement means that the square of the standard deviation estimated from each of these samples is also an estimate of the same value. The formula for the standard error of the difference, $\hat{\sigma}_D = \sqrt{\hat{\sigma}_1^2/n_1 + \hat{\sigma}_2^2/n_2}$, requires the estimated value of the square of the standard deviation of each of the two populations. In the present example, it is assumed that this value is the same for both populations. It can be mathematically proved that this common value is best approximated by taking a weighted average of the two sample estimates, using degrees of freedom as weights. This average will be represented by the symbol σ_a^2. Thus the single best estimate of the square of the common population standard deviation is given by the formula

$$\sigma_a^2 = \frac{(n_1 - 1)\,\hat{\sigma}_1^2 + (n_2 - 1)\,\hat{\sigma}_2^2}{(n_1 - 1) + (n_2 - 1)} = \frac{14(240) + 19(324)}{14 + 19} = \frac{9,516}{33} = 288.4$$

This value is then substituted in the usual formula for the standard error of the difference:

$$\hat{\sigma}_D = \sqrt{\hat{\sigma}_a^2/n_1 + \hat{\sigma}_a^2/n_2} = \sqrt{288.4/15 + 288.4/20} = \sqrt{19.2 + 14.4} = \sqrt{33.6} = 5.8$$

Now that the standard error of the difference has been determined, the analysis proceeds in the usual way. Assume that an extremely large number of pairs of samples is selected at random from two normal populations with identical means and standard deviations, one sample in each pair being drawn from one population and one sample from the other. Assume that, although the sample size for one population may be different from that of the other population, the sizes of samples drawn from the same population are equal. Assume that in each pair of samples the sample mean corresponding to the first population is consistently subtracted from that corresponding to the second, and that this difference is divided by the standard error of the difference estimated from each pair of samples by the method illustrated in the previous paragraph. Because an extremely large number of pairs of samples is taken, an extremely large number of these ratios will be generated. It can be mathematically proved that these ratios are t values. The probability of obtaining a given t value can be determined from Appendix Table V. However, because two samples are employed, the number of degrees of freedom is two less than the number of items in both samples.

With respect to the present example, the difference between the sample means of suppliers A and B is $160 - 150 = 10$, $\hat{\sigma}_D = 5.8$; t therefore equals $10/5.8 = 1.72$, and the number of degrees of freedom is $15 + 20 - 2 = 33$. Appendix Table V indicates that t values are not given for situations in which the number of degrees of freedom exceeds 30. The reason for this is that when the number of degrees of freedom exceeds 30, the probability of obtaining a particular t value can be very closely approximated by referring to the Table of Areas under a Normal Curve (Appendix Table IV). In this example, this table indicates that the probability of obtaining a t value as high as or higher than 1.72 on one side of the curve is .0427 ($.5000 - .4573 = .0427$). This means that the probability of obtaining a t value as high as, or higher than, 1.72 on either side of the curve (that is, a positive or negative 1.72 value) is $2 \times .0427 = .0854$. Thus the hypothesis that there is no difference between these sample means would be accepted at the 5-percent significance level. The probability of obtaining a difference as large as the one obtained is greater than 5 percent. To illustrate the direct use of Appendix Table V in this type of situation, assume that the sample sizes in this problem had been 15 and 14. Under these conditions, the degrees of freedom would have been $15 + 14 - 2 = 27$. Appendix Table V indicates that a t value as high as 2.052 would occur only 5 percent of the time. The t value obtained in this problem—namely, 1.72—is less than this, and the hypothesis would therefore be accepted at the 5-percent level.

Summary

This section examined situations in which the sample size is small and the population standard deviation is unknown. In these situations, several of the principles and procedures applicable when the sample size is large are not relevant. Sampling theory can be reliably applied only within a more restricted framework. In order to generalize from small samples, the original population must be normally, or very close to normally, distributed. This restriction does not apply, of course, to large samples. It is imposed for the following reason.

All the sampling applications discussed in this chapter require the utilization of the standard error of the mean or the standard error of the difference. These standard errors can be evaluated exactly if the actual standard deviations of the original population are known. Even when these standard deviations are unknown, they, and therefore the standard errors, can be reliably estimated from sample results, if the samples are large. However, if the samples are small—that is, if each sample is composed of fewer than 30 items—the population standard deviations, and therefore the standard errors, cannot be reliably approximated. The usual techniques, in other words, can no longer be employed. It is now necessary to use the t distribution. Applications relating to confidence intervals and tests of significance involving a single sample mean can be made, if the *original populations are normally distributed*, by referring to the t distribution. Applications relating to tests of significance that involve two sample means can be made, again by referring to the t distribution, if both of the original populations are normally distributed *and* if the two population standard deviations are equal.

SUGGESTED READINGS

Bryant, Edward. *Statistical Analysis.* New York: McGraw-Hill Book Company, Inc., 1960, chap. 5.

Dixon, W. J., and F. J. Massey. *Introduction to Statistical Analysis.* New York: McGraw-Hill Book Company, Inc., 1951, chaps. 7, 9.

Freund, J. E., and F. J. Williams. *Modern Business Statistics.* Englewood Cliffs, N.J.: Prentice-Hall, Inc., 1961, chaps. 8, 9, 10.

Moroney, M. J. *Facts from Figures.* Baltimore: Penquin Books, Inc., 1957, chaps. 13, 14.

Richmond, Samuel. *Principles of Statistical Analysis.* New York: The Ronald Press Company, 1964, chaps. 6, 7.

Walker, H. M., and Joseph Lev. *Statistical Inference.* New York: Holt, Rinehart and Winston, Inc., 1953, chaps. 5, 6, 7.

QUESTIONS

1. Compare the meaning of the standard deviation and the standard error of the mean.
2. Is a difference of 1 standard error of the mean more, or less, significant than a difference of 3 standard errors? Explain.
3. State the meaning of the term "confidence interval."
4. What is the meaning of the term "significant difference"?
5. What is meant by the expression "90-percent confidence level"?
6. What is the "sampling distribution of the mean"?
7. State clearly the two possible approaches to the problem of increasing the reliability of a sample.

8. Which indicates greater reliability of a sample, a standard error of the mean of $4 or one of $16? Why?

9. Distinguish between type I and II errors.

10. "Chance occurrences must be distinguished from those due to some other cause." Discuss.

11. In random sampling, what is the relation between an increase in the size of the sample and an increase in its accuracy?

12. For a fixed sample size, what is the relation between the size of the confidence interval and the confidence level?

13. How will an increase in sample size affect the confidence level associated with a fixed size of interval? How will it affect the size of the confidence interval associated with a fixed confidence level?

14. What is sampling variation?

15. Distinguish between the area of acceptance associated with a 5-percent significance level and that associated with a 2-percent level.

16. Distinguish between the area of rejection associated with a one-tailed test conducted at a 5-percent level of significance, and the area of rejection associated with a two-tailed test conducted at a 5-percent level.

17. What is the relation between type I and II errors for a fixed sample size?

18. Under what conditions should the t distribution be used to construct a confidence interval?

19. Under what conditions can the t distribution be used to test for a significant difference between two sample means?

PROBLEMS

1. A sample of the useful life of shoe heels measured in terms of miles is presented in the frequency distribution below. Assuming the true mean of the life of these heels to be 76.5 miles, is there a significant difference between the sample mean and the theoretical mean? Explain.

PRODUCT SAMPLE FROM REINFORCED TISSUE SHOE
HEEL COMPANY TESTED FOR WEARING QUALITY

No. of miles	No. of heels
25 but under 35	15
35 but under 45	20
45 but under 55	27
55 but under 65	21
65 but under 75	17
	100

2. The Evertite Shoe Company has taken two random samples to test the wearing quality of the company's soles. The results of these samples are presented below:

	Sample I	Sample II
Mean	45 miles	40 miles
Standard deviation	12 miles	9 miles
Number of soles	65 soles	37 soles

  (a) Establish the 80-percent confidence interval in Sample I.
  (b) State whether or not there is a significant difference between the two sample means.
3. A random sample of 65 items is drawn from a universe known to be approximately normal. The sample mean is $60 and its standard deviation is $1.60.
  (a) Compute the standard error of the mean.
  (b) Establish the 95-percent confidence interval.
  (c) Establish the 98-percent confidence interval.
  (d) Establish the 80-percent confidence interval.
4. Assume a random sample of 65 items drawn from a universe known to be approximately normal, with a mean of $60 and a standard deviation of $1.60.
  (a) Test the hypothesis that the true mean of the distribution from which the sample is taken is $68. Illustrate by a simple sketch.
  (b) Test the hypothesis that the true mean of the distribution from which the sample is taken is $59.70. Illustrate by a simple sketch.
5. Assume the existence of a moderately skewed universe. If a large number of random samples of 60 items each is drawn from this universe and their means arranged in a frequency distribution, what shape would the distribution assume?
6. A comparison of two brands of paint gave the following results when tested for coverage:

	Texas Brand	Happy Brand
N	122 gallons	145 gallons
$\bar{X}$	150 sq. feet	153 sq. feet
σ	9.9 sq. feet	15.6 sq. feet

  (a) Is the difference between the averages significant?
  (b) State the probability that the difference is a chance occurrence.
7. The average number of children in a sample of 82 families is 4.85. The standard deviation of the sample is 1.98 children.
  (a) What is the standard error of the mean?

(b) Assume that the standard deviation stays the same. How many families must we include in a sample if we want to get a standard error of .1?

8. Following is a frequency distribution presenting the results of a test applied to a sample of 100 Wearever Everwearing Tires.

WEAREVER EVERWEARING TIRES
(Test Sample)

Mileage per tire	No. of tires
5000 but under 15,000	1
15,000 but under 25,000	5
25,000 but under 35,000	10
35,000 but under 45,000	24
45,000 but under 55,000	35
55,000 but under 65,000	16
65,000 but under 75,000	8
75,000 but under 85,000	1
	100

(a) If the theoretical length of life of these tires is 48,840 miles, what is the possibility that the difference between the average of the sample and the average of the universe is due to chance? Is this difference significant?

(b) If in another sample of 401 tires the average mileage is 53,572 miles with a standard deviation of 16,000 miles, what is the possibility that the difference between the two sample means is due to chance? Is this difference significant?

(c) Using the results of the sample in (b) above, establish the 80-percent confidence interval.

9. Assume that a census has been taken and the average wage found to be $66.32. If a sample of 901 men yields an arithmetic mean of $67.53 with a standard deviation of $15.00, what is the possibility that the difference between the two averages is due to chance?

10. A random sample of 50 items is drawn from a universe of high-grade bonds known to be distributed in an approximately normal fashion. The arithmetic mean of the sample is $200 and its σ is $7.00

(a) Establish the 99-percent confidence interval.

(b) Establish the 90-percent confidence interval.

(c) Establish the 60-percent confidence interval.

(d) What is the possibility that the mean of the universe is $205 or more? Illustrate by a simple sketch.

(e) What is the possibility that the mean of the universe is $198 or under? Illustrate by a simple sketch.

11. State whether or not the following distributions are likely to approximate normal, and discuss why.
   (a) The diameter of 100,000 marbles produced by a machine process in a marble factory
   (b) A random sample of wages paid to workers in a large industrial area
   (c) The distribution of sample means around the mean of the universe—assuming the universe is slightly skewed

12. Assume that you are playing a game with a pair of dice. In this game, 7 is a winning number. Your opponent is extremely fortunate in that he throws 7's quite frequently. Applying the customary levels of significance presented in the chapter, what should be your reaction if your opponent throws so many 7's that the probability of their appearing in such profusion is (a) .04, (b) .008, (c) .00004

13. A cathode-ray tube manufacturer has attempted, by introducing an inspection system, to reduce the number of defective tubes produced. The number of defective tubes is presented in the following table for two 10-week periods. One 10-week period precedes the introduction of the inspection system, and the other period follows its introduction. Except for the inspection system, production conditions throughout the entire 20-week period were unchanged.

DEFECTIVE TUBES PER WEEK

Week	No inspection	Week	Inspection
1	28	11	20
2	22	12	19
3	14	13	13
4	36	14	10
5	36	15	20
6	19	16	18
7	25	17	19
8	33	18	16
9	30	19	17
10	26	20	15

   (a) Is there a significant difference between the average number of defectives produced per week prior to the inspection system and the average number per week produced after the system?
   (b) How significant is the difference?

14. Assume that A and B in each of the following examples represent samples to be compared. Determine the significance of the difference between their means, assuming that each sample comes from a normal population with the same σ.

Example I		Example II		Example III	
A	B	A	B	A	B
4	56	42	82	66	60
14	30	24	84	30	48
34	48	6	46	54	84
14	4	30	50	12	12
34	12	18	58	18	96

15. A large insurance company is interested in the difference in annual sales between employees who have had a college statistics course and employees who have not been so privileged. The following table presents annual sales of these employees during their first five years of employment. The two groups are basically similar except for their previous training in statistics. Does the company have reason to believe that previous training in statistics is to the employee's advantage?

AVERAGE ANNUAL SALES

Had statistics		Did not have statistics	
Salesman	Sales	Salesman	Sales
Antoine	$18,000	Anastasia	$18,000
Bergnan	8,000	Bones	4,000
Carson	10,000	Cooler	6,000
Delaney	8,000	Danet	4,000
Erp	16,000	Ergrams	6,000
Farragut	4,000	Fooster	8,000
Geronomo	10,000	Gandry	3,000
Hesperin	6,000	Hentry	4,000
Ishnell	8,000	Ivanhod	6,000
Jones	12,000	James	5,000

16. If a given manufacturing process is working correctly for Company A, the steel rods produced will have a breaking point of 800 pounds per square inch, with a standard deviation of 80 pounds per square inch. A sample of 82 items is randomly selected, and it is found that the sample mean is 725 and that the sample standard deviation is 70. These steel rods are essential to the safe operation of racing cars. In answering the following questions, carry all calculations to the nearest tenth.

(a) Is the difference between the sample mean and the population mean significant?

(b) Is this difference important?

(c) Construct the 85-percent confidence interval.

(d) Why is the lower limit of the above interval important in this problem? Why is the higher limit important?

(e) Instead of producing its own steel rods, Company A can pur- chase—at the same price as its own cost of manufacture—these steel rods from Company B or Company C. Company B sends over a trial lot. In examining a random sample of 101 items selected from this lot, Company A finds that the sample mean is 700 and the sample standard deviation is 72. For Company C, the same experiment yields a sample mean of 690 and a sample standard deviation of 70.

(1) If Company A were to purchase its steel rods instead of manu- facturing them, does it make any difference which company it does business with?

(2) Should Company A do business with either Company B or Company C?

17. A random sample of the scores obtained on entrance exams by 50 students at XYZ college was taken. X represents the score on a single examination, $\Sigma X = 4500, \Sigma X^2 = 2025, \Sigma(X - \bar{X}) = 0, \Sigma(X - \bar{X})^2 = 2000$. You are interested in attending this college. Employing the 99-percent confidence interval, what is the lowest score you can allow yourself to obtain and still be accepted?

18. A pilot study indicates that the standard deviation of a certain popu- lation is 20. What size sample should be taken in order to obtain an estimate of the population mean that has a 99-percent confidence level and a confidence interval of size $8?

19. A random sample of 50 steel sheets is selected from a carload of steel sheets. The breaking point of each steel sheet in the sample is tested. The results are illustrated in the table below. The buyer specifies that the mean breaking point be 30 pounds per square inch.

(a) Is the difference between the mean of the sample and the specified mean significant?

(b) Is the difference important? Explain.

No. of pounds per square inch applied before breaking point reached	No. of sheets
25 but under 35	8
35 but under 45	10
45 but under 55	13
55 but under 65	10
65 but under 75	9

20. The National Warehouse Company spends $20,000 each year for gloves for its employees. Historically, two companies have been the major suppliers of gloves. In order to take advantage of quantity

discounts, National decides that it should do all its purchasing with one firm. To this end, National takes two random samples of gloves, one from each supplier, and tests each glove for durability. The results are presented below. Does it make any difference which supplier National selects to do business with? Explain.

	Sample from Supplier A	Sample from Supplier B
Mean number of units of friction applied before glove deemed unusable	85	75
Standard deviation	18	16
Number of gloves	65	37

21. A random sample of 82 steel sheets is selected from a carload of steel sheets. Each steel sheet in the sample is tested for its breaking point. The mean number of pounds per square inch applied before the breaking point is reached is 50, and the standard deviation is 13. The buyer specifies that the mean breaking point be 30 pounds per square inch.
    (a) Is the difference between the mean of the sample and the specified mean *significant?*
    (b) Is the difference *important?* Explain.
22. The American Dynamo Company, a large manufacture of machine tools, spends $300,000 each year on steel rods. In the past, the company efficiency expert had persuaded the company to purchase its steel-rod requirements from two separate suppliers in equal amounts, so that the company would not be overly dependent on any one supplier. A newly hired efficiency expert, on the other hand, persuades the company to purchase all its requirements from one supplier, in order to take advantage of quantity discounts. To this end, the company takes two random samples of steel rods, one from each supplier, and tests each rod for its breaking point. The results are presented below. Does it make any difference which supplier American selects to do business with? Explain

	Sample from Supplier A	Sample from Supplier B
Mean number of units of pressure applied before rod breaks	72	92
Standard deviation	16	18
Number of rods in sample	122	145

23. The Auto Worker's Union wishes to estimate the mean weekly income of automobile factory workers with 99.9-percent confidence. They wish the size of the confidence interval to be no greater than $8. On the basis of previous studies they believe the population standard deviation to be $15. What size sample should they take? Carry all calculations to the nearest hundredth.

24. A medical drug is mass-produced. If the number of units of ingredient X exceeds 88 units by very much, people using the drug can become violently ill. Would the firm attempt to minimize a type I or type II error? In defending your answer be sure to define these two types of errors.

25. Assume, in the above problem, that the number of units of ingredient X contained in the final product is known to approximate, very closely, a normal curve. Assume that a random sample of 8 final products is selected, and that the number of units of ingredient X in each product is determined. Assume that the sum of the squared deviations of each item from the sample mean is 110.

    (a) What is the area of rejection if a 5-percent significance level is employed (consider whether a one-tailed or two-tailed test is appropriate)?

    (b) Assume that the firm is willing to risk a type I error of 5 percent and a type II error of no more than .1 percent when the true mean exceeds the desired mean by as much as, or more than, 4 units. What sample size should it select?

26. A firm purchases cases of specially made metal bolts at a fixed price. The supplier states that each case contains 200 bolts. The firm naturally wishes to guard against accepting cases that contain less than 200 bolts. The firm randomly selects a sample of 10 cases from a lot of 492 cases, and counts the number of bolts in each of these 10 cases. The sample mean is 189 bolts and the sum of the squared deviations of the number of bolts in each of the 10 cases from this mean is 225. Carry *all* the following calculations to the *nearest tenth* only.

    (a) Would you accept the entire lot of 492 cases on the basis of these sample results? Employ a 5-percent significance level.

    (b) Assume that the firm now takes a sample of 36 cases. The sample mean is now 190 bolts and the sum of the squared deviations of the number of bolts in each of the 36 cases from this mean is 5040. Assume that the actual mean for the population of 492 cases is 190 bolts. Assume that the firm is actually not very much concerned as long as the number of bolts per case is, on the average, at least over 195. However, if the actual population mean is actually 195 or less, costs are significantly affected. Assume that the firm is willing to risk a type I error of 2 percent and a type II error of no more than 1 percent when the actual population mean is 195 or less. What size sample must the firm take? (Use the best estimate of the population σ that you can find anywhere in this problem.)

27. Two random samples were taken. One pertained to the annual incomes of doctors in the Boston area and the other to incomes of lawyers in the Boston area. The results are summarized below. Are these results consistent with the hypothesis that the two sample means were drawn from the same normal population?

	Doctors	Lawyers
Sample size	10	20
Sample mean	$14,000	$10,000
$\Sigma(X - \bar{X})^2$	12,160,000	5,760,000

28. A firm produces its own metal rods. It wants the breaking strength to be 140 pounds per square inch. If the breaking strength of the rods actually produced is greater than this, greater expense than is necessary will be incurred. If the breaking strength is less than 140 pounds, the quality of the firm's product will be too low. Assume that the standard deviation of the population is 15 pounds per square inch, the sample size is 36, and that the significance level is 5 percent. Assume that the true mean is actually 150 pounds per square inch. Let the probability of a type I error be represented by the symbol α, and the probability of a type II error by the symbol β.

(a) What is the probability of a type I (α) error?

(b) What values of $\bar{X}$ will lead to a rejection of the hypothesis?

(c) What is the probability of a type II (β) error?

(d) If the significance level is lowered to 1 percent, what is the probability of a type I error?

(e) What values of $\bar{X}$ will now lead to a rejection of the hypothesis?

(f) What is the probability of a type II error?

(g) What do you conclude about the size of β as α decreases, with the sample size fixed?

(h) Assume that the true mean is actually 145. If $\alpha = 5$ percent, what's β?

(i) What do you conclude about the size of β, the closer the actual mean is to the hypothetical mean?

(j) Assume that $n = 100$ and that the actual mean is 150. For $\alpha = 5$ percent, what's β?

(k) What do you conclude about the size of β as n increases, with α fixed?

(l) Assume that $n = 100$ and the actual mean is 150. For $\beta = 2.1$ percent, what is α?

(m) What do you conclude about the size of α, for fixed β, as n increases?

(n) What size sample is necessary in order that the probability of a type I error is 5 percent and the probability of type II error is at most 2 percent when the actual mean differs from the hypothetical mean by as much as 8 pounds per square inch?

(o) Assume, now, that the firm purchases these metal rods at a fixed price. The firm is now interested only in preventing the purchase of rods with too low a breaking point. A one-tailed test is now appropriate. Under this assumption, what will be the answer to question (n)?

CHAPTER EIGHT

Further Sampling Applications: Qualitative Data

The last two chapters have applied probability and sampling theory to *quantitative* or *continuous* data. This is data which result from *measurement*. For example, the variable to which the data correspond could be the breaking strength of metal rods. A given rod can be measured and its breaking strength determined, for example, as 170.2 pounds per square inch. Or the variable to which the data correspond could be the yearly income of doctors in the Boston area. The income of a doctor in this area could be measured and determined, let us say, to be $14,143. Another type of data has extremely important sampling applications in the world of business and economics. It is called *qualitative* or *discrete* data. These data result from *counting* and not from measuring. For example, the variable to which the data correspond may be the number of defective electronic tubes in a given lot. This number is determined by counting the number of such tubes in the specified lot. Or the variable may be the number of residents in the Boston area who prefer candidate X. This number is determined by counting the number of such residents in the given area.

This chapter is mainly concerned with the application of sampling theory to qualitative data. To this end, the following sections will discuss, in order, two important probability theorems, the binomial distribution, proportions, and the chi-square distribution.

TWO PROBABILITY THEOREMS

The applications discussed in the previous chapter depend only on the definition of probability formulated in Chapter 6. Other important applications can be derived, as pointed out in Chapter 6, by employing one or more of the many theorems based on this probability definition. Two of these probability theorems, the addition theorem and the multiplication theorem, will be presented now. Because this discussion will utilize the probability terminology developed in Chapter 6, the reader is advised to review pages 135–136 before continuing.

Assume that several *events* are *mutually exclusive*. According to the addition theorem for mutually exclusive events, the *probability that either 1 of 2 or more of these events will occur is the sum of the probabilities corresponding to each of the events occurring singly*. As an illustration, assume that an experiment consists of drawing a single card from a normal deck of fully shuffled playing cards. The events, a king and queen, are mutually exclusive because, if a king results from the single draw, it is impossible for the event, a queen, to occur simultaneously. However, the events, a king and a spade, are not mutually exclusive because it is possible for both events to occur simultaneously (a king of spades) on a single draw. According to the addition theorem, the probability of obtaining either a king or queen on a single draw is the sum of the probabilities corresponding to each of these events occurring singly. The probability that a king may occur is 4/52, and the probability that a queen may occur is also, in this instance, 4/52. Therefore the probability that either a king or a queen may occur is $4/52 + 4/52 = 8/52 = 2/13$. By employing the same theorem, we find the probability that either a red 3, a black 4, a 5, a king, or a queen of spades may occur on a single draw is $2/52 + 2/52 + 4/52 + 4/52 + 1/52 = 13/52 = 1/4$.

The addition theorem is concerned with whether *either one* of several events will occur in a single experiment. The multiplication theorem is concerned with whether *each of 2 or more* events will occur in a specified order in two or more experiments. The multiplication theorem that will be employed in this chapter applies specifically to *independent* events. By definition, 2 or more events are independent if the occurrence of any one of them has no effect on—that is, does not affect the probability of—the occurrence of any of the others. For example, assume that two experiments are performed, each consisting of the drawing of a single card from a deck of ordinary playing cards. Assume you desire to determine the probability of selecting a king followed by a queen. If the card selected on the first draw is replaced before the second card is drawn, the 2 events are independent. The explanation is that the probability of obtaining a queen on the second draw is in no way affected by what occurred on the first draw. The probability of obtaining a queen on the second draw will always be 4/52. Assume, now, that the card selected on the first draw is not replaced before the second card is drawn. The two events are no longer independent. The probability of obtaining a queen on the second draw now depends on what occurred on the first draw. If the first draw resulted in the selection of a queen, the probability of obtaining a queen on the second draw is 3/51. The reason is that, because the first card was not replaced, there are only 51 cards remaining and only 3 of these are queens. If, however, the first draw resulted in a card other than a queen, the probability of obtaining a queen on the second draw is 4/51. Thus, the probability of obtaining a queen on the second draw, in this instance, depends on what event occurred in the first draw.

The multiplication theorem for independent events is as follows: The *probability that each of 2 or more events will occur in a specified order is the product of the probabilities corresponding to each of the events occurring singly*. As an illustration, assume that two experiments take place, each consisting of the drawing of a single card from a full deck of ordinary playing cards. Assume, further, that the card selected on the first draw is replaced before the second card is selected. The probability of obtaining a king followed by a queen is $4/52 \times 4/52 = 16/2704 = 1/169$. The probability of obtaining a king followed by a queen, black three, and ace of spades, in that order and assuming immediate replacement after each draw, is $4/52 \times 4/52 \times 2/52 \times 1/52 = 32/7,311,616 = 1/228,488$.

The two probability theorems just presented will be employed below to develop the sampling applications of the binomial distribution.

BINOMIAL DISTRIBUTION

This section will discuss sampling applications that come under the heading of the binomial distribution. This distribution, and therefore the applications derived from it, is relevant in the analysis of qualitative data. It can be safely applied only in situations in which each of the following conditions are met:

1. All possible outcomes in a single experiment can be classified into one of two possible categories. Or, to express the idea differently, all possible outcomes in a single experiment have just one of two characteristics or distinguishing features.

2. There are only 2 possible events in a single experiment, these events being mutually exclusive.

3. The outcome of a given experiment is not influenced by that of any other experiment—that is, the outcomes of all experiments are independent.

4. The probability of each of the 2 possible events is the same in each experiment.

The following example will illustrate a situation in which the above conditions are satisfied.

A box contains 4 blue metal disks and 2 red metal disks. These 6 disks have identical physical properties (for example, they have the same shape, weight, thickness, and surfaces). An experiment consists of shaking the box and selecting, at random, a single disk. After the color of the disk is recorded, the disk is immediately replaced in the box. Because there are 6 disks in the box, each experiment has 6 possible outcomes. Each of these outcomes can be placed into only one of two categories—it is either blue or red. There are only 2 possible events in a single experiment—the occurrence of a blue disk or a red disk—and these events are mutually exclusive. If a series of experiments is performed, the probability of obtaining, for example, a blue disk is not influenced by the outcome of any other experiment. The explanation is that, because the disk selected on a particular experiment is replaced before the next experiment is performed, in each experiment one disk is always being selected from 6 disks, 4 of which are blue. Finally, the probability of each event is the same in each experiment, because there always are, for example, 4 blue disks in a total of 6 disks.

The probability of obtaining a blue disk in a single experiment is $2/3$. In evaluating this probability, the predetermined probability definition is relevant, because each of the possible outcomes is equally likely and all possible events are mutually exclusive. The 6 outcomes are equally likely because the experiment is completely random and the disks are physical duplicates, so that there is no reason, inherent in the nature of the experiment, why any one disk is more likely to be selected than any other. Because 4 of the possible 6 outcomes have the characteristic blue, the probability of obtaining a blue disk in a single experiment is $4/6 = 2/3$. Similarly, the probability of obtaining a red disk is $1/3$. As these events are mutually exclusive, the probability of obtaining either a blue or red disk on a single trial is, according to the addition theorem, $2/3 + 1/3 = 3/3 = 1 = $ absolute certainty. It will be useful, in what follows, to let p designate the probability that a particular event—for example, a blue disk—occurs on a single experiment. The expression $(1-p)$ will therefore represent the probability of obtaining a red disk. In general, if p represents the probability of obtaining a particular event in a binomial experiment, $(1-p)$ will represent the probability of obtaining the other event. In the present illustration, $p + (1 - p) = 2/3 + 1/3 = 3/3 = 1$.

Assume, now, that 2 disks are drawn, the first being replaced before the second is drawn. The probability of obtaining a blue disk on each trial is, employing the multiplication theorem, $p \cdot p = 2/3 \cdot 2/3 = 4/9$. Similarly, the probability of obtaining 0 blue disks—that is, 2 red disks—is $(1 - p) \cdot (1 - p) = 1/3 \cdot 1/3 = 1/9$. The probability of obtaining 1 blue disk cannot be determined in as straightforward a manner as the above probabilities. The probability depends on the number of ways in which just 1 blue disk can be selected in these two experiments. It should be apparent that there are just two ways: a blue followed by a red, and a red followed by a blue. These possibilities will be designated by BR and RB. The probability of obtaining a blue followed by a red is $p \cdot (1 - p) = 2/3 \cdot 1/3 = 2/9$. The probability of obtaining a red followed by a blue is $(1 - p) \cdot p = 1/3 \cdot 2/3 = 2/9$. Because these two series of events are mutually exclusive, the probability that either one of them occurs is the sum of their separate probabilities: $2/9 + 2/9 = 4/9$. Thus the probability of selecting just 1 blue disk in two draws is $4/9$. Table 8-1 summarizes the probabilities of obtaining 2, 1, or 0 blue disks in these two experiments. It is interesting to note that the sum of the probabilities of these three series of events is 1. Accordingly, you are absolutely certain to obtain either 2, 1, or 0 blue disks in two draws.

Table 8-1

	Ways in which result can occur	Probability of each way	Probability of result
Possible result			
2 blue disks	BB	4/9	4/9
1 blue disk	BR	2/9	4/9
	RB	2/9	
0 blue disks	RR	1/9	1/9
			9/9 = 1

Assume, now, that 4 disks are drawn, the disk selected on a given experiment being replaced before the next experiment is performed. The probability of obtaining 4 blue disks—that is, a blue disk on each of the four experiments—is $p \cdot p \cdot p \cdot p = 2/3 \cdot 2/3 \cdot 2/3 \cdot 2/3 = 16/81$. The probability of obtaining 1, 2, or 3 disks depends on the number of ways in which, respectively, 1, 2, or 3 disks can be selected in four experiments. One blue can be selected in any one of the following four ways: BRRR, RBRR, RRBR, RRRB. The probability of each of these ways is

$$BRRR: p \cdot (1 - p) \cdot (1 - p) \cdot (1 - p) = p(1 - p)^3 = 2/3 \cdot (1/3)^3$$
$$= 2/3 \cdot 1/27 = 2/81$$
$$RBRR: (1 - p) \cdot p \cdot (1 - p) \cdot (1 - p) = p(1 - p)^3 = 2/3 \cdot (1/3)^3$$
$$= 2/3 \cdot 1/27 = 2/81$$
$$RRBR: (1 - p) \cdot (1 - p) \cdot p \cdot (1 - p) = p(1 - p)^3 = 2/3 \cdot (1/3)^3$$
$$= 2/3 \cdot 1/27 = 2/81$$
$$RRRB: (1 - p) \cdot (1 - p) \cdot (1 - p) \cdot p = p(1 - p)^3 = 2/3 \cdot (1/3)^3$$
$$= 2/3 \cdot 1/27 = 2/81$$

With the use of the addition theorem, the probability that any one of these four series of events occurs is shown to be $8/81$. Therefore the probability of obtaining 1 blue disk is $8/81$.

Two blue disks can be selected in any one of the following six ways: BBRR, BRBR, BRRB, RRBB, RBRB, RBBR. The reader should prove to himself that there is no other sequence of 4 events that results in exactly 2 blue disks. As illustrated below, the probability of each of these series of 4 events is $4/81$, and, according to the addition theorem, the probability of obtaining 2 blue disks is $24/81$.

BBRR: $p \cdot p \cdot (1 - p) \cdot (1 - p) = p^2(1 - p)^2 = (2/3)^2(1/3)^2$
$$= 4/9 \cdot 1/9 = 4/81$$
BRBR: $p \cdot (1 - p) \cdot p \cdot (1 - p) = p^2(1 - p)^2 = (2/3)^2(1/3)^2$
$$= 4/9 \cdot 1/9 = 4/81$$
BRRB: $p \cdot (1 - p) \cdot (1 - p) \cdot p = p^2(1 - p)^2 = (2/3)^2(1/3)^2$
$$= 4/9 \cdot 1/9 = 4/81$$
RRBB: $(1 - p) \cdot (1 - p) \cdot p \cdot p = p^2(1 - p)^2 = (2/3)^2(1/3)^2$
$$= 4/9 \cdot 1/9 = 4/81$$
RBRB: $(1 - p) \cdot p \cdot (1 - p) \cdot p = p^2(1 - p)^2 = (2/3)^2(1/3)^2$
$$= 4/9 \cdot 1/9 = 4/81$$
RBBR: $(1 - p) \cdot p \cdot p \cdot (1 - p) = p^2(1 - p)^2 = (2/3)^2(1/3)^2$
$$= 4/9 \cdot 1/9 = 4/81$$

In a similar fashion, the reader should be able to show that the probability of obtaining 3 blue disks is $32/81$. Table 8-2 summarizes the probabilities of obtaining 4, 3, 2, 1, or 0 blue disks in 4 draws. The sum of these probabilities is 1, which is consistent with the obvious fact that you are absolutely certain to obtain either 4, 3, 2, 1, or 0 blue disks in 4 draws.

A General Formula

The groundwork for the derivation of the formula for a binomial probability has now been laid. It should be apparent that if a particular result can occur in several ways the probability of each of these ways is the same. For example, if 4 disks are drawn, the result (1 blue) can occur in any of the following four ways: BRRR, RBRR, RRBR, RRRB. The probability of each of these ways, as indicated in a preceding paragraph, is $2/81$. A general formula that will always give the appropriate answer in problems of this sort is $p^x \cdot (1 - p)^{n-x}$. This is the same expression that appeared several times in the previous paragraphs. In this formula, p represents the probability that the event in question occurs on a single experiment, n represents the number of experiments performed, and x represents the number of times the event is to occur in n experiments. By applying this formula to the present example, $p = 2/3$, $x = 1$, and $n = 4$, so that $p^x \cdot (1 - p)^{n-x} = (2/3)^1 \cdot (1/3)^3 = 2/81$. This is the same answer obtained above. Note that $(1 - p)$ is just another expression for the probability of obtaining a red disk, and $(n - x)$ is just another expression for the number of times a red disk is to occur.

A formula has been developed that will give the *probability* of *one* of the ways in which the particular result can occur. Can a formula also be developed that will give the *number* of ways in which the particular result

Table 8-2

	Ways in which result can occur	Probability of each way	Probability of result
Possible result			
4 blue disks	BBBB	16/81	16/81
3 blue disks	BBBR	8/81	
	BBRB	8/81	
	BRBB	8/81	32/81
	RBBB	8/81	
2 blue disks	BBRR	4/81	
	BRBR	4/81	
	BRRB	4/81	
	RRBB	4/81	24/81
	RBRB	4/81	
	RBBR	4/81	
1 blue disk	BRRR	2/81	
	RBRR	2/81	
	RRBR	2 81	8/81
	RRRB	2/81	
0 blue disks	RRRR	1/81	$\dfrac{1/81}{81/81 = 1}$

can occur? The answer is "yes." In practice, it is not necessary to list all possibilities separately. In other words, because each of the different ways has the same probability, binomial probabilities can be determined directly from a formula. The formula that gives the number of ways in which a particular result can occur is

$$\frac{n!}{(n - x)!x!} \quad {}^{1}$$

[1] This is the general formula for the number of distinguishable permutations of n objects, x of one kind and $n - x$ of another kind.

The symbol, $n!$, is read "n factorial," and designates a mathematical operation in which n, which can be any positive number, is multiplied by a series of numbers, each number in the series having a value that is one less than the number preceding it, the last number in the series being 1. By definition, 0! is equal to 1. For example, if n is 5, $n!$ would be $5 \times 4 \times 3 \times 2 \times 1 = 120$. If n is 15, x is 11, and therefore $n - x$ is 4, then $(n - x)!$ would be $4 \times 3 \times 2 \times 1 = 24$. The number of ways that 2 blue disks can be selected in four experiments would thus be

$$\frac{n!}{(n - x)!x!} = \frac{4!}{2!2!} = \frac{4 \times 3 \times 2 \times 1}{2 \times 1 \times 2 \times 1} = 6$$

The general formula for a binomial probability can be obtained by combining the formulas developed in the last two paragraphs. It is $B = \frac{n!}{(n - x)!x!} p^x(1 - p)^{n-x}$. For example, the probability of obtaining 2 blue disks can be calculated directly as

$$B = \frac{4!}{2!2!} \cdot \left(\frac{2}{3}\right)^2 \cdot \left(\frac{1}{3}\right)^2 = \frac{24}{4} \cdot \frac{4}{9} \cdot \frac{1}{9} = \frac{96}{324} = \frac{24}{81}$$

This answer, of course, agrees with that obtained above for the same problem. Similarly, if 6 disks are drawn from a bowl containing 150 blue and 50 red disks, the probability of obtaining 4 blue disks is[2]

$$B = \frac{n!}{(n - x)!x!} p^x(1 - p)^{n-x} = \frac{6!}{2!4!} \left(\frac{3}{4}\right)^4 \left(\frac{1}{4}\right)^2 = \frac{1215}{4096} = .2966$$

Some Applications

To see how binomial probabilities can be applied to different situations, assume that it is known that 70 percent of the 300,000 people listed in the Boston, Massachusetts, telephone directory are males. Obviously, 30 percent, or 90,000 people, are females. Assume, further, that a market-research team is seeking people to interview. What is the probability that a sample of 5 people randomly selected from the telephone directory will contain 3 females? Binomial probabilities can be used to answer this question because the four conditions specified at the beginning of the section on the binomial distribution are satisfied.

This can be readily seen if the selection of each of the 5 persons in the sample is viewed as a single experiment, so that five experiments are performed. Then all the approximately 300,000 possible outcomes in each experiment can be classified into one of two possible categories (male or

---

[2] Assume, of course, that each disk is replaced after each draw. Because there are 200 disks and because 150 of these are blue, the probability of selecting a blue disk on a single draw is $^{150}/_{200} = \frac{3}{4}$.

female). Only 2 events (male or female) can occur in a single experiment, and these are mutually exclusive. All events being considered are, practically speaking, independent. This final condition holds because the sample size is so small relative to the population size. For example, even if the first 4 persons selected are females, the probability of selecting a female on the fifth experiment is still approximately 30 percent (there would be 299,996 people left to choose from, and 89,996, or 89,996/299,996 = .29999 $\cong$ .3 = 30 percent, of them are females. Similarly, the probability of selecting a male on the fifth trial is still approximately 70 percent (210,000/299,996 = .70001 $\cong$ .7). The reader should satisfy himself that the probabilities of selecting a male or female on the second, third, or fourth experiment are even closer, respectively, to 70 or 30 percent.

The probability of obtaining 3 females in this sample of 5 can be determined, therefore, by employing the formula for a binomial probability just developed. This probability is

$$\frac{n!}{(n-x)!x!}\, p^x(1-p)^{n-x} = \frac{5!}{2!3!}\,.3^3(.7)^2 = \frac{120}{12}\,(.027)\,.49 = .1323$$

What is the probability of obtaining a majority of females in this sample? A majority occurs if there are *either* 3, 4, *or* 5 females in the sample. These three series of events are mutually exclusive because if, for example, 3 of the 5 persons are females, the possibility that 4 or 5 of them are females is automatically excluded. This means that the addition theorem of probability can be employed to determine the probability that any one of the three series will occur. The reader will recall, from the beginning of this chapter, that this probability is the sum of the probabilities corresponding to each of the events occurring singly. The probability of selecting exactly 3 females was just determined to be .1323. The probability of selecting 4 females is similarly calculated as

$$\frac{5!}{1!4!}\,(.3)^4(.7)^1 = .0284$$

and the probability of selecting 5 females is

$$\frac{5!}{0!5!}\,(.3)^5(.7)^0 = .0024$$

The probability of selecting 3, 4, or 5 females—that is, the probability of obtaining a female majority—is therefore .1323 + .0284 + .0024 = .1631.

As another illustration of the use of binomial probabilities, assume that a supplier of electronic tubes guarantees a manufacturer that not more than 10 percent of any lot shipped will be defective. A lot of 2,000 tubes is shipped, and a sample of 4 tubes is selected at random. Three of these are found to be defective. If you were the manufacturer, would you accept or reject the entire lot? Assume that your decision must be based entirely on the results of this one sample.

As a starting point, note that the supplier indicated that, at most, 10 percent would be defective. Pose the hypothesis that exactly 10 percent of the 2000 tubes are defective. The results of the procedure to be presented will hold, even more strongly, if actually fewer than 10 percent of the tubes are defective. The crucial question, then, is, "What is the probability of obtaining as many as 3 defective tubes in a sample of 4 selected at random from a population in which 10 percent of the tubes are defective?"

This problem satisfies the conditions necessary for the application of binomial probabilities. First, the 2,000 possible outcomes (corresponding to the 2,000 tubes that could be selected) can be placed in just one of two possible categories (defective or not defective). Second, just 2 mutually exclusive events—a defective or a good tube—are possible in each experiment (an experiment being represented by the selection of a single tube). Third, the events are independent, because the sample size (4) is small relative to the population (2,000). The probability of obtaining exactly 3 defectives is therefore

$$\frac{4!}{1!3!} (.1)^3 (.9)^1 = \frac{24}{6} (.001)(.9) = .0036$$

The probability of obtaining 3 or more defectives is equal to the probability of obtaining either 3 or 4 defectives. The reader should verify that the probability of obtaining 4 defectives is .0001. The probability of obtaining 3 or more defectives in a sample of 4 is therefore .0036 + .0001 = .0037.

If the hypothesis is true—that is, if the population is 10-percent defective—a result as bad as (or worse than) the one actually obtained would be expected only .37 percent of the time. The reader should verify that if the number of defectives in the population is actually less than 10 percent (for example, 8 percent), the probability of obtaining the above result would be even more remote. Because the probability derived is less than the normal significance levels of 5 percent and 1 percent, the hypothesis is rejected. In other words, the manufacturer would conclude that the population is really more than 10-percent defective, and on this basis he would reject the entire lot.

Mean and Standard Deviation of the Binomial Distribution

In a previous section, the random selection of disks from a bowl was discussed. There were 6 disks in the bowl, 4 blue and 2 red, and after each draw the disk selected was immediately replaced, so that successive draws were always made from a bowl containing exactly 6 disks. Assume that 10 draws are made and that the number of blue disks obtained is recorded. This number could be any value between 0 and 10. Assume that 10 more draws are made and the number of blue disks obtained recorded. Assume that this process is repeated 10,000 times. A frequency distribution could be set up that would indicate the number of times that 0 blue disks were obtained in a series of 10 draws, the number of times that 1 blue disk was obtained, and so on up to the number of times that 10 blue disks were obtained in 10 draws. It is meaningful, in this situation, to ask how many

Table 8-3. HYPOTHETICAL RESULTS OF TEN THOUSAND SAMPLES OF TEN DISKS EACH FROM A POPULATION, TWO THIRDS OF WHICH CONTAIN BLUE DISKS AND ONE THIRD RED DISKS
(Assuming Replacement)

No. of blue disks in a sample of 10 disks X	*No. of samples in which specified no. of blue disks was obtained* f	fx
0	0	0
1	3	3
2	30	60
3	163	489
4	569	2276
5	1367	6835
6	2276	13656
7	2601	18207
8	1951	15608
9	867	7803
10	173	1730
	10,000	66,667

$$\mu = \frac{\Sigma fx}{\Sigma f} = \frac{66,667}{10,000} = 6.6667$$

blue disks were obtained *on the average* over the 10,000 sets of 10 draws each. That is, what is the mean number of blue disks obtained in the 10,000 sets of 10 draws?

This arithmetic mean could be calculated in the usual way from the frequency distribution constructed from the results of the 10,000 sets of 10 draws. Assume that these results are as presented in Table 8–3. The mean number of blue disks is calculated to be 6.67. In a similar fashion, the standard deviation of this distribution could be calculated.

It can be mathematically proved that as the number of sets of draws is increased both the mean and standard deviation of the resulting frequency distributions approach a specific value. That is, assume that first 50, then 100, then 1000, then 5000, and so on, sets of 10 draws are made. Assume that the mean and standard deviation of the distribution composed of 50 sets of draws is computed. Then assume that the mean and standard deviation of the remaining distributions are computed. As the number of sets of draws increases from 50 to 100, 1000, and so on, both the mean and standard deviation computed from the resulting distributions will be successively closer to a specific value. These two values are called, respectively, the mean and standard deviation of the binomial distribution.

In practice, it is not necessary to perform, for example, 1 million sets of experiments in order to determine approximately the mean and standard deviation of a particular binomial distribution. It can be mathematically proved that the mean (denoted by μ_B) and standard deviation (denoted by σ_B) of a binomial distribution can be determined, respectively, from the following formulas:

$$\mu_B = np$$
$$\sigma_B = \sqrt{np(1 - p)}$$

As before, p is the probability that a particular event occurs, and n is the number of items in the sample, or, expressed differently, the number of experiments performed (draws made) in a single series or set. For example, in the situation just described, $p = 2/3$ and $n = 10$; in the electronic-tube situation, $p = .1$ and $n = 4$; and in the interviewing situation, $p = .3$ and $n = 5$. Thus, μ_B and σ_B for a particular binomial distribution depend entirely on p and n.

The interviewing situation described earlier will be utilized to illustrate the application of these formulas. In this illustration, $n = 5$ and $p = .3$. If an extremely large number of samples of size 5 is taken,[3] on the average the number of females in each sample will be $np = 5(.3) = 1.5$, and the standard deviation will be $\sqrt{np(1 - p)} = \sqrt{5(.3).7} = \sqrt{1.05} = 1.02$

The usefulness of these formulas will become particularly evident after examination of the next section.

Normal Curve Approximation to the Binomial

A bowl contains 6 disks that are identical physically. Three are blue and 3 red. This is exactly the situation described earlier, except that there are 3 instead of 4 blue disks, the probability, p, of obtaining a blue disk therefore being ½ instead of ⅔. Table 8-4 shows the probability of obtaining 0, 1, or 2 blue disks if a sample of 2 is selected at random with

[3] Assume that the 5 names drawn in each sample are replaced after each sample is taken so that the number of items in the population is always 300,000 before each new sample is taken.

replacement. Table 8-4 also shows the probability of obtaining 0, 1, · · ·, 6 blue disks if a sample of 6 is selected, 0, 1, · · ·, 12 blue disks if a sample of 12 is selected, and 0, 1, · · ·, 20 blue disks if a sample of 20 is selected. These probabilities are calculated, of course, from the binomial formula

Table 8-4.   PROBABILITIES OF OBTAINING 0, 1, 2, · · ·, TWENTY BLUE DISKS IN SAMPLES OF TWO, SIX, TWELVE AND TWENTY DISKS SELECTED FROM A POPULATION IN WHICH 50 PERCENT OF THE DISKS ARE BLUE

n = 2		n = 6		n = 12		n = 20	
No. of blue disks in sample	Prob- ability	No. of blue disks in sample	Prob- ability	No. of blue disks in sample	Prob- ability	No. of blue disks in sample	Prob- ability
0	.2500	0	.0156	0	.0002	0	.0000
1	.5000	1	.0938	1	.0029	1	.0000
2	.2500	2	.2344	2	.0161	2	.0002
		3	.3125	3	.0537	3	.0011
		4	.2344	4	.1208	4	.0046
		5	.0938	5	.1934	5	.0148
		6	.0156	6	.2256	6	.0370
				7	.1934	7	.0739
				8	.1208	8	.1201
				9	.0537	9	.1602
				10	.0161	10	.1762
				11	.0029	11	.1602
				12	.0002	12	.1201
						13	.0739
						14	.0370
						15	.0148
						16	.0046
						17	.0011
						18	.0002
						19	.0000
						20	.0000

developed earlier. Assume that 10,000 samples of sizes 2, 6, 12, and 20 are taken. Table 8-5, which is based on the probabilities shown in Table 8-4, shows the expected number of samples that will have 1, 2, and so on, blue disks for each of the four sample sizes. For example, because the probability of obtaining 2 blue disks in a single sample of 6 disks is .2344, the expected number of samples, out of 10,000 samples, that will have 2 blue

Table 8-5.   EXPECTED RESULTS OF TEN THOUSAND SAMPLES OF TWO DISKS EACH, SIX DISKS EACH, TWELVE DISKS EACH, AND TWENTY DISKS EACH FROM A POPULATION IN WHICH 50 PERCENT OF THE DISKS ARE BLUE

(Assuming Replacement)

	$n = 2$		$n = 6$		$n = 12$		$n = 20$
No. of blue disks in sample	No. of samples in which specified no. of blue disks was obtained	No. of blue disks in sample	No. of samples in which specified no. of blue disks was obtained	No. of blue disks in sample	No. of samples in which specified no. of blue disks was obtained	No. of blue disks in sample	No. of samples in which specified no. of blue disks was obtained
0	2,500	0	156	0	2	0	0
1	5,000	1	938	1	29	1	0
2	2,500	2	2,344	2	161	2	2
		3	3,125	3	537	3	11
		4	2,344	4	1,208	4	46
		5	938	5	1,934	5	148
		6	156	6	2,256	6	370
				7	1,934	7	739
				8	1,208	8	1,201
				9	537	9	1,602
				10	161	10	1,762
				11	29	11	1,602
				12	2	12	1,201
						13	739
						14	370
						15	148
						16	46
						17	11
						18	2
						19	0
						20	0

FIGURE 8–1

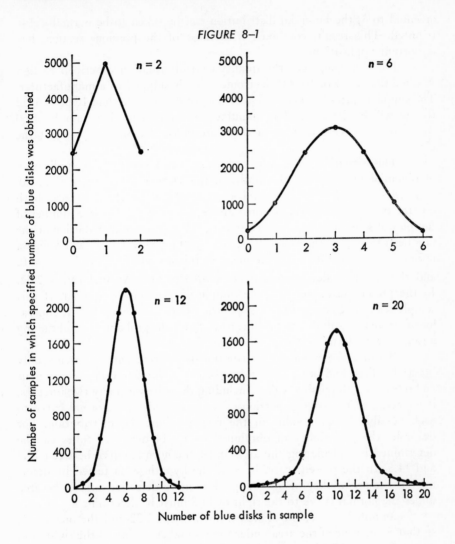

Number of blue disks in sample

disks is .2344 × 10,000 = 2,344. Figure 8-1 shows the frequency distributions of Table 8-5 graphically. It is obvious that, as the sample size increases, the shape of the frequency distribution definitely tends to approach more and more that of a normal curve.

This apparent tendency can be generalized. It can be mathematically proved that, for a given p, as the sample size increases the binomial distribution resembles more and more closely a normal curve. The closer p is to .5, the smaller the sample size necessary to achieve a close resemblance to the normal curve. In practice, a workable rule is that if n is greater than or equal to 50 *and* if np and $n(1 - p)$ are both greater than or equal to 5, the binomial distribution can be taken to be normally distributed. This result, combined with those of the previous section, has important applications.

For example, take the quality-control situation described earlier. Assume that a lot of 10,000 electronic tubes is shipped to a manufacturer. The supplier states, as a condition of sale, that not more than 10 percent of the lot will be defective. The manufacturer takes a random sample of 60 tubes and discovers that 14 of them are defective. Should he reject the entire lot?

This situation meets the conditions necessary for the application of binomial probabilities. In addition, the sample size is more than 50, and $np = 60 \times .1 = 6$, and $n(1 - p) = 60 \times (1 - .1) = 54$ are both greater than 5. Therefore, as noted above, if an extremely large number of samples of size 60 is selected at random, the frequency distribution of the number of samples that have $0, 1, 2, \cdots, 60$ defective tubes will follow a normal curve. Furthermore, the mean of this distribution will be $np = 6$, and the standard deviation will be $\sqrt{np(1 - p)} = \sqrt{60(.1)(.9)} = 2.32$. In the present example, just one sample of 60 items is selected. If this sample really does come from a population that is .1 defective, or, equivalently, from a population with a mean 6, what is the probability of obtaining a sample with 14 or more defective tubes?

Because the binomial distribution is discrete and represents only integral values, and because its normal curve approximation is continuous and represents all possible values including those between any two integers, it is necessary to assign a portion of the area under the normal curve to each possible integral value in the relevant binomial distribution. For example, the probability of obtaining *exactly* 14 defective tubes can be determined by calculating the area under the normal curve between 13.5 and 14.5. In the present case, because the hypothesis is tested by determining the probability of obtaining 14 or more defective tubes, the area under the normal curve to the right of 13.5 must be determined.

As noted above, the standard deviation is 2.32 and the mean is 6, so that 50 percent of the area under the normal curve lies to the right of 6. The difference of 7.5 between 13.5 and 6 therefore represents 3.23 standard deviations. The table of areas under a normal curve (Appendix Table IV) shows that the probability of obtaining a value as high as this if the hypothesis is true is .0006. Because this probability is less than the usual significance levels of .05 and .01, the hypothesis would be rejected. The manufacturer would conclude that the number of defectives in the entire lot is more than the specified 10 percent. A one-tailed test was employed because the manufacturer is interested only in determining whether the percentage of defectives is significantly *greater* than .1. If the percentage is less than .1, the quality obtained would be higher than the minimum specified in the contract, and the manufacturer would have no cause for rejecting the lot.

As a final example, take the market-research situation described earlier. Thirty percent of the people listed in the Boston telephone directory are known to be females. If a sample of 100 is selected at random, what is the probability of obtaining a majority of females? A female majority occurs if 51 or more of the people in the sample are females. Because $n = 100$ is greater than 50, and because $np = 30$ and $n(1 - p) = 70$ are both greater than 5, if an extremely large number of samples of size 100 is selected at random, the distribution of the number of females in each sample will follow a normal curve. The mean of this normal curve is $np = 30$, and the standard deviation is $\sqrt{np(1 - p)} = \sqrt{100(.3)(.7)} = 4.58$. The probability of obtaining 51 or more females in a single sample can therefore be determined by calculating the percentage of the area under the normal curve to the right of 50.5. The difference between the mean of 30 and the value 50.5 is 20.5. This difference represents 4.48 standard deviation $(20.5 \div 4.58 = 4.48)$. The 4.48 standard deviations correspond to virtually 50 percent of the area under a normal curve. That is to say, approximately 0 percent of the area lies to the right of 50.5, and therefore it is practically impossible to obtain a female majority in a single sample of 100 people.

The following two sections will continue the discussion of the application of sampling theory to qualitative data. The sampling distribution of a proportion will be examined first.

PROPORTIONS

The previous section was mainly concerned with determining the probability that a specific *number* of items, out of a sample of n items, would possess a particular characteristic. For example, in a sample of 100 people, what is the probability that 51 are female? Or in a sample of 60 electronic tubes, what is the probability that 14 are defective? A very closely related problem situation is one in which the question is, "What is the probability that, in a sample of 100 people, .51, or 51 percent, are female?" Or, in a sample of 60 tubes, "What is the probability that .17, or 17 percent, are defective?" The major interest in these situations is, not the *number* of items in a sample that have a particular characteristic, but the *proportion* of items.

Take the by now very familiar situation of the bowl containing 6 disks. Assume that 3 of these are blue and 3 red. The population proportion of blue disks, therefore, is $\frac{3}{6} = .5$. Assume, as before, that 10,000

Table 8-6. *EXPECTED RESULTS OF TEN THOUSAND SAMPLES OF TWENTY DISKS EACH FROM A POPULATION IN WHICH 50 PERCENT OF THE DISKS ARE BLUE*
(Assuming Replacement)

(1)	(2)	(3)	(4)	(5)	(6)	(7)
X No. of blue disks in sample	P = X/20 Proportion of blue disks in sample	No. of samples (f) in which specified no. and proportion occured	fP	$(P - \bar{P})$	$(P - \bar{P})^2$	$f(P - \bar{P})^2$
0	.00	0	.00	− .50	.2500	.0000
1	.05	0	.00	− .45	.2025	.0000
2	.10	2	.20	− .40	.1600	.3200
3	.15	11	1.65	− .35	.1225	1.3475
4	.20	46	9.20	− .30	.0900	4.1400
5	.25	148	37.00	− .25	.0625	9.2500
6	.30	370	111.00	− .20	.0400	14.8000
7	.35	739	258.65	− .15	.0225	16.6275
8	.40	1201	480.40	− .10	.0100	12.0100
9	.45	1602	720.90	− .05	.0025	4.0050
10	.50	1762	881.00	.00	0	.0000
11	.55	1602	881.10	.05	.0025	4.0050
12	.60	1201	720.60	.10	.0100	12.0100
13	.65	739	480.35	.15	.0225	16.6275
14	.70	370	259.00	.20	.0400	14.8000
15	.75	148	111.00	.25	.0625	9.2500
16	.80	46	36.80	.30	.0900	4.1400
17	.85	11	9.35	.35	.1225	1.3475
18	.90	2	1.80	.40	.1600	.3200
19	.95	0	.00	.45	.2025	.0000
20	1.00	0	.00	.50	.2500	.0000
		10,000	5,000.00			125.0000

$\bar{P} = \Sigma f P / \Sigma f = 5,000/10,000 = .5$ $\sigma = \sqrt{\Sigma f(P - \bar{P})^2/\Sigma f} = \sqrt{125/10000} = .0125$

samples of 20 disks each are selected[4] and that the number of blue disks in each sample is recorded. Table 8-5 summarizes the expected frequency distribution reflecting the number of blue disks obtained in each of the 10,000 samples. The proportion of blue disks in each sample is obtained

[4] Again, each disk is immediately replaced after each draw.

simply by dividing the number of blue disks obtained by the sample size, which, in this instance, is 20. For example, 46 of the samples contained 4 blue disks, and therefore in 46 of the samples the proportion of blue disks will be $\frac{4}{20} = \frac{1}{5} = .20$. The results of these divisions are presented in Table 8-6 (columns 1–3).

In Figure 8-2, the graph of the frequency distribution of the *number* of blue disks obtained (columns 1 and 3, Table 8-6) is compared with the graph of the frequency distribution of the *proportion* of blue disks obtained (columns 2 and 3, Table 8-6). It is apparent that both graphs have the same shape and both tend to be normally distributed. In fact, if the sample size were as large as 50, the graphs would be almost perfect replicas of normal curves. As this statement implies, if the distribution of the *number* of blue disks is normally distributed, the distribution of the *proportion* of blue disks will be normally distributed. Because the number of disks is normally distributed when $n \geq 50$, $np \geq 5$, and $n(1 - p) \geq 5$, the proportion of blue disks will be normally distributed when these same conditions are met. The distribution of the proportion, constructed in this way, is called the sampling distribution of a proportion. This concept, of course, is identical with that of previous chapters relating to the sampling distribution of the mean or of the difference between means.

Table 8-6 also shows the calculation of the mean and the standard deviation of the distribution of proportions (columns 1-7). These measures are calculated in the usual manner:

$$\bar{P} = \frac{\Sigma fP}{\Sigma f} = .5, \sigma = \sqrt{\frac{\Sigma f(P - \bar{P})^2}{\Sigma f}} = \sqrt{.0125}$$

Here, P represents the value of a typical item in the distribution—namely, a proportion—$\bar{P}$ represents the mean proportion, f represents the number of samples in which the particular P value was observed, and Σf represents the number of samples taken. Fortunately, it is not necessary to take 10,000 samples in order to approximate the mean and standard deviation of a distribution of proportions. As before, let n designate the number of items (for example, disks) in each sample, and let p designate the probability of obtaining, for example, a blue disk in a single experiment (that is, the proportion of blue disks in the population). Further, let μ_p and σ_p designate, respectively, the mean and standard deviation of a sampling distribution of proportions. Then it can be mathematically proved that these measures can be calculated from the following formulas:

$$\mu_p = p$$
$$\sigma_p = \sqrt{\frac{p(1 - p)}{n}}$$

simply by finding the number of blue disks that fall in class sizes which are in this interval, 9, 10, 11, . . . out of the 100 samples. [illegible] 4 blue disks, and thus have most of their samples who seek [illegible] blue disks with limits 9, 10 at 20. The results of such a count are given in Table 8–2 (column 5).

FIGURE 8–2

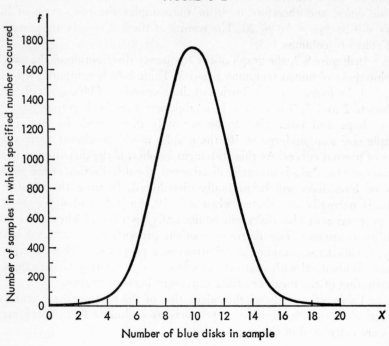

Number of blue disks in sample

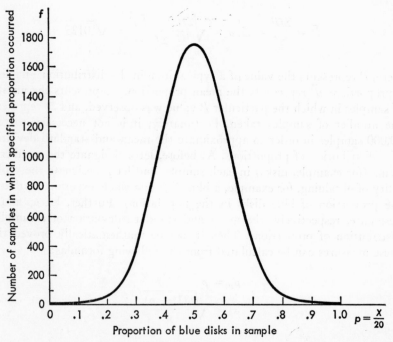

Proportion of blue disks in sample $p = \dfrac{X}{20}$

The reader may more easily recall and understand these formulas if he notes that the distribution of proportions was derived by dividing the number of blue disks in each sample in the original (binomial) distribution by n. The formulas given above can also be derived by dividing the corresponding formulas for the original (binomial) distribution by n. The next two sections will show how these formulas can be productively applied to problems involving tests of significance and confidence intervals.

Tests of Significance

In general, the conditions that must be satisfied before the formulas relating to proportions can be applied are the same as those relating to the binomial distribution. These have been stated earlier and will not be repeated here. The same problem situations introduced to illustrate the application of the binomial distribution will be employed to illustrate the applications of the sampling distribution of a proportion.

Assume that last year 30 percent of the people listed in the Boston telephone directory were females. Has this proportion changed over the year? To answer this question, pose the hypothesis that the population proportion is .3 today. Take a sample of, for instance, 100. Assume that the sample proportion is .1. What is the probability that, in a sample of 100 people, .1 of them are females if the hypothetical population proportion is .3? To express it another way, what is the probability of obtaining a difference as large as (or larger than) .2 (.3 − .1 = .2) between the hypothetical proportion and the sample proportion in a sample of 100?

Because $n > 50$, $np > 5$, and $n(1 - p) > 5$, the sampling distribution of the proportion is normally distributed. The mean of this distribution is $\mu_p = p = .3$, and the standard deviation is $\sigma_p = \sqrt{p(1 - p)/n} = \sqrt{.3(.7)/100} = .0458$. The difference between the hypothetical proportion and the sample proportion is therefore 4.37 standard deviations (.2 ÷ .0458 = 4.37). The table of areas under a normal curve shows that the probability of obtaining a difference as great as this is much less than 1 percent. Therefore the hypothesis would be rejected. The proportion of females in the population is significantly different from .3.

As a second example, assume that a manufacturer receives a shipment of 10,000 electronic tubes. Assume he takes a sample of 60 tubes and finds that .17, or 17 percent, are defective. The contract specifies that not more than .1 may be defective. Should the lot be rejected? In this situation, $\sigma_p = \sqrt{.1(.9)/60} = .0387$. The difference between the hypothetical and sample proportions, .17 − .1 = .07, represents 1.81 standard deviations. The difference is too great to be attributable to sampling variation, and the lot would be rejected at the 5-percent significance level, assuming that a one-tailed test is employed (it would be accepted if a two-tailed test were used).

Confidence Intervals

In tests of significance, a population proportion is assumed and the sample result is compared to the hypothetical or assumed population proportion. Assume, now, that no assumption is made regarding the population proportion, and that the sample result is to be employed to estimate the population proportion. The procedure introduced in the previous chapter will be followed. That is, a confidence level is first specified. Assume this to be 95 percent. Then 1.96 standard deviations is added to, and subtracted from, the sample proportion. This procedure, remember, is valid only if the distribution of proportions is normal. As pointed out several times earlier, if $n \geq 50$, $np \geq 5$, and $n(1 - p) \geq 5$, the distribution will be normal. The limits determined by adding and subtracting 1.96 standard deviations make up the 95-percent confidence interval for the population proportion.[5]

For example, assume that a market-research team wants to know what proportion of the people listed in the Boston telephone directory are females. A sample of 100 is selected at random, and .2, or 20 percent, are females. According to the procedure outlined above, 1.96 standard deviations should be added to, and subtracted from this value. But the formula for the standard deviation, $\sigma_p = \sqrt{p(1 - p)/n}$, requires the population proportion, and this is unknown. The sample proportion is therefore employed as an estimate of the population proportion. The standard deviation is then calculated as $\sigma_p = \sqrt{.2(.8)/100} = \sqrt{.0016} = .04$. The research team would be 95-percent confident that the population proportion is between $.2 - 1.96(.04) = .2 - .0784 = .1216$ and $.2 + 1.96(.04) = .2 + .0784 = .2784$.

CHI-SQUARE DISTRIBUTION

The chi-square distribution has very many applications in situations that involve the testing of hypotheses concerning discrete or qualitative

---

[5] Strictly speaking, the limits determined in this way must be interpreted as a very close approximation to the true confidence limits. The reason is that the formula for the standard deviation requires knowledge of the population proportion, and this is unknown. If the sample proportion is substituted for the population proportion in this formula, and the confidence limits constructed in the usual way, the limits so derived will typically be very close to the true limits. The true upper and lower limits can be calculated, respectively, from the rather complex formulas:

$$\text{upper limit} = \frac{2p + z^2/n + \sqrt{z^2/n[4p(1 - p) + z^2/n]}}{2(1 + z^2/n)}$$

$$\text{lower limit} = \frac{2p + z^2/n - \sqrt{z^2/n[4p(1 - p) + z^2/n]}}{2(1 + z^2/n)}$$

In these formulas, z equals 1.96 for a 95-percent confidence level, 2.58 for a 99-percent confidence level, and so forth.

data. The general procedure is to

1. Formulate a hypothesis
2. Determine the number of times that each of several events would be *expected* to occur if the hypothesis were true, each number being termed an "expected frequency"
3. Record the number of times that each of the several events *actually* occurred, each such number being termed an "actual frequency"
4. If there is a difference between the actual and expected frequencies, determine the probability that such a difference will occur if the hypothesis is, in fact, true, and accept or reject the hypothesis by comparing this probability to the usual significance levels
5. Determine the probability referred to above by computing the measure defined, below, as chi-square and given the symbol χ^2

The following examples will illustrate this general procedure. As in previous sections, the first example has been picked in order to emphasize certain theoretical aspects of the general problem situation. Later examples stress business applications.

A Theoretical Example

Assume that a bowl contains 10 metal disks that are identical except for color, 2 being red, 2 white, 2 blue, 2 black, and 2 green. A sample of 100 is selected at random. As in previous examples, each disk is immediately replaced after each draw so that there are always 10 disks in the bowl before each draw. Because each color is equally represented in the population before each draw, the expectation is that each color should be equally represented in each sample. Thus, in a sample of 100 items, the expectation is that each color should be selected 20 times. That is, if many hundreds of samples of 100 disks are selected, the *average* number of red disks in each sample will be 20, the *average* number of blue disks will be 20, and similarly for the remaining three colors. Nonetheless, in any *one* sample, the five colors may not be equally represented; if they are not, the sample will reflect the play of chance. The actual number of disks of each color, however, should not be too different from 20. An objective measure of what is "too different" is provided by the chi-square distribution.

Let f_e, signifying "expected frequency," represent the number of times that each event is expected to occur in a single sample of n items. In the present illustration, there are 5 possible events—the selection of a red, white, blue, black, or green disk. n equals 100. And f_e equals 20 for the number of red disks expected in a single sample of 100 items, 20 for the number of blue disks, and similarly for the other three colors. Let f_a, signifying "actual frequency," represent the actual number of times that each event occurs in a sample of n items. Assume, now, that a single sample of 100 disks is taken and that the results are as shown in the first two columns of Table 8-7. Calculate for each possible event the measure $(f_a - f_e)^2/f_e$. Table 8-7 also shows this set of calculations. The sum of these measures for all possible events is given the symbol χ^2 and referred to as the chi-square value. Thus, by definition, $\chi^2 = \Sigma[(f_a - f_e)^2/f_e]$. The last column of Table 8-7 shows that in the present example $\chi^2 = .50$.

On examining the formula for χ^2, it is apparent that, for each event, the closer the actual frequency, f_a, is to the expected frequency, f_e, the smaller is their difference, $f_a - f_e$, the smaller is the numerator in the formula for χ^2, and the smaller is χ^2. Now, if the hypothesis relating to a particular problem is correctly stated, f_a will typically be very close to f_e.

Table 8-7. HYPOTHETICAL RESULTS OF SAMPLE OF ONE HUNDRED DISKS SELECTED, WITH REPLACEMENT, FROM A POPULATION CONTAINING AN EQUAL NUMBER OF RED, WHITE, BLUE, BLACK, AND GREEN DISKS

	Actual no. of disks of specified color in sample f_a	*Expected no. of disks of specified color in sample* f_e	$f_a - f_e$	$(f_a - f_e)^2/f_e$
Color of disk				
red	21	20	1	.05
white	19	20	−1	.05
blue	20	20	0	.00
black	18	20	−2	.20
green	22	20	2	.20
	100	100	0	.50

Thus, if the hypothesis is correct, the expected value of χ^2 will be relatively small. If the hypothesis is incorrect, f_a will typically be very different from f_e, and χ^2 will be relatively large. As this statement implies, the larger the value of χ^2, the smaller the probability that the particular hypothesis is true.

The probability of obtaining a particular χ^2 value, if the particular hypothesis is true, can be mathematically determined. In problems such as these, the distribution that shows the probabilities of obtaining all possible χ^2 values is called the chi-square distribution. Tables have been prepared (for example, see Appendix Table VI) that show the χ^2 values which would occur a certain percentage (for example, 5 percent, 1 percent) of the time if the hypothesis is true.

In order to use these tables, the number of "degrees of freedom" relevant to the problem must be determined. The reader will recall this term from the discussion of the t distribution in the previous chapter. In situations in which the chi-square distribution is applied, the number of degrees of freedom is determined as follows. If all the possible events, and therefore all the actual frequencies (f_a), are arranged in a *single* row or a *single* column, the number of degrees of freedom is equal to the number of possible events minus one. In the present example involving metal disks, there are 5 possible events and 5 possible actual frequencies, and these are arranged in a single column (Table 8-7). The number of degrees of freedom for this problem is therefore $5 - 1 = 4$. Often, in problems involving the chi-square distribution, the possible events are arranged in several rows and columns rather than in a single row or column. For such problems, the number of degrees of freedom is determined differently. How the calculation is made will be discussed in a later section.

The procedure, outlined at the beginning of this section, for testing hypotheses involving the chi-square distribution will now be illustrated, with the use of the example above. First, a hypothesis is formulated, as follows: "The five colors—red, white, blue, black, and green—are equally represented in the population." Second, the expected frequencies for each of the 5 possible events are determined. If the hypothesis is true, there should be, on the average, an equal number of disks representing each color in the sample; if a sample of 100 items is selected, there should be, therefore, $100 \div 5 = 20$ disks representing each color. Third, a sample is taken and the actual number of disks representing each color is recorded. Hypothetical results are shown in Table 8-7. Fourth and fifth, the probability of obtaining the observed differences between the expected and actual frequencies is determined by computing χ^2, determining the relevant number of degrees of freedom, and examining Appendix Table VI.

As shown in Table 8-7, $\chi^2 = .50$. The number of degrees of freedom was shown, in a previous paragraph, to be 4. The computed value of χ^2, .50, is therefore located, in Appendix Table VI, in the row corresponding to 4 degrees of freedom. The two χ^2 values in the proper row in the Appendix Table that are closest to it are .429 and .711, the former being lower and the latter being higher. A value as high as .429 would occur 98 percent of the time and a value as high as .711 would occur 95 percent of the time. Because the computed value of χ^2 lies between these two values, it would occur between 98 and 95 percent of the time. Because these probabilities are well above the usual significance levels of 5 and 1 percent, the hypothesis would be accepted in this example. This is as it should be, as the hypothesis was known to be true at the outset—that is, each color was known to be equally represented in the bowl.

Needless to say, in practical applications a sample is taken in the first place because the true nature of the population is not known for certain. The purpose of the sample is to test some hypothesis concerning the unknown population. Examples of such situations will now be discussed.

An Example from Personnel

A firm is in the process of deciding which of four salesmen it should promote to the position of sales manager. Each salesman has about the same background and experience, and the sales territory of each has about the same sales potential. In this situation, the firm feels that the performance of the salesmen in the field should be compared, the job of sales manager going to the salesman with the best selling record. However, even if all the salesmen had equal ability, their records should be expected to differ simply because of the play of chance. The question that the firm must answer, therefore, is whether the selling records of some of the salesmen are significantly better than those of others. If there is no significant difference between the selling records, the firm must look for another criterion on which to base the selection of one man for promotion.

Table 8-8.   SALES RECORDS OF FOUR SALESMEN

	Actual average weekly sales f_a	Expected average weekly sales f_e	$f_a - f_e$	$(f_a - f_e)^2/f_e$
Salesman				
A	20	21	−1	.048
B	22	21	1	.048
C	18	21	−3	.429
D	24	21	3	.429
	84	84	0	.954

The first two columns of Table 8-8 show the number of units that each salesman sold, on the average, each week over the past three months. To determine whether the sales records are significantly different, the five steps outlined above will be followed. First, the hypothesis that four salesmen have equal ability is formulated. Second, the expected frequencies are determined. If the hypothesis is true, each salesman should sell the same number of units on the average. Because the total number of units sold by all four salesmen is 84, the number that each of the four would be expected to sell is determined as $84 \div 4 = 21$. Third, the actual frequencies are recorded. Table 8-8 shows the theoretical frequencies, the actual frequencies, and the difference between the theoretical and actual frequencies. Fourth and fifth, the probability that such differences occur, if the hypothesis just formulated is true, is determined by calculating χ^2, determining the number of degrees of freedom, and examining Appendix Table VI.

Table 8-8 also shows χ^2 to be .954. There are four possible events—the occurrence of a sale for salesman A, the occurrence of a sale for Salesman B, for C, and for D—and four possible actual frequencies. Furthermore, these events and frequencies are arranged in a single column. Therefore the number of degrees of freedom is determined as $4 - 1 = 3$. The computed value of χ^2, .954, is located in the row corresponding to 3 degrees of freedom in Appendix Table VI. The two χ^2 values in the table that are closest to .954 are .584 and 2.366. The probability of obtaining a χ^2 value as high as these values is, respectively, 90 and 50 percent. Because the computed value of χ^2 (.954) lies between the two values obtained from the table, the probability of obtaining a value as high as .954 must be between 90 and 50 percent. Because both of these values are above the usual significance levels, the hypothesis is accepted. There is no significant difference between the selling records of the four salesmen. The firm must search for some other criterion to use as the basis of promotion.

If, on the other hand, the computed value of χ^2 had been, say, 12.000, the hypothesis would have been rejected. This value would have been higher than the value, 11.345, in the table that corresponds to the 1-percent significance level. In this event, the firm would have some justification for narrowing down the choice to less than the four being considered.

An Example from Marketing

As another illustration of the application of the chi-square distribution, assume that an automobile manufacturing firm is bringing out a new model. In order to map out its advertising campaign, it wants to determine whether the model will appeal most to a particular age group or equally to all age groups. The firm takes a random sample from persons attending a preview of the new model and obtains the results summarized in Table 8-9. How do you think the firm should conduct its advertising campaign with respect to this model?

What the firm is really interested in is whether the number of favorable responses differs significantly from age group to age group, account being taken of the differences in the total number of responses for each age group. In other words, could the four samples representing the four age groups have come from populations having the same proportion of favorable responses?

Again, this question will be answered by following the five steps outlined at the beginning of this section. First, the hypothesis that the four samples come from populations with the same proportion of favorable responses is formulated. Second, the expected frequency for each event is determined. There are eight possible events, two for each of the four age groups. For example, the occurrence of a favorable response in the "under 20" age group is one event, the occurrence of an unfavorable response in the same group is another event, and so on for the other three groups. The total number of responses for all groups is 480, 310 or 310/480 = 64.6 percent of which are favorable, and 170, or 35.4 percent, of which are unfavorable. If each sample actually does come from a population with the same proportion of favorable responses, the proportion just obtained, .646, can be used as an estimate of the common population proportion of favorable responses, and the proportion .354 can be used as an estimate of the common population proportion of unfavorable responses. The expected frequencies for each event can then be determined by multiplying the total number of responses for each age group by these proportions. For example, there were 200 responses in the "under 20" group. If this sample really did come from a population where the population proportions of favorable and unfavorable responses were respectively, .646 and .354, the expected frequencies for

Table 8-9.   ACTUAL RESULTS OF A RANDOM SAMPLE OF PERSONS ATTENDING A PREVIEW SHOWING OF A NEW MODEL AUTOMOBILE

	Age groups				
	Under 20	20–39	40–59	60 and over	Total
Persons who					
Liked the car	146	78	48	38	310
Disliked the car	54	52	42	22	170
	200	130	90	60	480

favorable and unfavorable responses would be, respectively, .646 × 200 = 129 and .354 × 200 = 71. The expected frequencies for the three other age groups are determined in a similar manner. These calculations are summarized in Table 8-10.

The third step in the general procedure—the recording of the actual frequencies for each possible event—has already been completed (Table 8-9). Step four, making a test of significance, requires the calculation of χ^2. This task is most easily accomplished by rearranging the data presented in Tables 8-9 and 8-10 according to the format of Table 8-11. The first column of this table, titled "row-column," indicates how the data is to be rearranged. For example, the number "1–1" indicates that the frequency appearing in the *first* row and *first* column in Table 8-9 is to be recorded in the first row of the column headed by f_a, the number "1–2" indicates that the frequency appearing in the *first* row and *second* column in Table 8-9 is to be recorded in the second row of the column headed by f_a, and the number "2–3" indicates that the frequency appearing in the *second* row and *third* column in Table 8-9 is to be recorded in the seventh row of the column headed by f_a. The frequencies appearing in Table 8-10 are to be transferred, in a similar fashion, to the column headed by f_e. χ^2 can then be calculated in the usual manner. Table 8-11 shows that $\chi^2 = 12.45$.

Because all the possible events and actual frequencies were initially arranged in more than one column and row, the method previously given

Table 8-10. EXPECTED RESULTS (ASSUMING HYPOTHESIS IS TRUE) OF A RANDOM SAMPLE OF PERSONS ATTENDING A PREVIEW SHOWING OF A NEW MODEL AUTOMOBILE

	Age groups				
	Under 20	*20–39*	*40–59*	*60 and over*	*Total*
Persons who					
Liked the car	129	84	58	39	310
Disliked the car	71	46	32	21	170
	200	130	90	60	480

Table 8-11. CALCULATION OF χ^2 FOR DATA OF TABLES 8-9 AND 8-10

	f_a	f_e	$f_a\text{-}f_e$	$(f_a\text{-}f_e)^2$	$(f_a\text{-}f_e)^2/f_e$
Row–Column					
1–1	146	129	17	289	2.24
1–2	78	84	− 6	36	.43
1–3	48	58	−10	100	1.72
1–4	38	39	− 1	1	.03
2–1	54	71	−17	289	4.07
2–2	52	46	6	36	.78
2–3	42	32	10	100	3.13
2–4	22	21	1	1	.05
	480	480	0		12.45

for determining the relevant number of degrees of freedom cannot be employed. In situations in which the possible events and actual frequencies are initially arranged in more than one column and more than one row, the number of degrees of freedom is determined by the formula $(r - 1)(c - 1)$, where r designates the number of rows and c designates the number of columns. In the present example, there are two rows and four columns, so that the number of degrees of freedom is $(2 - 1)(4 - 1) = 1 \times 3 = 3$.

The probability of obtaining a χ^2 value as large as the one obtained—namely, 12.45—if the hypothesis is true, is now determined in the usual way. Appendix Table VI shows that, with 3 degrees of freedom, the χ^2 value closest to the computed value is 11.345, such a high value occurring only 1 percent of the time. Therefore the probability of obtaining a χ^2 value as large as the one obtained if the hypothesis is, in fact, true is less than 1 percent. Because this probability is below the usual significance levels, the hypothesis is rejected. That is, the proportion of favorable responses does differ significantly from group to group.

An examination of Table 8-9 will show that the younger age groups prefer this particular model to a significantly greater degree than do the older age groups. Given these results, the firm can, of course, undertake various courses of action. For example, it can concentrate all its advertising efforts on the younger age groups, because this is the group that appears to be most interested. On the other hand, the firm can regard advertising expended on the younger age groups as unnecessary, because they are already interested. In this event, the firm can concentrate advertising on the older age groups, where the initial resistance seems to be greatest.

The reader should not be upset because the statistical test, in this illustration, could lead to either one of two conflicting courses of action. This is a good place to stress the fact that the techniques of statistical inference, by themselves, usually do not solve all of management's problems. These techniques are useful, mainly, in that they limit the number of alternatives that management must consider and focus management's attention on the more important aspects of the over-all problem. In the present example, management knows more than it did before the statistical test: it now knows which age group has the greatest initial resistance to, and also which has the greatest initial interest in, the product. How management decides to use this information is another problem.

An Example from Production

A firm has several hundred machines, all of the same type. It is about to replace all these machines with a new model. Four machines, each produced by a different machine manufacturer, are being considered. The four machines cost about the same, have the same rate of output per hour, and have the same service and parts guarantees. The firm would like to know whether the quality of output produced on the machines is the same, or whether one or more of the machines produces a higher-quality product than the others. To determine this, the firm picks four machine operators of equal ability and asks each to familiarize himself completely with one of the four machines. When this training has been accomplished, the firm has each of the four operators work for a week with the machine with which he is familiar. At the end of the week, the firm

examines the output turned out by each machine. These results are summarized in Table 8-12. Is there a significant difference between the quality
of output, as measured by the number of good, fair, and poor pieces,
produced by the different machines?

The by now familiar sequence of five steps will be followed. First,
the hypothesis that the quality of output is the same for all machines is
formulated. Second, the expected frequencies are determined. There are
12-possible events—three quality grades of output for each of four machines.
For example, the occurrence of a "fair" piece of output from machine A
is one possible event, the occurrence of a "good" piece from machine B is
another. As Table 8-12 shows, the total number of pieces produced is
210, 127/210 = 60.5 percent of which are good, 48/210 = 22.8 percent of
which are fair, and 35/210 = 16.7 percent of which are poor. If the quality

Table 8-12.   ACTUAL QUALITY OF OUTPUT TURNED OUT
BY FOUR DIFFERENT MACHINES

| | No. of pieces of output rated | | | |
	Good	Fair	Poor	Total
Machine				
A	40	5	5	50
B	30	15	9	54
C	32	17	11	60
D	25	11	10	46
Total	127	48	35	210

of output from each machine really were the same, the proportion of
the pieces produced that is rated good should be the same for each machine,
as should be the proportion rated fair and poor. Estimates of these common
proportions have been calculated above. The theoretical frequencies for
each possible event can be determined by applying these proportions to the
sample sizes corresponding to each machine. For example, 50 pieces were
turned out by machine A; the expected number of good pieces would
therefore be 50 × .605 = 30, the expected number of fair pieces would
be 50 × .228 = 11, and the expected number of poor pieces would be
50 × .167 = 8. The expected frequencies for all 12 events are shown in
Table 8-13.

The third step, the recording of the actual frequencies, has already
been summarized in Table 8-12. Steps four and five are as follows. Table
8-14, which follows the format introduced in the previous section, presents
the calculations necessary for the computation of x^2. x^2 is shown to be

Table 8-13.   *EXPECTED QUALITY OF OUTPUT (IF HYPOTHESIS IS TRUE)*
TURNED OUT BY FOUR DIFFERENT MACHINES

| | No. of pieces of output rated | | | |
	Good	Fair	Poor	Total
Machine				
A	30	11	8	49*
B	33	12	9	54
C	36	14	10	60
D	28	10	8	46
				209†

* Does not total 50 because of rounding.
† Does not total 210 because of rounding.

Table 8-14.   *CALCULATION OF χ^2 FROM DATA OF TABLES 8-12 AND 8-13*

	f_a	f_e	$f_a - f_e$	$(f_a - f_e)^2$	$(f_a - f_e)^2 / f_e$
Row–column					
1–1	40	30	10	100	3.3
1–2	5	11	− 6	36	3.3
1–3	5	8	− 3	9	1.1
2–1	30	33	− 3	9	.3
2–2	15	12	3	9	.8
2–3	9	9	0	0	.0
3–1	32	36	− 4	16	.4
3–2	17	14	3	9	.6
3–3	11	10	1	1	.1
4–1	25	28	− 3	9	.3
4–2	11	10	1	1	.1
4–3	10	8	2	4	.5
	210	209*	1†		10.8

* Does not total 209 because of rounding.
† Does not total 0 because of rounding.

10.8. Because all possible events and actual frequencies were initially
arranged in four rows and three columns, the number of degrees of freedom
relevant for this problem is $(4 - 1)(3 - 1) = 3 \times 2 = 6$. Appendix Table
VI shows that when the number of degrees of freedom is 6, the two values
in the table that are closest to the computed χ^2 value are 10.6 and 12.6.

This fact implies that the probability of obtaining a χ^2 value as large as the one obtained, if the hypothesis is true, is between 10 percent and 5 percent.

If a .1 significance level is employed, the hypothesis would therefore be rejected. The quality of output produced on the four machines would be significantly different. As this statement implies, machine A would be considered superior to machine D. Whether machine A would be considered superior to machines B and C, both of which show about the same results, could be determined by running another chi-square test for machines A, B, and C. Of course, if, for example, a 5-percent significance level had been initially employed, the different machines would not be considered significantly different with respect to quality of output. In situations such as the present, where the management decision clearly hinges on a selection of significance levels, the reader will do well to review the previous chapter's discussion of type I and II errors.

Sample Size

In general, two conditions relating to sample size must be satisfied before the chi-square test can be meaningfully applied. First, the total number of observations, or putting it differently, the sum of the actual frequencies for all possible events, must be at least 50. Second, the *theoretical* (that is, expected) frequency for each possible event must be at least 5.[6]

SUGGESTED READINGS

Bross, Irwin. *Design for Decision*. New York: The Macmillan Company, 1953.
Bryant, Edward. *Statistical Analysis*. New York: McGraw-Hill Book Company, Inc., 1960.

[6] For exceptions to these general rules, see H. M. Walker and Joseph Lev, *Statistical Inference* (New York: Holt, Rinehart and Winston, Inc., 1953), pp. 106–107. One set of rules that should be employed when the expected frequencies for each event are small and when the possible events are arranged in two rows and two columns involves the use of *Yates' correction for continuity*. In this type of situation the following rules should be observed. (1) Follow the five steps outlined throughout this section. If the hypothesis is accepted, Yates' correction is not necessary. (2) If the hypothesis is rejected, apply Yates' correction. This correction involves the adjustment of the usual χ^2 formula to the following form:

$$\chi_c^2 = \sum \frac{(|f_a - f_e| - .5)^2}{f_e}$$

In this adjusted formula, $|f_a - f_e|$ means that if the computed difference is negative the minus sign is to be ignored, so that all differences, positive or negative, are to be treated as positive. For example, $2 - 4$ would be treated as $+2$ and not -2, so that the numerator would become $(2 - \frac{1}{2})^2 = (1\frac{1}{2})^2$. (3) If the hypothesis is still rejected after the correction, no further adjustment is required. (4) If the hypothesis is rejected without Yates' correction and accepted with the correction, a more tedious procedure, described in Walker and Lev, *op. cit.*, pp. 103–105, must be employed.

Cohen, Lillian. *Statistical Methods for Social Scientists.* Englewood Cliffs, N.J.: Prentice-Hall, Inc., 1954.

Croxton, F. E., and D. J. Cowden. *Applied General Statistic* (2nd ed.). Englewood Cliffs, N.J.: Prentice-Hall, Inc., 1954.

Dixon, W. J., and F. J. Massey. *Introduction to Statistical Analysis.* New York: McGraw-Hill Book Company, Inc., 1951.

Freund, J. E., and F. J. Williams. *Modern Business Statistics.* Englewood Cliffs, N.J.: Prentice-Hall, Inc., 1961.

Grant, Eugene. *Statistical Quality Control.* New York: McGraw-Hill Book Company, Inc., 1964.

Hoel, P. G. *Elementary Statistics.* New York: John Wiley & Sons, Inc., 1960.

Mode, Elmer. *Elements of Statistics* (3rd ed.). Englewood Cliffs, N.J.: Prentice-Hall, Inc., 1961.

Morgenstern, Oskar. *On the Accuracy of Economic Observations.* Princeton, N.Y.: Princeton University Press, 1950.

Moroney, M. J. *Facts from Figures.* Baltimore: Penquin Books, Inc., 1957.

Neter, John, and William Wasserman. *Fundamental Statistics for Business and Economics.* Boston: Allyn and Bacon, Inc., 1961.

New England Telephone and Telegraph Company. *Sampling Can Work for You.*

Richmond, Samuel. *Principles of Statistical Analysis.* New York: The Ronald Press Company, 1964.

Rosander, A. C. *Elementary Principles of Statistics.* Englewood Cliff, N. J.: D. Van Nostrand Company, Inc., 1951.

Schlaifer, R. *Introduction to Statistics for Business Decisions.* New York: McGraw-Hill Book Company, Inc., 1961.

Vance, L. E., and John Neter. *Statistical Sampling for Auditors and Accountants.* New York: John Wiley & Sons, Inc., 1956.

Walker, H. M., and Joseph Lev. *Statistical Inference.* New York: Holt, Rinehart and Winston, Inc., 1953.

Wilks, S. S. *Elementary Statistical Analysis* (rev. ed.). Princeton, N.J.: Princeton University Press, 1949.

QUESTIONS

1. Distinguish between the addition and multiplication theorems of probability.

2. How are the addition and multiplication theorems employed to derive the general formula for calculating binomial probabilities?

3. What conditions must be satisfied before the binomial distribution can be used in sampling applications?

4. "One part of the general binomial probability formula indicates the *probability* of *one* of the ways in which a particular result can occur, and another part indicates the *number* of ways in which the result can occur." Explain this statement.

5. Under what conditions is the normal curve a valid approximation to the binomial distribution? to the sampling distribution of a proportion?

6. Does the normal curve approximation to the binomial save calculating time?

7. How can the formulas for the mean and standard deviation of the sampling distribution of a proportion be derived from those of the binomial distribution?

8. What is the general procedure employed when the chi-square distribution is used to test a hypothesis?

9. How are degrees of freedom calculated, in a chi-square application, when all possible events and actual frequencies are originally arranged in a single row or column? when they are originally arranged in several rows and columns?

10. What conditions relating to sample size must be satisfied before the chi-square test can be meaningfully applied?

11. Distinguish between continuous and discrete data.

PROBLEMS

1. A single unbiased die is thrown twice in a row. What is the probability of coming up with a
   (a) 3 both times?
   (b) 3 *and* 4, in *that* order?
   (c) 3 *and* 4, in *any* order?
   (d) 3 both times or a 4 both times or a 3 and 4 in any order?
   (e) If you were offered 2.5:1 odds against coming up with a 3 and 4, in any order, show why you would or would not accept them.
   (f) If two unbiased dice are thrown simultaneously, what is the probability of throwing a total point count of 5 before throwing a total point count of 11, all other point counts being ignored?

2. A gambler offers the following bet: If you throw a die *three* times in succession, and if either a 4 *or* a 5 turns up *each* time, he will pay $30 for each $1 that you bet. Would you, as a "percentage player," take this bet?

3. Two boxes sit side by side on a counter. The first box contains 20 golf balls, 5 of which are white, 4 red, and 11 black. The second box contains 10 golf balls, 4 of which are white and 6 of which are red. A game of chance consists of one person's drawing, while blindfolded, one ball from each box.
   (a) What is the probability that 1 red and 1 white ball will be selected?
   (b) What is the probability of drawing either a white or red ball and a black ball?
   (c) What is the probability of drawing 2 red balls or 1 white ball and 1 black ball, or 2 white balls or 2 black balls?

4. If a manufacturing process is working correctly, 10 percent of the items turned out will be defective. A sample of 7 items is taken.
   (a) What is the probability that exactly 3 of these items will be defective?

    (b) What is the probability that no more than 5 will be defective?

    (c) If 3 items were defective, would you, as a quality control inspector, take any action? Why?

5. If a manufacturing process is working correctly, 2 percent of the items turned out will be defective. A sample of 8 items is taken.

    (a) What is the probability that 6 of the items will be defective?

    (b) If 6 items were defective, would you, as a quality control inspector, take any action?

6. A manufacturing process is intended to produce electrical fuses with no more than 1 percent of them defective. It is checked every hour by trying 10 fuses selected at random from the hour's production. If one or more of the 10 fails, the process is halted and carefully examined. If in fact its probability of producing a defective fuse is .01, what is the probability that the process will needlessly be examined in a given instance?

7. A manufacturing process turns out certain items, 2 percent of which are defective. A random sample of 250 items is selected.

    (a) What is the probability of obtaining exactly 16 defective items?

    (b) What is the probability of obtaining 16 or more defective items?

    Use the normal curve approximation to answer these questions.

8. Firm X mass-produces electric razors. It knows that if the manufacturing process is working correctly, 92 percent of the razors produced will be in good operating order and 8 percent will be defective. It selects, at random, 10 razors from the production line, and discovers that 4 of these are defective. Should the firm undertake an inspection of the production process?

9. A television manufacturer purchases a particular type of tube from an outside supplier. The supplier states that no more than 5 percent of the tubes shipped at any one time will last less than 600 hours. The manufacturer wants to make certain that each shipment meets this specification, because if more than 5 percent of the tubes are defective his service department will not be able to handle the number of TV sets that will be returned for repair. Furthermore, if too many sets have to be returned, his reputation will be damaged. A large lot of tubes is received. A sample of 100 tubes is randomly selected from this lot, and it is found that 14 of these tubes burn out before 600 hours have elapsed. Should the firm contact the supplier?

10. Town X has a population of 20,000. According to previous election results, 40 percent of the population are Republicans, 30 percent are Democrats, 20 percent are Independents, and 10 percent are "other." A random sample of 50 is selected.

    (a) What is the probability of obtaining 20 (40 percent) Republicans?

    (b) What is the probability of obtaining 15 (30 percent) Democrats?

    (c) What is the probability of obtaining 10 (20 percent) Independents?

(d) What is the probability of obtaining 5 (10 percent) "other"?

(e) It actually turns out that 12 of the people in the sample are Republicans, 18 are Democrats, 15 are Independents, and 5 are "other." Would you accept the hypothesis that 40 percent of the people in the population are still Republicans?

Answer question (e) using, first, the binomial probability distribution and, second, the concept of the sampling distribution of a proportion.

11. A college attempts to maintain a religious "balance" in its student body so that 30 percent of its students are Catholics. Of course, not every student accepted by the college will actually enroll in the college, and for this reason there might be an "inbalance" in any one year. A sample of 100 students is selected at random, and it is found that 25 percent of them are Catholics. Is the sample result consistent with the goal of the college with respect to religious balance?

12. A movie producer is bringing out a new movie. In order to map out his advertising campaign, he wants to determine whether the movie will appeal most to a particular age group or whether it will appeal equally to all age groups. The producer takes a random sample from persons attending a preview showing of the new movie, and obtains the following results:

	Age groups			
	Under 20	*20–39*	*40–59*	*60 and over*
Liked the movie	146	78	48	38
Disliked the movie	54	52	42	22
Indifferent	20	10	9	8

How do you think the firm should conduct its advertising campaign with respect to this movie?

13. A public-opinion survey is attempting to discover whether the people's preference for candidate X varies with the section of the country in which they reside. The following results are obtained from a questionnaire sent to 200 persons selected at random. What would you conclude?

	No. of persons with stated preference			
	North	*South*	*East*	*West*
Preference for Candidate X				
For	28	20	60	30
Against	8	8	7	5
Indifferent	7	10	11	6

CHAPTER NINE

Statistical Quality Control and Sample Design

Many of the examples in previous chapters have come from the area known as statistical quality control. Attention will now be directly focused on this very important field of statistics. The present chapter will also briefly examine sample designs other than that employed throughout this text.

STATISTICAL QUALITY CONTROL

"The primary function of the quality-control activity is the *prevention of defects*."[1] Progressive management is always interested in the quality of its product. The prevention of defects, or at least a reduction in their number, is the hope of most such managements. Quality control requires "a program of coordinated inspection procedures from the machine or process level through final acceptance based on sound statistical principles."[2] Statistical quality control involves the statistical analysis of the inspection data derived from these procedures. Such analysis is based on the principles involved in the normal curve and sampling presented in the preceding chapters.

A quality-control program is planned with three basic purposes in view:

1. To obtain maximum assurance that the smallest possible amount of nonacceptable material will be produced at each stage of production

[1] G. W. Ireson and E. L. Grant, *Handbook of Industrial Engineering and Management* (Englewood Cliffs, N.J.: Prentice-Hall, Inc., 1955), p. 987. Italics in original.

[2] This statement and a great deal of the material in this chapter are from an excellent pamphlet, *An Introduction to Statistical Quality Control* (Washington, D.C.: Bureau of Ordnance, Department of the Navy, 1950).

2. To bring about the separation of nonacceptable lots of material from acceptable lots of material

3. To make certain that inspection at final acceptance will judge a given lot of material uniformly, regardless of where the items are produced or who inspects them

An excellent feature of quality control is that it is easy to apply. Once the system is established, it can be operated by personnel who have not had extensive specialized training or a highly mathematical background. It may appear difficult only because the statistical principles on which it is based are unrecognized or unknown. However, as these principles are actually based on common sense, the quality-control method finds wide application.

The armed forces have a special interest in quality control because most of the items they use are produced in tremendous quantity by mass-production techniques. Private companies also have an interest and do excellent work along these lines. Many large manufacturers have published pamphlets relating to quality control with specific application to their own problems.[3]

There is an increasing realization of the possibilities existing in the techniques of quality control. Those familiar with these ideas and possessing active imaginations are continually finding new areas within which these techniques can be applied. An example of this is the Bendix Manufacturing Company's application of quality control to sources from which it purchases materials and parts to be used in Bendix products.[4] This company believes that by using this type of control it can be certain that the items being purchased will be completely suitable. As soon as the items being purchased from a particular supplier fall below a certain standard, the supplier is warned. This procedure helps the supplier to correct his own processes immediately. If the situation is not corrected, another source of supply is located. Although the explanation here is neccessarily brief, the general idea is apparent and indicates the application of quality-control techniques to fields other than mass production within one company.

Quality control per se has become popular in manufacturing because it has proved to be a system for maintaining high standards of manufacturing quality at the minimum possible cost. It brings about many savings in production cost by decreasing waste, eliminating rework, and reducing the amount of inspection necessary. Besides assuring a high, uniform quality of product, it provides a measure of product quality understood by both the producer and consumer of the product. By providing this

[3] Bernard P. Goldsmith, *Acceptance Sampling of Reliable Tubes* (Waltham, Mass.: Raytheon Manufacturing Company, 1954).

[4] H. C. Newton, "'Vendor Rating' for Quality Control," *Tele-Tech & Electronic Industries* (February 1955), pp. 71, 140–143.

measure of quality, it helps to ensure the acceptance of the product by the purchaser.

There are four principle steps in the application of statistical principles to manufacturing. They are

1. The recognition of the presence of "piece-to-piece" variation in the items
2. The recognition of a pattern and its consistency
3. The recognition of the ability to predict
4. The recognition of a relation between a sample and the universe of items—that is, the population

"Piece-to-Piece" Variation

Imagine that a company is producing springs. One of the requirements is that the springs have a certain amount of deflection—"spring"—to them. According to the first step listed, it must be recognized that regardless of the care taken in producing these springs they will all vary slightly. A sample of 100 springs could be taken and the amount of deflection in each measured by applying a uniform pressure or weight to each spring in the sample. The "piece-to-piece" variation would be shown by the individual measurements of the deflection of individual springs.

The springs could then be assorted in several piles according to their deflection. Those with the least deflection could be placed in a pile on the left; those with more deflection placed in various piles to the right; and those with most deflection in a pile on the extreme right. If this is done, it will be found that more springs will fall in the middle piles than at either end.

Recognition of a Pattern

Now, according to the second step, it is possible to recognize a pattern and its consistency. Three histograms are presented in Figure 9-1. Histogram A illustrates a possible grouping of the 100 springs taken in the sample. B illustrates the pattern resulting from a sample of 1000 springs and C one from a sample of 1,000,000 springs. In the chapter on the normal curve, a definition was presented that was said to be associated with quality control. The definition states that the normal curve is the shape of the distribution of a large number of measurements around the unknown true value of a physical quantity. Many times, in a mass-production process, if the process is operating correctly, all the items being manufactured will have an equal opportunity to be affected by such things as temperature, vibration, and the like, and therefore, although the items may differ from one another, they will form a normal curve around the average. The histograms indicate that the larger the size of the sample the more likely the curve is to be normal—that is, the more likely it is exactly to represent the universe from which it is taken.

The measurement of large numbers of units of any mass-produced item always results in a definite, persistent pattern. The pattern may appear as a skewed curve; but whether it is skewed or normal, the pattern will be consistent. The reason for such consistency is that "chance" is always at work in the production of machine-made products. In the manufacture of springs, for example, the diameter of the wire, the play

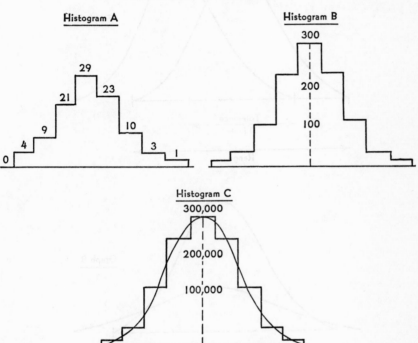

FIGURE 9–1.   Histograms

of gears, and the like will affect each piece separately, and differences caused by each will tend to cancel one another.

The important point, however, is that for *every* manufacturing process a pattern of variation in the items produced will *always* exist. Of even greater importance is the fact that for a particular process the same pattern will be repeated as long as only the same chance causes are at work.

Ability to Predict

Naturally, if this pattern repeats itself consistently, the third step— the recognition of the ability to predict—should be easy. If something repeats itself, it can certainly be predicted. As long as the same pattern recurs in manufacturing a product, it can be taken as an assurance that no new cause of variation has affected the process.

Based on this consistent repetition of a pattern, proper limits of a process in the future can be established, if we assume that there is no basic

FIGURE 9–2

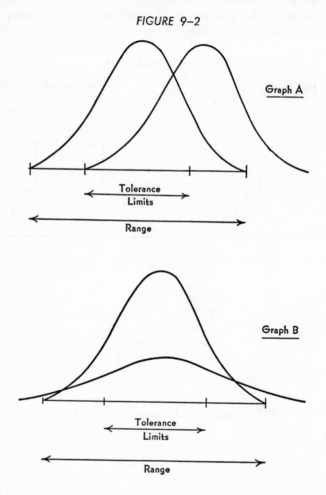

change in the process itself. It will then be considered that production is "good" when the pattern is repeated within the tolerance limits established. If the pattern is within these tolerance limits, there is assurance that the entire production is acceptable. There is no need for concern about each individual item because the process itself is "in control" within the tolerance limits established.

Now, if the pattern changes, something must be wrong. Variation means that the product is affected not only by the usual small chance factors but also by some basic change in the conditions affecting production. It is necessary to find the cause of this variation and eliminate it. A basic change will be indicated by one of two possible variations in the pattern. These two possible variations are indicated by the two curves presented in Figure 9-2.

Graph A represents a variation caused by some factor such as tool wear. As a tool wears, the average size of the product will change. The change in size causes the distribution to shift, as is indicated in Graph A. However, the deviation around this average will remain about the same because the random factors causing the deviation have not changed. In other words, although the shape of the curve remains the same, the average and the entire curve will shift, causing a considerable number of the pieces to be outside one of the tolerance limits.

On the other hand, changes such as those caused by material instability result in greater piece-to-piece variation and cause the pattern to flatten out so that both extremes are beyond the tolerance limits. For example, suppose a shipment of wire is received which is of the correct average diameter but extremely unstable—that is, much too thick in some places and too thin in others. Although the average size product will remain the same, the deviation around this average will change. The deviation is indicated in Graph B.

In either of these illustrations quality suffers and material is wasted. If there is a working quality-control system, it is possible to spot such trouble immediately and correct the entire process. This adjustment, cannot, obviously, be made if the items are tested only after the entire lot has been produced. It should also be pointed out that this type of testing is different from a system which has as its purpose only the elimination of defective pieces. Testing only in order to screen defective pieces does not correct and maintain quality by controlling the production process itself.

Relation between Sample and Universe

The fourth step in the application of statistical principles to business was listed above as the recognition of a relation between a sample and the universe of items. To obtain control of the manufacturing process, it is necessary to find whether the production pattern has remained consistent. A sample selected at random, of the items produced, will indicate whether the pattern is being maintained. Quite often only 5 or 10 pieces are necessary for this purpose in a particular instance. It is true that the larger the sample, the more accurate the picture of the universe; but, in any firm, economy is of great importance. For this reason, the risks in sampling have to be considered in the light of whatever best balances the dual problem of accuracy and economy. Sampling usually gives a more accurate picture than would a 100-percent test, because much more attention and more refined methods can be applied to the individual pieces. A few pieces can be given an extremely thorough examination, which, because of the limitations of economy, would be impossible for the entire universe.

As previously stated in discussing the sampling distribution of the mean, the average of any sample taken will fall within narrower limits

FIGURE 9–3

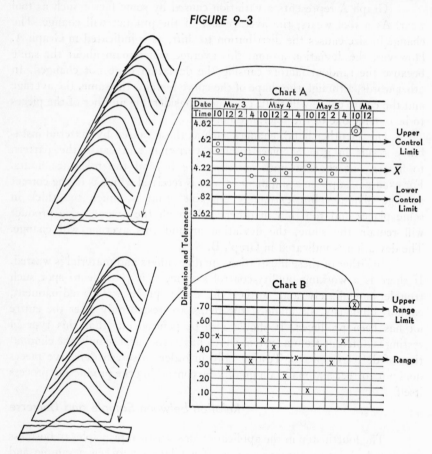

around the true mean of the universe than will the individual items themselves. The explanation is that the average of a sample of pieces manufactured is affected by all the items in the sample and the highs will average out the lows—that is, the large measurements will tend to balance the small. As in the determination of a confidence interval, limits in quality control are called "control limits." If the average of a sample falls outside these limits, it is almost certain that some significant cause has entered the production process. Something else is affecting production besides the expected small chance factors.

Control Charts

A control chart provides an easy method of continuously checking the process to find out whether the pattern is repeating itself or has changed. Actually, the control chart is two charts. One chart concerns itself with averages; the other has to do with the range. These are presented in Figure 9-3.

Chart A represents that portion of a control chart used to record sample averages. Small samples of the items being manufactured are taken from the process at specified intervals of time. The averages of these samples are plotted on the control chart. If the averages fall within the control limits, the indication is that the pattern of the distribution has not changed. If the averages fall outside of these limits, the indication is that the difference between the required average size of the item being produced and the average of the sample is so great that it is extremely significant. The difference is too large to be assumed as being due to chance only.

Chart B represents the portion of a control chart used to record sample ranges. The previous portion of the chart indicates the center of the sample; this part indicates its spread. As each sample is taken, the difference between the highest and lowest value in the sample is found. If these ranges fall inside the control range, obviously the spread of the pattern has not changed significantly.

It is not expected that a student will be a quality-control expert after such a brief presentation. It is hoped, however, that the purpose of a quality-control system and the simplicity of its application may be appreciated.

SAMPLE DESIGN

All the samples discussed in this text are designed so that the items included in the sample are selected according to the method of *unrestricted* (or *simple*) *random sampling*. Other sample designs are not employed, for four reasons. First, unrestricted random sampling is the logical starting point for any discussion of sample designs; this method would therefore have to be treated before other methods are introduced. Second, the basic principles of statistical inference are the same for most of the other sample designs, the only differences occurring in such details as standard-error formulas and shapes of sampling distributions. Third, a detailed discussion of other sample designs would change the orientation of the text from that of introductory general statistics to one of advanced specialized statistics. Fourth, more is known about the theory and application of unrestricted random sampling than about any of the other sample designs.

Although sample designs other than unrestricted random sampling are not examined and utilized, they will be briefly discussed in this section, so that the reader will have additional insight into the wide scope of possible applications in the general area of statistical inference. In order to be better able to compare and contrast the basic elements of unrestricted random sampling with those of other sample designs, the discussion will begin with a review of unrestricted random sampling.

Unrestricted Random Sampling

When unrestricted random sampling is employed, each item in the universe must have an equal chance of being included in the sample. In addition, every possible combination of items must also have an equal opportunity of being chosen. Thus, if a sample of 10 balls is drawn from a universe composed of red and black balls that are homogeneous except for color, every ball in the universe must have exactly the same chance of being a part of the sample. Similarly, every possible combination of 10 balls must also have this opportunity. It should be evident that these conditions cannot be met if haphazard sampling methods are employed, but can be realized only as a result of careful planning.

If all the items in the universe can be numbered, an unrestricted random sample may be obtained in two ways. The numbers corresponding to the items can be enclosed in capsules and placed in a globe from which a group may be drawn at random. The items corresponding to the numbers selected in this manner compose the random sample. Whenever a capsule is drawn for inclusion in the sample it must be replaced before the next drawing. If it is not replaced, the nature of the universe will be altered somewhat. Although this variation is of little importance if the size of the population is large, with smaller populations it assumes some significance The same results can be obtained by the use of a table of random numbers (Appendix Table II). The numbers in this table have themselves been selected at random. A starting point should be selected at random, perhaps by placing a pencil on the page while the eyes are closed. The digits in the number so located identify the first item in the sample. Additional numbers are obtained by moving in any direction in the table. This procedure will result in a random sample because the random numbers and their position in the table are themselves the result of chance selection.

Unfortunately, it is often impossible or impractical to identify and number each item in the universe. Under these circumstances, methods must be developed that will approximate the conditions of random sampling. If directories are available, this problem is frequently solved by selecting page numbers and items on pages at random. In so doing, as a matter of convenience, rules are often adopted that alter the chances of the inclusion of items or combinations of items in the sample. For example, when directories are employed, the rule might call for the drawing of only one item from any individual page; in this way the incorporation in the sample of combinations composed in total or in part of more than one item on any one page would be precluded. Similarly, if the sampling procedure called for taking every tenth item on a list, combinations of items not separated by nine spaces could not become part of the sample. Obviously, in these and similar instances, all possible combinations of items do not have an equal chance of selection, even though the sampling method is random in nature. Such samples are called *restricted* random samples.

Restricted Random Sampling

Three sample designs that come under the general heading of restricted random sampling will be discussed. These are *stratified random sampling, cluster random sampling,* and *systematic random sampling.* Bear in mind that the standard-error formulas and the shapes of the relevant sampling distributions for these sample designs are different from those relating to unrestricted random sampling.

Often characteristics of the universe that are either known or believed to be significant with respect to the problem at hand have already been ascertained. As a result, the random-sampling methods can be restricted in such way that they permit this knowledge to improve the sample. For instance, if differences in sex are known to influence the rate of absenteeism of industrial workers in a certain community and if a previous census has shown that 70 percent of such workers are men, the quality of the sampling results in a study of absenteeism can be improved if a 70-percent weight in the sample is assigned to data collected from male workers. Had a simple unrestricted random sample been taken, as a result of pure chance either more or less than 70 percent of the items in the sample might have come from men. This chance error might, if the sex element were significant with respect to absenteeism, produce a similar error in the conclusions drawn from the sample. However, when the 70-percent weight is assigned to male data this source of error is eliminated.

The simplest method of achieving this weighting would be to control the drawing of the sample in such a manner that 70 percent of the items would come from men and 30 percent from women. However, this method need not always be followed. If the individual variations in absenteeism had been much greater among the women, a larger sample might have been needed in order to obtain accurate results for the female portion of the working force than would have been required for the men, whose behavior was much more stable. In these circumstances, even though a larger sample might have been taken among the women, the conclusions obtained from the smaller sample conducted among male workers would be assigned 70 percent of the total weight in determining final sample results, because 70 percent of the population is composed of men. Careful stratification sometimes permits amazingly accurate results from relatively small samples. It is also quite useful when dealing with skewed populations; for example, there is no need to worry, as there would be if unrestricted random sampling were being employed, about missing the important but small high-income group in a salary survey. Stratification systems can be based on any known significant characteristic or group of characteristics. Area, income, sex, race, age, size, occupation, and education are a few of those more commonly employed.

The above discussion pertained to stratified sampling. Its purpose was to divide the population into groups or *strata* such that there are (1) as much homogeneity as possible within strata and (2) as great a difference as possible between strata. In cluster sampling, however, just the reverse is true. The population is divided into groups or *clusters* such that there are (1) as much heterogeneity as possible within clusters and (2) as small a difference as possible between clusters. The reason for this procedure is that, in stratified sampling, once the strata have been established, certain elements *in each strata* are selected at random. In cluster sampling, once the clusters are established, *certain* clusters—not all clusters—are selected at random, with all the elements or merely a random sample of the elements in each of the *selected* clusters being employed in the study.

Clusters are usually selected on a geographical or time basis. The chief advantage of this design is that it is usually less expensive than an unrestricted random sample of the same size. For instance, it would not be necessary to travel all over the country to interview persons in a national survey, as it might quite well be if an unrestricted random sample is taken. Its disadvantage is that the standard error is typically greater than that of an unrestricted random sample of the same size.

Systematic random sampling involves an ordering of the population such that, for instance, every 20th (or 10th, or 3rd, and so forth) item in a list is sampled. Its advantage lies in the ease with which a sample can be selected. Its disadvantage is that it could lead to the wrong conclusion if there is a systematic pattern in the population. For example, a salary study for a firm may involve working with a pay-roll listing of employees that is organized by department, there being 20 persons in each department, the 20th person being the highest-salaried person in the department. Here, a systematic sample, designed so that every 20th person in the list is selected, would greatly overstate the salary picture.

Directed Samples

Occasionally the limitations of time or budgets may preclude taking either random or stratified random samples. In such circumstances, a sample composed of items believed to be representative is frequently employed. Whether such a sample will be adequate depends on the skill, knowledge, and experience of the person making the selection. This type of sampling is most appropriate when the universe is dominated by a few large items that must be included in a sample in order to make it representative. For example, a sample of primary copper producers in the United States would be very misleading if Anaconda and Kennecott were not included. It must be noted that conclusions based on probability analysis, which are commonly used in the analysis of random samples, cannot be employed with directed samples.

Statistical Inference and Other Sample Measures

Throughout these four chapters on statistical inference, emphasis has been placed on the relation between the sample mean and the population mean. The reason is that the mean is usually the most commonly sought characteristic of a population. However, often it is also important to conduct tests of significance and construct confidence limits for other measures that can be computed from a single sample, such as the standard deviation. Although the standard errors and sampling distributions of the various measures of dispersion, skewness, and kurtosis are not treated in this text, they are known and discussed, from both the theoretical and the applied points of view, in more advanced texts. The basic principles of statistical inference developed in this text with respect to the arithmetic mean can be applied as well to these other, less commonly employed but nonetheless important, measures. This fact is pointed out at the end of this part of the text, which deals explicitly with statistical inference, in order to emphasize further the wide range of applications of the principles developed in these four chapters.

SUGGESTED READINGS

An Introduction to Statistical Quality Control. Washington, D.C.: Bureau of Ordnance, Department of the Navy, 1950.

Cochran, W. G. *Sampling Techniques.* New York: John Wiley & Sons, Inc., 1953.

Deming, W. E. *Some Theory of Sampling.* New York: John Wiley & Sons, Inc., 1950.

Dixon, W. J., and F. J. Massey, Jr. *Introduction to Statistical Analysis.* New York: McGraw-Hill Book Company, Inc., 1951, chap. 9.

Grant, E. L. *Statistical Quality Control.* New York: McGraw-Hill Book Company, Inc., 1964.

Hansen, M. H., W. N. Hurwitz, and W. G. Meadow. *Sample Survey Methods and Theory* (2 vols.). New York: John Wiley & Sons, Inc., 1953.

Spurr, W. A., L. S. Kellogg, and J. H. Smith. *Business and Economic Statistics.* Homewood, Ill.: Richard D. Irwin, Inc., 1954, chap. 20.

Wallis, W. A., and H. V. Roberts. *Statistics: A New Approach.* Glencoe, Ill.: The Free Press of Glencoe, Inc., 1956, chap. 16.

1. Imagine that you are taking samples of a product being mass-produced.
   (a) What will be the effect on the curve representing this product if there is a basic change in manufacturing conditions caused by some factor such as tool wearing?
   (b) What will be the effect on the curve representing this product if there is a change caused by some factor such as material instability?
2. Is it true that one function of a typical control chart is to test continuously a hypothesis concerning the true mean? Discuss.
3. Describe the two parts of a typical control chart and state (a) why these charts are used, (b) how they are used, (c) what they indicate.
4. In quality control a shift (change) in the arithmetic mean and a change in the range represent different kinds of production problems. Explain.
5. Quality control means more than just the elimination of defective pieces. Explain.
6. List the four steps in the application of statistical principles to manufacturing.
7. What is meant by unrestricted random sampling?
8. Assume that you are to conduct a random sample of the students in the university. Describe two methods of securing an unrestricted random sample and one method of obtaining a restricted random sample.
9. Could an unrestricted random sample of a student body be achieved in the following ways?
   (a) Take one name selected at random from each page of the student directory.
   (b) Take all the names on one page that was selected at random.
   (c) Take every twentieth name from the directory.
   (d) Take all the names beginning with a single letter that was selected at random.
10. Would the responses to a questionnaire constitute a random sample? If not, enumerate as many factors as you can think of that would introduce non-random considerations.
11. Why is it possible to achieve greater sampling accuracy through careful stratification?
12. Suggest a basis of stratification to be employed in sampling public opinion or economic issues.
13. On what factor does the success of directed sampling usually depend?
14. Under what conditions is directed sampling most advisable?
15. Describe your plan for obtaining the following samples:
    (a) An unrestricted sample of the entire population of the United States

    (b) The most economical but adequate restricted sample of the entire population of the United States

    (c) A directed sample of the manufacturing costs of the manufacturers of television sets

    (d) A stratified sample of the wage of construction labor

16. Of the procedures listed below, which would provide the best sample for determining the distribution of income within a community?

    (a) Mailing a questionnaire to every 10th person listed in the telephone directory

    (b) Recording the adjusted gross income from every 10th return filed with the Bureau of Internal Revenue office in the community.

    (c) Interviewing every 10th person passing a given street corner on a given day

    (d) Calling at every 10th house on every 10th street listed in the city directory

17. Are the following statements true, false, or a combination of truth and falsehood?

    (a) Unrestricted random sampling means that each item in the universe has an equal chance of being included in the sample.

    (b) Directed sampling is not a form of random sampling but rather involves deliberate choice of items.

    (c) Careful stratification reduces the size of the sample necessary to achieve a given level of accuracy.

Part Four

FORECASTING

CHAPTER TEN

Correlation

The discussion thus far has been concerned with the behavior of a single set of values. We have considered the techniques of collecting and analyzing data pertaining to some individual attribute of the universe under study. In statistical analysis, however, it is often necessary to discover the degree to which two or more different groups of values are related to each other in their movement. Frequently the student of economics or business wants to know whether a series of values varies directly or inversely with another series. If, when there is a change in the values in one group there is a consistent change in the values of the other, the groups are said to be correlated. Should this relation be sufficiently close, the values of one series can be used to estimate reliably the values of the other.

In some instances a cause-and-effect relation is clearly evident. For example, the connection between the amount of rainfall in a given area and the amount of corn raised in the same area is apparent. Usually, however, the association is not so obvious. Is there a close connection between the scores that applicants receive on an aptitude test and their performance after employment? Do prices fall at the same time wages fall? Such questions are sufficiently important to justify the devotion of time and energy in the hope of finding answers, even though the extent of relation is not clear at the outset.

In other instances the hope of finding such a relation is in some respects a last resort. One of the reasons why so much attention is being paid to the relation between cigarette smoking and lung cancer is the fact that until just recently other methods of research, in the attempt to find the cause of lung cancer, have proved to be unsuccessful.[1] Cigarette smoking has increased tremendously during the same time period in which the incidence

[1] Harold F. Dorn, National Institutes of Health, "The Relationship of Cancer of the Lung and the Use of Tobacco," *The American Statistician* (Washington, D.C.: The American Statistical Association, December 1954, vol. 8, no. 5), pp. 7–13.

of lung cancer has increased tremendously. One aspect of the research problem is therefore to discover whether cigarette smoking causes lung cancer, whether both have increased because of some third factor, or whether the relation is entirely one of chance.

The problem of analyzing the relation between different series should be broken down into three steps:

1. Determining whether a relation exists and, if it does, measuring it
2. Testing whether it is significant
3. Establishing the cause-effect relation, if any

Only the first two steps are taken up in this chapter. The third step in the analysis, that of establishing the cause-effect relation, is beyond the scope of statistical analysis. An extremely high and significant correlation between the increase in smoking and the increase in lung cancer would not prove that smoking causes lung cancer. The proof of a cause-and-effect relation can be developed only by means of an exhaustive study of the operative elements themselves.

By definition, when a group of items is recorded with respect to the values of two distinct variables and it is found that pairs of values tend to be associated, the two variables are said to be correlated. A variable, as the word is used in this definition, is any quantity that can have different (varying) numerical values in different situations. For example, at a dance arranged for couples only, each couple may be considered an item and the age of the man and the age of the woman the two variables under study. Assuming the usual type of dance, the younger men would come with the younger women and older men with older women. Hence one could say that there is a *relation* between the ages of the men and the women, or that they are *associated*. More technically, it could also be stated that a *correlation* exists between the two sets of ages. In the layman's language, if one is asked to guess the age of a man selected at random from the floor, without seeing him or having any other knowledge about who he is (and assuming a wide scattering of ages to be present), the guess will be more accurate if the age of his "date" is known.

The above relation is *direct* or *positive*—that is, the higher the age of the man, the higher, on the average, will be the age of the woman. On the other hand, a relation, or correlation, may be *inverse* or negative; in these circumstances, the higher the value of one variable, the lower (on the average) will be the value of the other. For example, during its season, an amusement park will normally show an inverse relation between the amount of rainfall and the number of customers. In brief, a correlation is a condition in which the value of one variable in a pair is directly or inversely related to the value of the other variable in the same pair.

A mathematical relation implies nothing in itself about cause and effect. In many instances extremely high correlation between two variables may be obtained when no meaning can be attached to the answer. There is, for example, extremely high correlation between some series representing the production of pigs and the production of pig iron, yet no one has ever believed that this correlation has any meaning or that it indicates the existence of a cause-effect relation.

THE SCATTERGRAM

The first step in correlation analysis is the preparation of a scattergram. On the scattergram, the original figures to be correlated are plotted. A plot enables the investigator to obtain a visual impression of the distribution of the paired values. In addition, some of the measures found while calculating correlation can also be plotted on this graph, to make the entire relation much more evident.

The standard procedure in correlation analysis is to have X represent the independent or "causal" variable and Y the dependent or "resultant" variable. On the scattergram, X is plotted on the horizontal axis and Y on the vertical. Figure 10-1 presents three scattergrams. Graph A pictures the grouping of plotted points from the lower left of the graph to the upper right. This grouping indicates positive correlation, because large values on the X axis are associated with large values on the Y axis and vice versa.

Graph B shows the grouping of plotted points from the upper left to the lower right. This grouping indicates negative correlation, because large values on the X axis are associated with small values on the Y axis, and large Y values with small X values.

The third graph, C, pictures the points plotted under conditions where no correlation is present. Here any size value of one variable may be paired with any size value of the other variable.

If, in a particular problem, the original values plotted on the scattergram fall as they do in either graphs A or B, the values would be correlated. Although calculation is needed to discover the extent of this correlation, it is evident on visual inspection alone that some association exists. It must be emphasized that knowledge of whether the correlation is positive or negative is equally valuable. The information provided by graph B is just as useful as that in graph A.

At this point an example will prove helpful. Consider the problem of a large company that employs a substantial number of salesmen. It would certainly be of value if this company could tell before hiring a man whether the individual being considered would turn out to be a success. If someone should suggest the use of an aptitude test that had worked very well in other firms, the immediate temptation might be to use it without verifying its validity. Conditions may not, however, be the same in the concern now considering the test. This company's product, customers, and the like may differ considerably from those of other firms. It is therefore necessary to make certain that the aptitude test will be valid in this particular instance. One method of finding out is to use the test

FIGURE 10–1

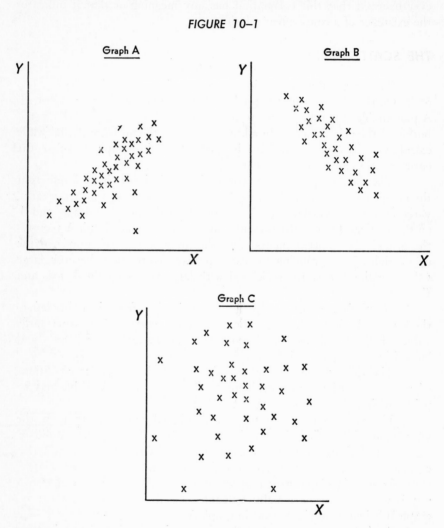

for a period of time without permitting hiring to be influenced. On the basis of the test scores obtained, forecasts of the estimated sales that each new salesman will make are prepared and then compared with the actual sales made by these men. A comparison between the actual sales made and the sales estimated on the basis of the aptitude test will indicate whether the test is valid for this particular company.

Table 10-1 contains all the data needed to calculate measures of correlation. Although only 5 salesmen are used so that for illustrative purposes the problem will be more manageable, in practice many more would be necessary.

The scattergram in Figure 10-2 presents the original figures—the test score and actual sales of each salesman. When this scattergram is examined, it can be seen that the plotted points cluster from the lower left to the upper right, indicating the presence of positive correlation.

The discussion in this chapter considers the technique applicable to a large group of items only because the theory involved is more understandable than that required for small samples. Since in most investigations the number of available items is sufficient to warrant our calling the groups large, no important practical difficulties should be encountered in not

Table 10-1

	Test scores X	Sales Y
Salesmen		
A	45	70
B	65	100
C	50	85
D	60	95
E	55	75

investigating small samples. In examining the calculations and charts, it must always be remembered that the small number of items is used solely to reduce the necessary arithmetic. It should require only a slight amount of imagination to regard the discussion and charts as relating to a large number, such as 200 salesmen.

THE REGRESSION LINE

Some measure is needed to represent the average relation between the X and Y variables. A straight line can be used to serve this purpose. In Figure 10-3 a "least squares" line has been fitted to the test scores and sales values. This is the same "least squares" line developed in connection with trend in Chapter 12. In correlation this is called the regression line; it indicates the estimated values of the dependent variable. In other words, if the line accurately depicts the relation under study it will enable the investigator to determine the Y values (sales) that on the average will be associated with any given value of X (test scores). The least squares *straight* line is used here for purposes of illustration because it describes the easiest relation to understand. In practice it might not turn out to be the line of best fit.

In the example, where the relation of test scores to sales is being examined, the question arises whether a person's sales can be predicted

FIGURE 10–2

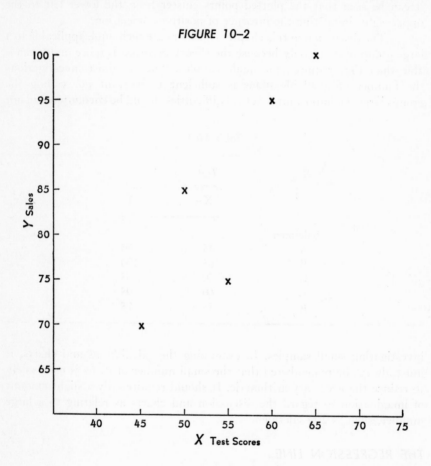

on the basis of his test score. In this particular problem, scores are the independent variable, X, and sales are the dependent variable, Y. The regression line represents the estimated sales. The original points on the scattergram were plotted using test scores and actual sales. The points on the regression line are located by plotting test scores from the X axis and estimated sales from the Y axis.

The estimated sales figures (which will be represented by the symbol Y_e) used to plot the regression line are obtained by fitting a least squares

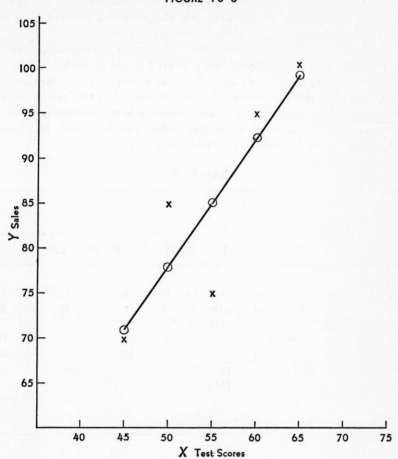

FIGURE 10–3

straight line to the original data. The formula for this straight line is

$$Y_c = a + bx$$

where

$$a = \frac{\Sigma Y}{N}$$

$$b = \frac{\Sigma x Y}{\Sigma x^2}$$

and x represents the difference between the average of the X values and each individual X value.

Now, as with the trend presentation in Chapter 12, *a* can be considered the "fulcrum" for the line. The line is balanced on this point. As will be indicated in the example, *a* is the estimated value of *Y* at the mid-point (arithmetic mean) of the *X* values.

b, on the other hand, determines the slope of the regression line. If *a* is thought of as the "fulcrum" for a lever, *b* would indicate its slope. If *b* is a plus value, it indicates that the lever is sloped from lower left to upper right; but if *b* is a minus value, it indicates that the lever is sloped from upper left to lower right. In correlation, *b* is the average number of units change in the dependent variable (sales) associated with every one-unit change in the independent variable (test scores).

Table 10-2

	Test scores	Sales								
	X	Y	x	xY	x²	Y_c	$Y - Y_c$	$(Y - Y_c)^2$	y	y²
Salesmen										
A	45	70	−10	−700	100	71	1	1	−15	225
B	65	100	+10	+1000	100	99	1	1	+15	225
C	50	85	− 5	− 425	25	78	7	49	0	0
D	60	95	+ 5	+ 475	25	92	3	9	+10	100
E	55	75	0	0	0	85	10	100	−10	100
	5)275	5)425		1475	250			160		650
				−1125						
	55	85								
				+ 350						

The calculations needed to compute the values of the regression formula are presented in Table 10-2. In this example, the arithmetic mean of the test scores, 55, is subtracted from each of the test scores to obtain small *x*. Multiplying these differences times each *Y* value (sales) gives the *xY* values requested in the *b* formula. Adding these values gives the numerator of the *b* formula. To get the denominator requires only squaring the *x* values and getting their total. *a* is extremely simple to get because it is merely the average of the *Y* values. Thus in this example,

$$a = 425/5 = 85 \quad \text{and}$$
$$b = +350/250 = +1.4$$

To get estimated *Y* (sales), it is necessary only to substitute these numbers for the letters in the formula

$$Y_c = a + bx$$

Thus for salesman A

$$Y_c = 85 + 1.4(-10) = 85 - 14 = 71$$

and for salesman D

$$Y_c = 85 + 1.4(+5) = 85 + 7 = 92$$

Also notice that for salesman E

$$Y_c = 85 + 1.4(0) = 85 + 0 = 85$$

verifying the preceding statement that at the mid-point of the X values a is the estimated value of Y. This is true because at the average of the X values small x is zero, so that in calculating the $Y_c = a + bx$ formula there is nothing to add or subtract from the a value at this point.

To locate the regression line, it is only necessary to take these estimated sales figures found in the Y_c column, plot them on the scattergram, and join the plotted points as in Figure 10-3. This line indicates the variability in Y (sales) that is associated with the variability in X (test scores).

The scattergram for this example, Figure 10-3, clearly indicates that the actual values differ from the regression-line values. In other words, all the variation in sales is not associated with the variability in test scores. Some factors causing a man to sell more or less of the product differ from factors causing him to get a high or low test score.

ACCURACY OF ESTIMATES

Because the estimated values differ from the actual values, some measure is needed to indicate how accurate the estimated figures are. A guess is in a sense an estimate, and as yet nothing has been done to indicate whether the estimates made in the example are any better than guesses.

Standard Error of Estimate

The standard error of estimate measures the accuracy of these estimates. It is calculated by means of the formula

$$s_y = \sqrt{\Sigma(Y - Y_c)^2/N}$$

Note that the standard error of estimate and the standard deviation (Chapters 5 and 6) are, in a sense, the same. Both are measures of dispersion, and they are calculated in the same way. The only difference between them is that the standard deviation measures the dispersion around a particular value (the arithmetic mean), whereas the standard error of estimate measures the dispersion around a line (the regression line).

A range of 1 standard deviation on one side of the arithmetic mean in a normal curve encompasses approximately 34 percent of the area under the curve; thus this range on both sides of the mean includes about 68 percent of the area. Similarly, if the actual points are dispersed around the regression line in a normal manner, approximately 34 percent of the plotted points will fall within a range of 1 standard error of estimate on one side of the regression line, whereas within that range on both sides of the line about 68 percent of the points will be located. As in the case of the standard deviation, plus and minus 2 standard errors of estimate would include about 95 percent of the plotted points and plus and minus 3 would include 99 + percent of the plotted points.

Calculating the standard error of estimate for the salesman example should contribute to an understanding of the nature and use of this measure. Notice in Table 10-2 the two columns headed $Y - Y_c$ and $(Y - Y_c)^2$. The first of these two columns is obtained by subtracting the estimated sales figures from the actual sales for each salesman. This procedure, of course, gives the difference in each instance between the estimated and actual values. Plus and minus signs are unimportant in these subtractions, because in the next column, $(Y - Y_c)^2$, each of these differences is squared. When these squared differences are totaled, the numerator of the s_y formula has been calculated. N is the number of salesmen in the example. Thus

$$s_y = \sqrt{160/5} = \sqrt{32} = 5.66$$

This measure can be plotted on the scattergram in Figure 10-4 by adding and subtracting the standard error of estimate from each of the estimated values.

Thus for salesman A

Estimated Sales	71	71
s_y	+ 5.66	− 5.66
	76.66	65.34

and for salesman B

Estimated Sales	99	99
s_y	+ 5.66	− 5.66
	104.66	93.34

Plotting each of the estimated values gives a new series of points on each side of the estimated values. The lines formed by connecting these points will be an equal distance from the regression line on each side.

Many assumptions underlie the interpretation of the standard error of estimate. Theoretically, if precise statements are to be made, the actual values should be infinite in number and should be affected only by chance. Nevertheless, even though these conditions are rarely encountered in practice, in the absence of serious distorting factors the same general

FIGURE 10–4*

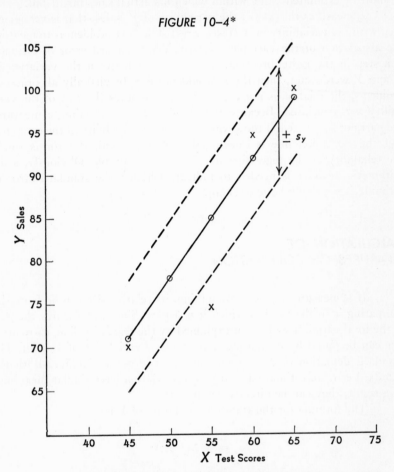

*Actually, on any of these diagrams, belts should not be used to describe distances around the regression line, because the sample is small. It must be emphasized that 5 items were used in the example only for brevity and clarity. Many more items should be used in practice, and these diagrams accurately picture the situation only if it is remembered that they apply to such a large group and not just to the 5 items actually plotted.

line of reasoning can be followed. If the distribution is reasonably normal, about 68 percent of the items would fall within the area between the two lines representing the standard error of estimate on the scattergram. Another way of stating this division is to say that 68 percent of the persons getting a score of 45 on this test, as did salesman A, would have sales between 65.34 and 76.66.[2] Thus the standard error provides a range within which an estimate has a certain probability of falling. Hence, if a new man should take the aptitude test, the standard error would indicate the range around the estimated value within which his actual sales might fall.

s_y measures the *part* of the variability of Y (sales) that is *not* associated with the variability in X (test scores). The next problem is to measure the association of the variables directly. The standard error of estimate is a step in the right direction. If the relation between the variation in X and Y were exact, then the s_y would be zero. In virtually all practical problems, the relation is not exact; thus s_y measures the *part* of the variability *not* associated. Because the standard error of estimate measures the part not associated, if the s_y value is large the reliability of the estimates and the regression line is questionable. If the standard error is small, the reliability of the regression line is more acceptable. Obviously, some arithmetic measure is needed to indicate whether the standard error of estimate is relatively large or small.

CALCULATION OF MEASURES OF CORRELATION

If s_y measures a *part* of something, its relative size can be found by comparing it to the total of which it is a part. Since s_y measures the *part* of the total variability of Y not explained by the regression line, its relative size can be found by comparing it to the *total* variability of Y itself. The standard deviation of Y is a measure of its total variability. Both the standard error of estimate and standard deviation have similar meanings; as a result, they can be directly compared.

The formula for the standard deviation of Y is

$$\sigma_y = \sqrt{\Sigma(y^2)/N}$$

y is found by subtracting each of the Y values (sales) from their average. These differences are then squared. The sum of these squared deviations is divided by the number of Y values to get an average. The square root of this average is the standard deviation of Y. If we use the y and y^2

---

[2] To make such a statement precisely correct, many definite assumptions are necessary concerning the factors affecting the variables, the distribution of the variables, and so forth. Such refinements have been omitted from this entire treatment of correlation. It is most important to understand the basic idea. Only then is it possible to appreciate such details. For the most complete treatment, see Mordecai Ezekiel, *Methods of Correlation Analysis* (New York: John Wiley & Sons, Inc., 1941); or Mordecai Ezekiel and Karl A. Fox, *Methods of Correlation and Regression Analysis* (New York: John Wiley & Sons, Inc., 1959).

columns from Table 10-2, the formula would read

$$\sigma_y = \sqrt{650/5} = \sqrt{130} = 11.4$$

This measure is plotted on the scattergram in Figure 10-5 together with s_y. The standard deviation represents the variation around the arithmetic mean; so 11.4, the σ_y, is added to and subtracted from the average of

FIGURE 10–5

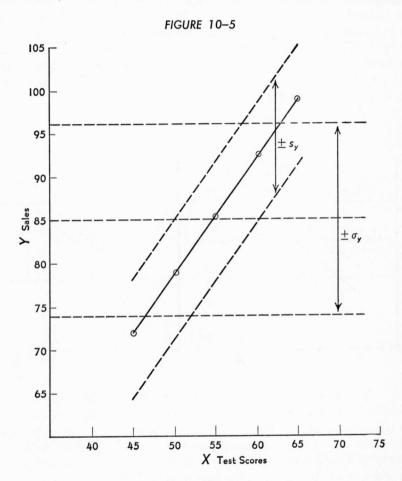

the Y values, 85; and the two values 96.4 and 73.6 are located on the vertical axis. A line is then extended across the scattergram at each of these values. To illustrate this idea more clearly, a line has been extended also across the scattergram at 85, the arithmetic mean of the Y values.

A rough idea of the amount of correlation can now be gained by a visual examination of the scattergram. The vertical distance between the regression line and the line on either side representing the standard error of estimate indicates the range of values within which about 68 percent of the items lie. This distance can be viewed as an indication of the *part* of the variability that is *not* associated. The σ_y, depicted by the vertical distance between the line representing the average of the Y variable and the lines on each side denoting the standard deviation, also encompasses about 68 percent of the values. This distance can be considered an indication of the *total* variability. Now, if the distance between the lines measuring the *part not* associated is small compared to the distance between the lines representing the total, most of the total must be associated. If the distance representing the *part not* associated is large when compared to that representing the *total*, most of the variation must not be associated and there would be very little correlation.

FIGURE 10–6

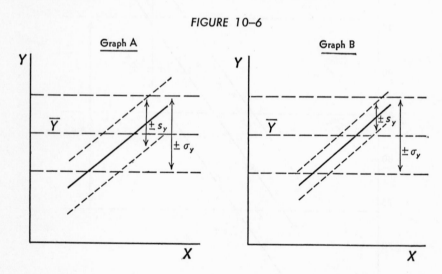

This type of comparison can be made by examining Figure 10-6. Graph A shows a condition where the vertical distance representing s_y is large compared with that representing σ_y. Correlation here is poor. In Graph B, the vertical distance depicting s_y is small compared with that depicting σ_y and correlation is good. If there were no correlation at all, s_y and σ_y would be equal and the lines would coincide.

The whole idea behind this approach to correlation is essentially simple. The standard deviation measures the dispersion of the items around their mean, whereas the standard error of estimate measures the dispersion of the same items around an average line—the least squares regression line. If the series of values represented by this least squares line is a better description of the relation between the variables than is the single value that the mean provides, the dispersion of the items around the line will be less than the dispersion around the mean. If the line perfectly depicts the relation, all the actual items will fall on it and there will be no dispersion at all. The less accurately the line describes the relation, the greater will be the extent of the dispersion. Where no correlation at all is present, the dispersion from the line will be as great as the dispersion from the mean. Consequently, a comparison of the standard error of estimate and the standard deviation indicates how much better a description of the relation the line provides than does the mean.

The measures of correlation commonly employed constitute mathematical expressions of this same relation. Because in actuality the squares of the standard deviation and the standard error of estimate accurately measure variation, they are employed in the formulas.

The Coefficient of Determination

The first important measure of correlation is the coefficient of determination. Its formula is

$$r^2 = 1 - s_y^2/\sigma_y^2$$

In the formula, this relation is expressed as a decimal fraction that can be easily converted into a percentage. The standard error of estimate squared—the part not associated—is divided by the standard deviation squared—the total variation. The resulting value multiplied by 100 is the percentage of the total variation *not* associated. By subtracting this percentage from 100 percent, the percentage associated is obtained. The great merit of the coefficient of determination is that it expresses the measurement of correlation in an easily understandable form. In the example,

$$r^2 = 1 - 32/130 = 1 - .246 = .754$$

These figures can be interpreted to the effect that .246 (25 percent) of the variation in Y (sales) is not associated with the variation in X (test scores). The coefficient of determination, r^2 (.754), indicates that about 75 percent of the variation is associated. Whether the nature of the relation is direct or inverse is determined by referring back to the b value in the regression-line equation. If the b is a plus value, the association is positive; if the b is a minus value, the association is negative.

The Coefficient of Correlation

The coefficient of correlation, r, is found by taking the square root of r^2. The coefficient of correlation is also a measure of how large the variation in the estimated values is in proportion to the variation in the original values.[3] In the example,

$$r = \sqrt{.754} = +.868$$

The possible values of the coefficient of correlation range from $+1$ to -1. If there is perfect positive correlation, Y varies directly with X and all Y variation is explained by the variation of X. When this is the situation, r will be $+1$. When there is perfect negative correlation where Y varies inversely with X and all variation is explained, r will be -1. Lesser degrees of correlation will result in smaller positive or negative values of the coefficient. The plus or minus sign attached to r indicates whether the relation is direct or inverse; positive coefficients indicate direct relation, negative coefficients denote inverse association. The sign of the coefficient of correlation is taken from the sign of b in the regression equation. If b is positive, r will be positive; if b is negative, r should be given a negative sign. Because the method of computation presented in this chapter always produces a positive r value, b must be checked in every instance to determine whether a negative sign should be used.

How large a value the coefficient of correlation should be to constitute good evidence of the association of the variables depends on the number of items in the sample. The larger the group of items, the smaller the r value that can be considered significant. This question of significance will be more thoroughly examined at the end of this chapter.

r is the most commonly used measure, but in some ways r^2 is preferable. The coefficient of correlation is an abstract number that does not have a direct meaning related to ordinary experience. On the other hand, the coefficient of determination, as noted above, can be interpreted as indicating the percentage of variation that is associated—an idea not difficult to grasp. Another problem arises from the use of a measure closely related to the coefficient of correlation. The square root of that portion of the formula subtracted from 1, .246 in the example, is called the coefficient of alienation. Now, if the portion of the formula subtracted from 1, representing the percentage not associated, happened to be .50, its square root would be .707. Under these conditions the coefficient of correlation would also be .707. It is at the very least confusing to say that alienation and correlation are both .707. Such a situation does not arise if the coefficient of determination is used.

[3] Both X and Y, test scores and sales, vary. Certain elements cause them to vary. Some of these elements affect both, whereas other elements affect only one of them. For example, knowledge of selling techniques might affect both the result on the aptitude test and the number of sales made. A physical characteristic, such as having only one eye located in the center of the forehead, might have absolutely no effect on a person's test score but might seriously affect the number of sales made. These examples indicate one element common to both variables and one element present in one but not the other. If all the elements affecting test scores and sales could be found, a proportion of the elements in each variable would be common. r^2 is the product of the two proportions of common elements and r is their geometric mean.

It should be noted that correlation can be found between more than two variables by the methods of partial and multiple correlation. Furthermore, many other relations than that depicted by a straight line may exist. In rank correlation, it is possible to compare such things as the standings of students in high school and in college to discover whether their position or standing is the same in both groups. Such techniques are, however, beyond the scope of this text.[4]

The more complex relations are based on the same theories and basic ideas that have been presented in the example of simple correlation. In any relation, the larger the coefficients of determination and correlation, the greater the association in the variability of the series considered.

OTHER RELATIONS

The formula used to calculate the coefficient of determination in the preceding discussion was

$$r^2 = 1 - s_y^2/\sigma_y^2$$

This formula made use of the relation between the standard deviation of the Y variable squared (σ_y^2), representing the total variation in that variable, and the standard error of estimate squared (s_y^2), representing the part of the variation not associated.

Although this is the easiest comparison to depict graphically, it might seem more logical to some to compare the total variation to the part associated rather than to the part not associated. The associated portion of the variation is represented by the standard deviation of the values of Y estimated by means of the regression line. These estimated values of Y differ from their mean because of the relation of the two variables described by the regression line. This variation is therefore associated and can be measured by the standard deviation of the estimated values. This measure is found by the formula

$$\sigma_{y_c} = \sqrt{\Sigma(y_c^2)/N}$$

y_c is found by subtracting each of the Y_c values from their average. These differences are then squared. The sum of the squared deviations is divided by the number of Y_c values to get an average. The square root of this average is the standard deviation of the Y_c values and represents the

[4] Admittedly, a certain amount of mathematical perfection is lacking in the formulas used in this chapter. This is an intended omission. Other methods may be slightly shorter and mathematically more refined, but this method has two outstanding advantages. The first of these is the simplicity of the algebra involved, which seems to be a prime consideration from the student's point of view. Secondly, the method used has a tremendous advantage in the relatively easy part-to-total comparisons that can be made and the simple graphs that can be drawn showing this comparison.

associated variation. If we use the y_c and y_c^2 columns from Table 10-3, this formula reads

$$\sigma_{y_c} = \sqrt{490/5} = \sqrt{98} = 9.89$$

r^2, the coefficient of determination, could now be found by directly comparing σ_y^2, representing the total variation, with $\sigma_{y_c}^2$, representing the associated variation. In the example this coefficient would be

$$r^2 = \sigma_{y_c}^2/\sigma_y^2 = 98/130 = .754$$

This approach compares the variation from the regression line (σ_{y_c}) to

Table 10-3

	Test scores X	Sales Y	Estimated sales Y_c	y_c	y_c^2
Salesmen					
A	45	70	71	14	196
B	65	100	99	14	196
C	50	85	78	7	49
D	60	95	92	7	49
E	55	75	85	0	0
			5)425		490
			85		

the variation of the original data (σ_y). If we follow this reasoning, correlation would be found by the formula

$$r = \sigma_{y_c}/\sigma_y = 9.9/11.4 = +.868$$

The plus sign is still obtained from the b value in the regression-line equation.

Notice that these formulas give the same answers that were found by the previous formula

$$r^2 = 1 - s_y^2/\sigma_y^2$$

The relation between these formulas is this:

$$\sigma_y^2 = \sigma_{y_c}^2 + s_y^2$$

In the example this relation would be expressed as

$$130 = 98 + 32$$

The total variation, represented by σ_y^2, is composed of two parts. One part, $\sigma_{y_c}^2$, is the associated variance; the other part, s_y^2, is the unassociated variance. Added together they must equal the total.

SHORT-CUT METHODS

The formulas used in the preceding sections of the chapter were selected because they are explainable in relatively simple terms. They use simple relations, such as a part-to-total comparison. If, however, it is desired to calculate the coefficient of correlation in as speedy a manner as possible, other formulas are available. An example of these is the "product-moment" method. This method permits computing r, when the relation between the variables is linear, without first obtaining the regression line and the standard error of estimate. The formula for this method is

$$r = \Sigma xy / N\sigma_x\sigma_y$$

All the symbols in this formula should be familiar. x and y represent

Table 10-4

	Test scores X	Sales Y	x	y	xy	x²	y²
Salesmen							
A	45	70	−10	−15	+150	100	225
B	65	100	+10	+15	+150	100	225
C	50	85	− 5	0	0	25	0
D	60	95	+ 5	+10	+ 50	25	100
E	55	75	0	−10	0	0	100
	5)275	5)425			+350	250	650
	55	85					

the deviations from the means of X and Y, and σ_x and σ_y are the standard deviations of X and Y. The calculations needed to compute the values of this formula are presented in Table 10-4. σ_y, the standard deviation of Y, has already been calculated by the formula

$$\sigma_y = \sqrt{\Sigma(y^2)/N}$$

and the σ_x is similarly found by the formula

$$\sigma_x = \sqrt{\Sigma(x^2)/N}$$

By using the data in Table 10-4,

$$\sigma_y = \sqrt{650/5} = \sqrt{130} = 11.4$$
$$\sigma_x = \sqrt{250/5} = \sqrt{50} = 7.07$$

With these values available, the product-moment formula is

$$r = \Sigma xy/N\sigma_x\sigma_y = +350/5 \cdot 7.07 \cdot 11.4 = +350/402.99 = +.868$$

The coefficient of correlation can be calculated much more efficiently by this method. The computations are easily adaptable to machine calculators, which permit a further increase in speed. It is important to note, however, that estimated values have not been calculated; in many instances, although they admittedly require additional effort, such estimates are necessary.

SIGNIFICANCE OF r:
THE z TRANSFORMATION

A previous section raised the question of how large a value of r is necessary to constitute good evidence that a significant degree of association or correlation exists between a dependent and independent variable. At that time it was pointed out that the answer depends on the number of observations available—the more observations, the smaller the value of r required. This answer is another of the many results provided by the type of analysis presented in Part III (Statistical Inference). The derivation of this answer will be examined in this section.

Some Examples

A firm purchases steel bars as an intermediate product in its over-all manufacturing process. Each of these bars is subjected to heat treatment as the next step in the manufacturing process. The amount of heat that each bar receives, however, depends on the breaking strength, which differs from bar to bar. The firm cannot test each bar for breaking strength directly, of course, because to do so would result in the destruction of each bar. However, if there is a significant relation between some characteristic, such as diameter at the center of each bar, and breaking strength, the firm can estimate the breaking strength of each bar without the necessity of destroying it.

The firm therefore selects 67 bars at random and statistically examines the relation between breaking strength and center diameter, obtaining an $r = .42$. If there is no relation, the population r will equal 0. The question, then, is, "What is the probability of selecting a random sample of 67 bars and obtaining a sample r of .42 if the population r is 0?" If we employ the results of Part III, if the probability is very small— for example, .05 or .01—we would reject the hypothesis that the population r equals 0 (that is, the difference between the sample r and the hypothetical population r would be statistically significant), and the firm would expect a valid relation to exist between breaking strength and diameter. (Whether this relation will solve the firm's problem, however, will depend on the accuracy of the estimate derived from the relation, and, as noted in a previous section, this accuracy depends on the standard error of estimate.)

As a second example, assume that 103 cities in the United States are picked at random and the relation between number of families in each city in 1964 and number of automobiles sold in each city in 1964 is analyzed statistically, yielding a coefficient of correlation of .82. An automobile manufacturer, who has access to census data relating to number of families in cities and towns all over the United States, is interested in knowing whether the apparent relation between number of families and number of automobiles sold is valid. If it is, he plans to allocate dealerships and set sales quotas on this basis.

If there is, in fact, no relation between these two variables, the population r will be 0. The relevant question, then, is "What is the probability of selecting a sample of 103 items at random and obtaining a sample r of .82 if the population r is actually 0?" Again, according to the results of Part III, if the probability is very small—for example, less than .05 or .01—the hypothesis that the population r equals 0 would be rejected; otherwise it would be accepted.

In both examples, the probability of obtaining a given sample r, if the population r is 0, is required. The following discussion of sampling theory shows how it can be obtained.

The z Transformation

Assume that an extremely large number of samples of size n is randomly selected with replacement from a population with a coefficient of correlation equal to some given value. To illustrate this point, 10,000 samples, each composed of 67 ($n = 67$) steel bars selected at random, could be examined to determine the relation between breaking strength and diameter. A sample r could be computed for each of the 10,000 samples, and a frequency distribution constructed. However, if the sample size is small and/or the population r is actually large (that is, close to 1), this "sampling distribution of r" will not be normally distributed around the population r; as a result, tests of significance based on the normal curve cannot be meaningfully employed.

The z transformation provides a way out of this dilemma. It can be mathematically proved that there is a mathematical relation[5] between a variable, called z, and the possible sample values of r such that (1) each r value corresponds to one and only one z value; (2) each z value depends only on the particular sample r obtained; (3) all z values corresponding to

[5] $z = \frac{1}{2} \log_e [(1 + r)/(1 - r)]$.

sample r's are normally distributed around the mean z value, which is equal to the single z value corresponding to the population r; and (4) the distribution of z values has a standard deviation, designated by the symbol σ_z, which can be calculated from the formula

$$\sigma_z = 1/\sqrt{n-3}$$

Thus any r value can be transformed to a z value. This transformation has been tabulated for all possible r values and is presented in Appendix Table VII. Thus an r of .82 becomes a z value of 1.16, and an $r = .42$ becomes a $z = .45$. Because the z distribution is normally distributed around the z value corresponding to the population r, there is only a 5-percent probability of getting a z value that differs from the z value corresponding to the population r by as much as $1.96\sigma_z$, only a 1-percent probability of obtaining a z value that differs from the z value corresponding to the population r by as much as $2.58\sigma_z$, and so on. This means, because each z value is uniquely related to an r value, the probability of obtaining different r values can be determined.

In the examples described earlier, the significance of r is determined as follows. In the first example, relating to the purchase of steel bars, $r = .42$ and $n = 67$. Appendix Table VII shows that $r = .42$ corresponds to $z = .45$, and $r = 0$ to $z = 0$. Furthermore, $\sigma_z = 1/\sqrt{n-3} = 1/\sqrt{64} = 1/8 = .125$

The particular z value, .45, obtained in the sample differs from the mean, 0, of all possible z values by 3.6 standard deviations:

$$(z - \bar{z})/\sigma_z = (.45 - 0)/.125 = 3.6$$

Because a difference as great as $2.58\sigma_z$ would occur only 1 percent of the time, the difference of $3.6\sigma_z$ would be considered significant. As $z = .45$ is significantly different from $\bar{z} = 0$, the r to which it corresponds, $r = .42$, would be significantly different from $r = 0$. That is, a $r = .42$ is too high, in this illustration, to be attributable to chance alone. The statistical evidence is not inconsistent with the existence of a positive relation between the breaking strength and diameter of the steel rods.

In the example pertaining to number of families and automobile sales, $r = .82$ and $n = 103$. Appendix Table VII shows that $r = .82$ corresponds to $z = 1.16$ and $r = 0$ to $z = 0$. Also,

$$\sigma_z = 1/\sqrt{103 - 3} = .1$$

Therefore

$$(z - \bar{z})/\sigma_z = (1.16 - 0)/.1 = 11.6$$

and, again, the sample results indicate a significant degree of relation between the dependent and independent variables.

Tests of Hypotheses concerning Values of r Other Than 0

The z transformation makes it possible to test hypotheses concerning values of r other than zero. For example, in the situation just discussed, should the hypothesis that the population r equals .3 be accepted? As before, the sample $r = .82$, the z value corresponding to it is 1.16, $n = 103$, and $\sigma_z = .1$. But now the hypothetical r is .3, and its corresponding z value (from Appendix Table VII) is .31. Thus a z value of 1.16 represents a difference of 8.5 standard deviations from a mean z value of .31:

$$(z - \bar{z})/\sigma_z = (1.16 - .31)/.1 = .85/.1 = 8.5$$

Therefore it would be concluded that the true population r is significantly higher than .3.

Sample Size and Significance of r

Earlier in the chapter it was pointed out that the greater the sample size, the smaller the value of r that would be required for significant correlation. This statement can now be illustrated. As noted above, when the sample size is 103, $\sigma_z = .1$. Now, as n (sample size) is reduced (for example, to 28), the standard deviation of the z distribution grows larger (if $n = 28$, $\sigma_z = .2$, in contrast to $\sigma_z = .1$ when $n = 103$). This relation implies that any given difference between a sample r and the hypothetical r will represent fewer standard deviations and therefore be less significant (that is, more probable to occur). For example, if, in contrast to the example discussed earlier, $n = 28$ instead of 103, the difference between $r = .82$ and $r = 0$ would represent $5.8\sigma_z$ $((1.16 - 0)/.2 = 5.8)$ instead of $11.6\sigma_z$. Though still significant, the difference is not as significant as it is in the earlier example.

To test his understanding of this point, the reader should verify that $r = .40$ is significant at the 5-percent level if $n \geq 27$, but not if $n < 27$. Thus if n is less than 27, r must be greater than .40 to be significant at the 5-percent level (for example, the reader can verify that if $n = 16$, r must equal .49).

CORRELATION AND FORECASTING

The importance of correlation and regression analysis in forecasting should be apparent by now. For this reason, just a few concluding remarks will be made.

If the correlation analysis has established that there is a relation between the dependent and independent variables, reliable forecasts of the dependent variable can be obtained by utilizing the derived regression equation. However, in order to use this equation to estimate future values of the dependent variable, values of the independent variable must be known. In the sales performance example employed in this chapter, this information presented no problem because each salesman would take a test as part of his job interview, and his probable sales performance over the coming period could be forecast. The value of the independent variable could always be determined in advance of the time period for which a forecast of the dependent variable was required.

However, this condition does not always exist. For example, if it has been determined that the quarterly sales of Company Z are closely related to United States shipments of fabricated steel products, Company Z's sales 3 quarters from now can be reliably forecast only if shipments of United States fabricated steel products 3 quarters from now are known. Because these shipments are not known now, they must be forecast. Thus, in order to forecast the dependent variable it is first necessary to forecast the independent variable. In some situations this procedure could result in a vicious circle that would provide no useful information for forecasting purposes.

However, if, for instance, a government or independent agency regularly makes 3-quarter forecasts of steel shipments that have been extremely accurate, Company Z's problem is solved. Or if Company Z can forecast these shipments more readily and/or accurately than they can make *direct* estimates of their own sales, the regression relation is useful.

Finally, if Company Z is fortunate enough to have its quarterly sales related to, let us say, steel shipped 3 quarters in the past, again reliable forecasts can be made. In a situation like this, steel shipments would be said to *lead* Company Z sales by 3 quarters. The correlation analysis would pair Company Z sales in each of the last, for example, 40 quarters with steel shipped *3 quarters before each of these 40 quarters.*

SUGGESTED READINGS

Chou, Y. L. *Applied Business and Economic Statistics.* New York: Holt, Rinehart and Winston, Inc., 1963, chap. 14.

Ezekiel, M., and K. Fox. *Methods of Correlation and Regression Analysis.* New York: John Wiley & Sons, Inc., 1959.

Neter, J., and W. Wasserman. *Fundamental Statistics for Business and Economics.* Boston: Allyn and Bacon, Inc., chap. 13.

1. When are two groups said to be correlated?
2. Does a high positive correlation between the increase in cigarette smoking and the increase in lung cancer prove that one causes the other?
3. Which would be more reliable—a weather forecaster whose predictions are always right or one whose predictions are always wrong?
4. "A least squares straight line will always correctly represent the average relation between two variables." Discuss.
5. Of what value is the regression line to the investigator if it accurately depicts the relation under study?
6. What would it mean if all the estimated values used to plot the regression line were the same as all the original values?
7. Which is preferable—a high positive or a high negative correlation?
8. Compare the meaning of the standard deviation and the standard error of estimate.
9. If the production of rice is the effect, and rainfall the cause, which would be designated as X and which as Y?
10. State clearly the meaning of the standard error of estimate.
11. Imagine a situation in which the standard deviation of the Y variable and the standard error of estimate are equal. State what the coefficient of correlation is in such an instance and why.
12. Assume the standard error of estimate to be zero. State what the coefficient of correlation is in such an instance and why. Assume that the standard deviation of Y is not zero.
13. The dispersion of the items around the regression line will be less than the dispersion of the items around the mean if ...?
14. When will the dispersion of the items from the regression line be the same as the dispersion of items around the mean?
15. Compare the meaning of r and r^2.
16. "A relation such as $r^2 = 1 - 568/400$ is impossible." Discuss.
17. Explain the meaning of the b in the least squares regression-line equation. What is it? What relation does it express?
18. $s_y^2/\sigma_y^2 = 0$ means...? Explain the meaning of this relation.
19. A coefficient of correlation of $-.88$ between television receivers produced per capita and the price of television receivers indicates what relation?
20. (a) What would be the value of the standard error of estimate if all the original points plotted on the scattergram fell on the regression line?
    (b) What would correlation be in such a situation?
21. Compare σ_y and σ_{y_c}.

22. State why $\sigma_y^2 = \sigma_{y_c}^2 + s_y^2$.

23. Compare the relations expressed by the formulas

$$r^2 = 1 - s_y^2/\sigma_y^2 \quad \text{and} \quad r^2 = \sigma_{y_c}^2/\sigma_y^2$$

24. (a) A study was made of circulation versus readership in relation to four Sunday Supplements. The study was made in Davenport, Illinois, and Fort Wayne, Indiana. The coefficient of correlation between "Readers per 100 Household Heads" and "Copies per 100 Families" was +.99. What conclusions can be made as a result of this study?

(b) The same type of study was made in the same locations in relation to six weekly magazines. In this study the correlation between circulation and readership was +.77. Why is the correlation between circulation and readership lower for magazines than it was for the Sunday Supplements considered in (a)? (SOURCE: Circulation vs. Readership, *NBC Study of Radio's Effective Sales Power*, New York: National Broadcasting Company, September 1952, pp. 15–16.)

PROBLEMS

1. Using the following data,
   (a) Calculate the coefficient of correlation.
   (b) Estimate the percentage of the group with lung cancer in a county where 15 percent of the group smoke heavily.

CITIZENS OF TIMBUTTWO IN 1965

County	Percentage of group smoking heavily	Percentage of group with lung cancer
A	10	5
B	20	15
C	25	10
D	35	25
E	30	20

2. Using the original information and the calculated standard error of estimate and standard deviation of Y, plot the data in question 1 above on a scattergram.

3. Using the following data,
   (a) Calculate r^2.
   (b) Calculate r.
   (c) Estimate the price per share of an issue with earnings of $5.50.

	Earnings per share	Price per share
Stock		
American Well	$4.80	$ 95.00
Boston Beans	4.50	101.00
Confrits	5.20	92.00
Delta Rudder	5.60	83.00
Everwearing Tire	5.40	89.00

4.

	Disposal personal income (billions)	Montbuck & Post sales (millions)
1960	206	1910
1961	254	1836
1962	284	1746
1963	314	2012
1964	322	2116

(a) Estimate Montbuck & Post sales when disposable personal income is $314 billion, as in 1957.
(b) How do you explain the difference between the estimated and actual sales for 1963?
(c) Compute the coefficient of correlation.
(d) Which of the two variables would be selected as X and which as Y? Why?

5.

	Rainfall (ounces)	Peanuts (hundred bushels)
Farm		
A	40	15
B	120	75
C	80	65
D	60	70
E	100	100

(a) What would be the estimated bushels of peanuts for a farm with 60 ounces of rainfall?
(b) Calculate the standard error of estimate and state its meaning in relation to the estimate made in (a).
(c) Calculate the coefficient of determination and state its meaning in relation to the two variables used.

6. The necessary calculations have been made to derive the values needed in a least squares equation using bond prices and bond yields. The average price of the 200 bonds considered was $150 and the average bond yield was $7. The b value in the equation is +$.50.

(a) Estimate the yield of a bond having a price of $156.

(b) The standard error of estimate is $1. Explain the meaning of this value as it applies to the estimate made in (a).

(c) The standard deviation of Y in this problem is $3. Compute the coefficient of correlation.

7. Using the following data,

(a) Estimate the number of persons passing all examinations if 3200 take all examinations.

(b) Calculate the standard error of estimate and state its meaning in relation to the answer in (a).

(c) Calculate the coefficient of correlation.

No. of Persons Passing C.P.C.U. Examinations
Compared to Number Taking the Examination

	No. taking all examinations	No. passing all examinations
1943	206	133
1944	263	172
1945	452	288
1946	556	361
1947	861	559
1948	1449	854
1949	2194	1333
1950	3066	1584
1951	2651	1418
1952	2252	1354
1953	2602	1455
1954	2865	1721
1955	2819	1682
1956	2697	1674
1957	2997	1819

Source: Application, Study Group and Examination Statistics for 1957 (Philadelphia: The American Institute for Property and Liability Underwriters Inc.).

8. Draw two scattergrams. On one, illustrate the relation between s_y and σ_y that would exist when there is good positive correlation; on the other, the relation that would exist when there is poor positive correlation.

9. Using the following data,

(a) Draw a scattergram.

(b) Calculate s_y.

(c) Calculate σ_y.

(d) Calculate the coefficient of correlation by relating σ_y to σ_{y_c}.

(e) Calculate the coefficient of correlation by relating σ_y to s_y.

(f) Plot the regression line, σ_y and s_y on the scattergram.

(g) Estimate the number completing all examinations if 5500 take examinations.

No. of Persons Taking Individual C.L.U. Examinations
and Number Completing All C.L.U. Examinations
(1948–1957)

	No. taking examinations	No. completing all examinations
1948	2885	250
1949	2967	341
1950	2794	449
1951	2310	380
1952	2539	367
1953	2775	391
1954	3177	397
1955	3630	407
1956	4176	435
1957	5034	561

Source: Table 6, "Significant Examination Data," *Annual Report of the American College of Life Underwriters* (Philadelphia: American College of Life Underwriters), p. 10.

10. The people of West Overage Valley make a living by raising cows and hens. It is finally decided that, for many reasons, the hens are becoming a public nuisance. It is the custom for people to bring cows with them when they come to the valley and to buy hens after arriving. The present residents decide to forbid anyone from settling who will probably acquire more than 75 hens.

Residents	Cows	Hens
A	15	100
B	35	50
C	45	30
D	20	70
E	55	20
F	10	120

(a) What is the coefficient of correlation?

(b) The Lone Stranger appears with 50 cows. How many hens will he probably acquire?

(c) John Chickenbill arrives with 25 cows. Will the residents permit him to stay?

11. (a) Using the following information, calculate the coefficient of correlation by the product-moment method.

(b) What does this answer indicate about the two methods of questioning?

LIST VERSUS FREE-RESPONSE QUESTIONS
CONCERNING PURCHASE OF DENTIFRICE
Percentage of sample
reporting purchase

	List	*Free response*
Colgate	27.7	29.9
Pepsodent	18.3	16.9
Chlorodent	11.9	15.1
Ammident	6.0	6.0
Ipana	5.9	6.0
Dr. Lyons	3.2	3.1
Listerine	2.8	1.7
Kolynos	0.9	0.5
Dr. West	0.7	0.6
Phillips	0.7	0.3
Squibb	0.4	0.2
Rexall	0.2	0.1
Others	6.8	6.6

SOURCE: Cross-Checks on Survey Data, *NBC Study of
Radio's Effective Sales Power* (New York: National Broadcasting Company, Sept. 1952), p. 14.

12. The following information is given:

$\Sigma(Y - \bar{Y})^2 = 100$, $\Sigma(Y - Y_c)^2 = 68$, $\Sigma Y = 20$, $\Sigma xY = 50$, $N = 20$,
$\Sigma(X - \bar{X})^2 = 80$, $\Sigma x^2 = 80$, $\Sigma X = 20$

(a) Calculate r^2, employing the product-moment method (carry all
calculations to the nearest tenth).
(b) Calculate r^2, employing the method that considers the relation
between the variability not associated and the total variability.
(c) Calculate the regression equation.
(d) Estimate Y, with 95-percent confidence, if $X = 2$.
(e) Is r statistically significant?

13. The following results have been computed by a statistician from data
for years of service (X) and weekly salary (Y) for 25 employees of a
retail store:

$\Sigma X = 80$ (years) $\Sigma x^2 = 5,500$ $\Sigma(Y - \bar{Y})^2 = 7,700$ $\Sigma(Y_c - \bar{Y}_c)^2 =$
$6,545$ $\Sigma Y = 1,240$ (dollars) $\Sigma xY = 5,000$

(a) Compute (to the nearest 10th) the equation for the line of regression.
(b) Compute (to the nearest 100th) the coefficient of determination,
using the concepts of "total," "explained," and "unexplained"
variation.

(c) Compute the coefficient of correlation, using the product-moment formula.

(d) Estimate, with 95-percent confidence, the salary of a person who has worked 5 years.

(e) Is r statistically significant?

(f) Is r statistically significant with respect to a population r of .2? (That is, could this sample have come from a population where the population r is .2?)

14.

UTAH, 1964

County	Average weekly disposable income per family	Average weekly consumption expenditure per family
A	80	70
B	60	50
C	70	65
D	40	40
E	120	80

(a) Compute (to the nearest 10th) the equation for the line of regression.

(b) Using the product-moment method, calculate the coefficient of correlation.

(c) Calculate the coefficient of determination, using the concepts of total, explained, and unexplained variation.

(d) Estimate, with 95-percent confidence, the average weekly consumption expenditure per family in a county that has average weekly disposable income per family equal to $100.

15. Shipments of cement by the Northeastern Cement Manufacturing Company and the value of new construction in the company's marketing area were as follows:

	X Value of new construction, billions of dollars (1957–1959 prices)	Y Shipment of cement, millions of barrels (average quarterly values)
1957	6.5	5.2
1958	9.9	7.3
1959	10.2	7.6
1960	10.8	8.2
1961	11.7	8.5
1962	13.9	9.5
1963	14.0	9.7

Carry all of the following calculations to the nearest hundredth.

(a) Calculate the coefficient of correlation.

(b) Assume that the value of new construction in the company's marketing area in 1964 is $18 billion at 1957–1959 prices. Predict the value of Y (average quarterly shipment of cement in millions of barrels).

(c) If the above assumption of $18 billion of new construction proves to be correct, how much reliance can be placed on the estimate for shipments?

CHAPTER ELEVEN

Index Numbers

Index numbers are introduced at this point in the text, not because they are directly used to prepare forecasts, but because many of the techniques employed in preparing forecasts utilize index numbers. For example, in correlation analysis either the dependent or the independent variable or both may be in the form of index numbers. Furthermore, the following chapters, particularly that dealing with seasonal indexes, will rely to a large extent on the concept of index numbers.

In addition to their use in forecasting, index numbers perform many other useful functions. These will be discussed in this chapter.

An index number is a special type of average that provides a measurement of relative changes from time to time or from place to place. The purpose of an index number is to represent, as fairly as one figure can, the average position of the many different figures from which it is calculated. Just as the arithmetic mean is used to represent a group of figures, the index number is used to represent the change taking place between two or more groups of figures selected from either different time periods or geographic locations. A narrower definition, which can be applied to indexes used to measure price variation, is that an index number "shows the average percentage change of prices from one point of time to another."[1]

In addition to providing a measure of relative change, index numbers also perform two additional services. In the first place, because they are numbers reduced to a more usable and understandable form, they are less unwieldly than large figures, such as total department store sales in dollars. They are percentages, which are easily compared. Secondly, although businesses are often reluctant to give out information concerning sales, profits, and the like, they may be induced to release some of the same data in the form of index numbers, which permit the absolute value of this

---

[1] Irving Fisher, *The Making of Index Numbers* (Boston: Houghton Mifflin Company, 1922).

restricted information to be concealed. Under such conditions, it is possible to present index numbers indicating whether a firm's profits or sales have increased or decreased over a period of years without revealing the total amount of these profits or sales.

METHODS OF CONSTRUCTION

There are many methods of constructing index numbers, and four of these are basic. In explaining these four methods, the techniques of computation will be illustrated through the use of steps rather than formulas, because index-number formulas appear quite formidable and give the impression of being extremely difficult and confusing. For the sake of simplicity and uniformity, in each instance a price index will be used as an example. This procedure should create no difficulty when other types of indexes are dealt with, because the basic method is the same, regardless of whether the index is one of prices, quantities, or values. It should be noted that, although an index number is a percentage, it is customary to omit the percent sign.

Relative of Aggregates Price Index

The name of each of the four methods to be presented suggests the technique of calculation. The first title, the "Relative of Aggregates Price Index," indicates that this index compares totals (aggregates) by changing the totals into percentages (relatives). This method involves the following steps:

1. Add the prices of the commodities included in the index for each year or place considered.
2. Divide each of the totals obtained by the total of the year selected as the base year.

For convenience only, the earliest year has been selected as the base year in Table 11-1, where an index number of this type is constructed to show the change in the price of coal, and in the examples used to illustrate the other methods. The base year is the year with which all other years are compared. Notice that the prices per ton of coal are added in each year. Next the sum of prices in the base year, $35.60, is divided into the sum of the prices in the given year, $37.12. The result gives a relative of 104, indicating that the prices of these commodities went up an average of 4 percent between 1962 and 1963. The relative for the base year (1962 in this example) is always 100.

This method has the unquestionable advantage of simplicity. In addition, should it ever become desirable to select a different year as the base of the index number, it is necessary only to use the totals in order to calculate the new index numbers. This base can be changed easily by using actual numbers, and no questionable manipulation of percentages is necessary.

For students who like formulas, the above computational procedure can be summarized by

$$RA = (\Sigma P_g / \Sigma P_b) \cdot 100$$

where RA designates Relative of Aggregates Price Index, ΣP_g designates

Table 11-1. RELATIVE OF AGGREGATES PRICE INDEX FOR THREE TYPES OF
COAL
(1962 = 100)

	1962 Price per ton	1963 Price per ton
Type of coal		
Anthracite	$12.80	$13.20
Bituminous	12.00	12.12
Coke	10.80	11.80
Totals	$35.60	$37.12
Index number	100	104

$$\$35.60\overline{)\$37.12} = 104.3 = 104$$

the sum of the prices of all goods in a given year, and ΣP_b the sum in the base year. In the above example,

$$RA = (37.12/35.60) \cdot 100 = 104$$

Average of Relatives Price Index

As the title indicates, this method involves getting an average of a group of relatives. The steps are

1. Express the price of each commodity as a relative by dividing the base-year price into the given-year price.

2. Add these relatives and get their average by dividing by the number of relatives.

In the example presented in Table 11-2, where once again an index of coal prices is constructed, relatives are calculated for each type of coal by dividing the 1963 price by the 1962 price. These relatives are added and the total 313 obtained. This total is divided by 3, the number of relatives in the column, and the average 104 obtained. In the base year, the relative for each commodity would be 100 and their average would, of course, be 100—the index for the base year. The index number derived by this method and the previous method are almost identical because the prices of the three types of coal are quite close to one another. Had they been considerably different, the two methods would have produced markedly different results.

The Average of Relatives method has an advantage over the preceding method. Although its computation is slightly more complicated, it permits a comparison of the values of each individual commodity involved. Thus it is possible to see clearly that coke coal rose 9 percent, an increase

Table 11-2.   *AVERAGE OF RELATIVES PRICE INDEX FOR THREE TYPES OF COAL*
(1962 = 100)

	1962	1962	1963	1963
	Price per ton	*Relatives*	*Price per ton*	*Relatives*
Type of coal				
Anthracite	$12.80	100	$13.20	103
Bituminous	12.00	100	12.12	101
Coke	10.80	100	11.80	109
Totals		300		313
Index numbers		100		104

$$3)\overline{313} = 104.3 = 104$$

far greater than that for the other two varieties of coal used in the example. Such a comparison was not possible in the Relative of Aggregates method.

This second method for constructing index numbers can be represented by the formula

$$AR = \frac{\Sigma \left(\frac{P_g}{P_b} \cdot 100 \right)}{N}$$

where AR designates the Average of Relatives Price Index, P_g/P_b the ratio of the price of a single good in a given year to the price of that good in the base year, $\Sigma(P_g/P_b \cdot 100)$ the sum of all these ratios (each multiplied by 100), and N the number of goods making up the group. In the above example

$$AR = 313/3 = 104$$

Relative of Weighted Aggregates Price Index

The preceding two methods have one great disadvantage in that the items included are not weighted according to their importance. If the commodities included in Table 11-3 are used, it would be a mistake to give the price of butter the same importance as the price of milk. Yet this is what is done when the Average of Relatives method is used—each price is implicitly assumed to be of equal importance. If, on the other hand, the Relative of Aggregates method is employed, butter, considering its high price, would be more important than milk, because all the prices

Table 11-3. **RELATIVE OF WEIGHTED AGGREGATES PRICE INDEX FOR THREE COMMODITIES**
(1938 = 100)

		1938			1964		
	Unit	Quantity consumed	Average price	Weighted price	Quantity consumed	Average price	Weighted price
Commodity							
Bread	loaf	12	$ .09	$1.08	12	$ .20	$2.40
Butter	pound	2	.40	.80	4	.75	1.50
Milk	quart	14	.13	1.82	16	.26	3.64
Totals				$3.70			$7.54
Index numbers				100			204
				$3.70)$7.54 = 204			

as quoted are summed to arrive at the aggregates. This method implicitly assumes that the significance of each item is measured by the value of the unit in terms of which its price is quoted. Actually, much more importance should be given to milk because it is consumed in much greater quantity than is butter.

If prices are to be weighted, they are usually weighted by quantities expressed in the units that the prices represent. Thus the price of milk is weighted by quarts of milk, the price of bread by loaves, and the like. Because of the importance of weighting in constructing an index number, much more will be said about it later. One point, however, must be stressed here. In a price index, price changes are measured; in a quantity index, quantity changes are measured, and so on. In measuring the change in anything, only the thing being measured can be permitted to change. For example, in measuring the change in prices by a price index, only prices can be permitted to change. Any weights selected must remain constant throughout. Thus, in the example in Table 11-3, the quantity of each item consumed by the average family in 1938 is used to weight the commodity prices in both 1938 and 1964.

The steps in constructing the Relative of Weighted Aggregates price index are

1. Weight the price of each commodity by multiplying the price each year by the weight selected.

2. Add these products to get the weighted aggregates.

3. Divide each of these totals by the weighted aggregate of the year selected as the base year.

In the example, the prices in 1938 and 1964 are weighted by multiplying them by the quantity consumed by the average family in 1938. These weighted figures are added; the result is a weighted total for 1938 of $3.70 and, for 1964, of $7.54. The 1938 total is then divided into the 1964 total; the result is a relative of 204. The index number for the base year would, as always, be 100.

This method has the same advantages as the Relative of Aggregates method in that it is relatively simple, and the base, if the same weights are used, is easily changed by using the totals to calculate a new index number. This method also has the advantage of introducing weights, thereby giving each commodity its proper importance in relation to the other commodities considered. It should be noticed, for instance, that in the example given in Table 11-3, butter is by far the highest-priced commodity. If the items had not been weighted, butter would have had the greatest effect on the index. After weighting the items, butter had the least importance in relation to the total of the commodities.

The following formula summarizes the computations required for this method:

$$RWA = [\Sigma(P_g \cdot W)/\Sigma(P_b \cdot W)] \cdot 100$$

Here, RWA designates the Relative of Weighted Aggregates Price Index, $P_g \cdot W$ the price of a product in a given year multiplied by the weight for that product, $\Sigma(P_g \cdot W)$ the sum of these weighted prices for a given year, and $\Sigma(P_b \cdot W)$ the sum of these weighted prices for the base year. In the present illustration,

$$RWA = (7.54/3.70) \cdot 100 = 204$$

Average of Weighted Relatives Price Index

The Average of Weighted Relatives method uses relatives, which indicate the change in price of each commodity, and weights these relatives according to the relative importance of each commodity. The steps in constructing this index number are

1. Compute a relative for each commodity by dividing the base-year price into the given-year price.

2. For each commodity, select prices and quantities sold from some single year. When the figures are multiplied together they give the value of the commodity sold during that year. These value totals will be employed as weights.

3. Weight the relative for each commodity by multiplying the relative by the value weight for that commodity.

4. Divide the total of the weighted relatives each year by the total of the value weights.

Table 11-4. **AVERAGE OF WEIGHTED RELATIVES PRICE INDEX FOR THREE COMMODITIES**
(1938 = 100)

		1938				1964		
	Unit	*Quantity consumed*	*Average price*	*Value weights*	*Relatives*	*Average price*	*Relatives*	*Weighted relatives*
Commodity								
Bread	loaf	12	$ .09	$1.08	100	$ .20	222	$240
Butter	pound	2	.40	.80	100	.75	188	150
Milk	quart	14	.13	1.82	100	.26	200	364
Totals				$3.70				$754
Index numbers				100				204
				$3.70)$754 = 204				

In the example given in Table 11-4, the prices in 1964 are divided by the prices in 1938; the result is a column of relatives. As will be explained in the discussion of weighting later in this chapter, values (not merely quantities, as in the preceding example) must be used to weight relatives. The prices in 1938, when multiplied by the quantities consumed in 1938, give value weights—the value of each commodity consumed in 1938. These value weights are multiplied by the relative for each commodity, and a series of weighted relatives obtained. Adding the weighted relatives gives a total of $754, and this total is divided by the total of the value weights, $3.70. This division gives the price index, 204, for these commodities in 1964 compared to the base year 1938. All base-year relatives equal 100; hence multiplying these by the value weights and then dividing their total by the sum of the value weights would give the base-year index 100.

It should be noticed that the index number found by this method in Table 11-4 and that of the preceding method found in Table 11-3 are identical. The same operations are performed in each method but in different order. The Average of Weighted Relatives method not only has the advantage of using weights, thereby giving each item its proper importance, but also enables a comparison to be made for each individual commodity involved. Thus it is possible to see that the price of bread increased 122 percent, much more than did the price of butter or milk. Of course, this advantage brings with it a disadvantage in that this index is somewhat more complicated to compute because it requires obtaining a relative for each item.

The formula that summarizes the calculation related to the construction of this type of index number is

$$AWR = \Sigma[(P_g/P_b) \cdot 100 \cdot W_v]/\Sigma W_v$$

where P_g/P_b is defined as in the formula for the Average of Relatives Price Index, $[(P_g/P_b \cdot 100 \cdot W_v)]$ is the price relative for a particular product in a given year multiplied by both the number 100 and the value weight for that product, $\Sigma[(P_g/P_b) \cdot 100 \cdot W_v]$ is the sum of all these weighted price relatives for a given year, and ΣW_v is the sum of the value weights. Thus, for the data of Table 11-4,

$$AWR = 754/3.70 = 204$$

PROBLEMS IN CONSTRUCTION

The four methods of index-number calculation presented in this chapter are, as was noted earlier, basic methods. Their usage is much like that of the accounting methods given in the first accounting course. These accounting methods are seldom met in practice in the identical form that they are presented in class, and yet they are basic to all accounting systems. Similarly, these four methods of index-number construction are also seldom met in practice in the identical forms that they have been presented in this chapter, and yet they are basic to all index-number construction.

Many problems are encountered in constructing a practical, workable index number. "What year should be the base year?" "What commodities should be included?" "What weights should be used?" These are among the many points that must be determined. Wesley C. Mitchell presents seven distinct operations involved in index-number construction:

1. Defining the purpose for which the final results are to be used
2. Deciding numbers and kinds of commodities to be included
3. Determining whether all these commodities shall be treated alike or weighted according to relative importance

4. Collecting actual prices of commodities selected and, in a weighted series, collecting data regarding relative importance

5. Deciding whether the form of the index number shall show average variations of prices or variations of a sum of actual prices

6. Choosing the base on which to compute relative prices if average variations are shown

7. Deciding on the form of average if averages are to be used[2]

Defining Purpose

The purpose of the index number is of central importance. The choice of commodities, of base year, and of weights all depends on the purpose of the measure to be calculated. Obviously, to get an index number of wholesale prices requires using different commodities, prices, and weights than would be used in the construction of an index number of retail prices.

Deciding Commodities to Be Included

As a general rule it can be stated that commodities whose physical characteristics are substantially uniform from market to market and year to year are preferable to other types. The change in the price of a particular grade of wheat, for instance, can be measured much more accurately than the change in the price of a man's suit. The quality of a particular grade of wheat remains the same from one year to another; the only thing that varies for each unit of wheat is the price. A man's suit, on the other hand, is not a uniform article, and the change in its price is much more difficult to measure accurately. The quality of a man's suit may vary with the price. For example, if an increase in the price of a suit from one year to another is accompanied by a corresponding increase in quality, then the price, in one sense, has not changed.

Another general rule is that the greater the number of commodities included in the index the more accurate will be the result. The prices of raw materials, manufactured products, farm products, and so on all vary in different ways. Raw-material prices, for example, show wider fluctuations than finished-commodity prices do. To make a general index number, such as an index of wholesale prices, samples must be taken from all the different groups that behave in peculiar ways.

Because different groups of prices fluctuate in their own distinct ways, it is necessary, when using an index number constructed by someone else, to study the list of commodities included in order to know what the index number really does measure. An index of wholesale prices cannot, for example, be used to indicate changes in the "cost of living" because the variations in retail prices are not the same as those in wholesale prices.

[2] Wesley C. Mitchell, *Bulletin 284* (Washington, D.C.: Bureau of Labor Statistics).

Determining Weights

Commodities are weighted so that each will influence the final result according to its relative importance. Actually, there is no question of using or not using weights, because commodities are always, in a sense, weighted. If a so-called unweighted index number is used, the problem of weighting is not explicitly recognized; nevertheless, weights are implicitly assigned. It has already been pointed out that, when the Relative of Aggregates method is employed, the implicit weights are the prices of the units included, whereas with the Average of Relatives method each commodity is implicitly weighted equally.

There really is no adequate reason for not weighting a group of commodities properly. Sometimes weights are not used because the collection of statistics indicating the relative importance of each item is extremely difficult, laborious, and expensive to assemble. In other peculiar situations, the people constructing the index number may believe that in the specific instance the results would not be significantly different if weights were used.

The problem of selecting weights is one of assigning importance. It should be clear that the significance of the price of a commodity usually depends on the number of units of the commodity that are sold. Consequently, when prices are being weighted, quantities sold are used as weights. On the other hand, when quantities are being weighted, the prices of these commodities are used as weights because the significance of a physical quantity depends on the price of the units. When either prices or quantities are expressed as relatives—that is, percentages of some base-period value—money value must be used to express their significance.

Once the weights have been selected, an important problem presents itself. Should these weights be changed periodically or kept constant? The answer depends on the purpose of the index number. Usually, an index number is intended to measure price change only or quantity change only—that is, to isolate the price or quantity change. In these circumstances, the weights must be kept constant.

If weights are kept constant, however, they will be inaccurate for most of the period covered by the index number. Few, if any, commodities maintain the same relative importance in the economy for even a very brief period of years. The longer the period of years covered by the index, the more their relative importance will probably change. As an extreme example, the decline in the use of whale oil for lighting purposes over the past 150 years might be mentioned. Certainly very few, if any, indexes— whether they are wholesale or retail, price or quantity—would be unaffected by the ever-occurring changes in the economy. The increased use of electricity and aluminum, the coming of radio and television, the increased use of prefabricated housing and frozen foods—all affect the economy and any indexes used to measure segments of the economy.

One of the outstanding problems in index-number construction is devising a weighting system that will accurately represent the commodities throughout the period covered by the index number. Many systems have been tried, such as getting the average importance of the commodities over a period of years, but no perfect system has yet been developed.

Collecting Data

Collecting the actual prices of the commodities included in the index number and, in a weighted series, collecting data regarding their relative importance are tremendous tasks. This is probably the main reason why indexes such as an index of wholesale prices are compiled by the federal government. It is difficult to imagine a private firm or agency with the facilities for obtaining the prices of hundreds of commodities from every major market in the United States each month or, for a smaller group of commodities and markets, each week. After a great deal of hard work, the federal government through the Bureau of Labor Statistics has managed to gather information of this type very successfully.

The proportions of this problem are so vast, however, that even the federal government does not attempt a census of all prices. It can be seen from this fact that the careful selection of samples is a necessary part of the problem of index-number construction. The compilation of adequate index numbers therefore requires a knowledge of the techniques of collecting and analyzing samples that were presented in Chapter 1 and Part 3. Because of a lack of data or extreme difficulties in ferreting out the needed information, the practical worker with index numbers is often forced to adopt techniques that are theoretically unsatisfactory, but a strong background of sampling techniques is necessary in any event.

Deciding the Form of the Index

If there is some advantage in measuring the change in price of each commodity included in the index, the index number must be in the form of an average of relatives. Each relative indicates the change in the price of each commodity. If this information is not needed, much less work is required to calculate the index number in the form of a relative of aggregates. This index number will show the variations of sums of actual prices.

Choosing the Base

The base year is the year to which all the others are compared. The base-year relative is always 100. This is a simple mathematical concept that exists in any division example: Whatever number is divided into another becomes 1 or 100 percent in relation to the answer. If an Average of Relatives type index is being computed, the relatives for each commodity in the base year are all 100. In any method of index-number calculation, the index number for the base year will always be 100, because the base-year value is always divided into the other year—given year—values.

There is considerable difficulty in selecting the year to use as the base precisely because it is the one to which the other years are compared. The base year must be one that permits comparison. If a year selected as the base came from the middle of a war-inflation period, the prices in all other years would be low by comparison. If a year were selected from the bottom of a depression, the prices in all other years would be high by comparison. Some base period must be selected which is "normal" in that it is neither a period of radically low or radically high prices.

At one time this selection may have been simpler than it is at present. In recent years it is impossible to find a year that can be agreed on as normal. A long depression, followed by World War II, a Korean War, and a long period of "cold-war" tension have provided a considerable number of years remarkably free of normality. For this reason recent practice has been to use the average prices for a group of years as a base. This method at least partially eliminates the effect of exceptionally high or low figures.

Even if some year or number of years is accepted as usable for a base, the problem is only temporarily solved. A base period too far in the past is, for most purposes, useless. One reason is that it is difficult to make accurate comparisons with a period too far in the past. The human ability to forget is a remarkable one. It seems unbelievable that many well-educated parents are unable to understand why their son finds it impossible to go through college on the same allowance that the parent had when he was in college. The price change in the past twenty years has been amazing, and yet it is difficult to remember the conditions existing twenty years in the past well enough to permit accurate comparison.

There are several other reasons why the base of an index number must be changed occasionally. Among these is that there is no interest in comparison with a base too distant in the past. Another is the fact that commodities change in importance to such a degree that a particular base period and series of weights will become meaningless.

For these reasons it is often desirable to bring the base of an index number more up to date by shifting the base to a more recent year. Shifting is also done if two index numbers are to be compared and each uses a different base period. Here it is necessary to shift the base of one so that they will both have the same base. The short method of base shifting is to divide all the index numbers in the series by the index number of the new base year. An example of this is found in Table 11-5. In this example two imaginary indexes are used. One represents the change in wages based on the year 1926, and the other indicates the change in profits based on 1930. As they stand in 1954, with a wage index of 250 and a profit index of 280, it would appear that profits rose more than wages. It is, however, senseless to make such a comparison as long as both indexes are based on different years. To compare them it is necessary that they both be based on the same year. In the illustration the profits index has been shifted so that the base year of both indexes is 1926. This shift was accomplished by dividing all the index numbers in the original profits index by 120, the original profits index for 1926, which is the year selected as the new base.

After shifting the base of the profits index to 1954 it appears that wages rose more than profits after 1926, because in 1954 the wage index is 250 and the shifted profits index is 233. If, however, the wage index had been shifted to the 1930 base year so that both indexes were based on 1930, it would appear that profits rose more than wages after 1930. In 1954

Table 11-5. BASE SHIFTING

	1926	1930	1934	1942	1947	1954
Index						
Wages	100	95	90	120	180	250
Profits	120	100	90	110	150	280
Profits shifted	100	83	75	92	125	233

the shifted wage index would be 263 and the profits index 280. These results seem at first to be contradictory but, if, expressed correctly, they are logical. Actually, they indicate only that wages rose more than profits after 1926 but profits rose more than wages after 1930. The comparison in each instance starts from a different base period. This fact illustrates another reason why the selection of a base period is of such paramount importance. The answer to the question "Did profits rise more than wages?" depends on the base year selected.

Deciding on Form of Average

If an Average of Relatives method is used, the question arises regarding which average should be used. The choice is determined by comparing the purpose of the index number with the characteristics of the different averages. Despite its disadvantages, especially the degree to which it is affected by extremes, the arithmetic average is the usual choice. One reason is that it is more widely understood than the other averages that might be more suitable in a particular situation, such as the geometric mean or median. Another is that, compared to such measures as the geometric-mean, the arithmetic mean is easier to compute and therefore involves less time and expense.

QUANTITY AND VALUE INDEXES

The material so far presented in this chapter specifically applies to the construction of a price index, a common type of index number. These general remarks, however, are equally applicable to quantity (output) and value indexes.

In calculating an unweighted quantity index, either by the Relative of Aggregates method or the Average of Relatives method, the only difference in procedure is that quantities instead of prices are totaled and compared. The same thing is true in calculating a quantity index by a weighted method, except that here, it must be emphasized, it is the quantities instead of the prices that would be allowed to vary from year to year.

Value of a product is found by multiplying its price times the quantity of the product. Thus, for example, the cost of all schools built in Texas times the number of schools would give the value of the schools in terms of total dollar cost. To calculate a value index for these schools would require only dividing this dollar value each year by the dollar value in a base year.

Nothing has been said in this chapter concerning the construction of an index measuring general business conditions. This type of index is a completely separate idea involving problems of time-series analysis not encountered in the construction of the usual index number. For this reason, the construction of indexes measuring general business conditions is included with the material on time series analysis.

COMMON INDEX NUMBERS

Information concerning specific index numbers used in practice can be obtained from the firm or government agency responsible for their preparation. It might be helpful to mention briefly a few of the most commonly used index numbers to indicate the type of information that is available.

Consumer Price Index

One of the most familiar index numbers, because of its wide use, is the Consumer Price Index compiled by the United States Department of Labor, Bureau of Labor Statistics, and published monthly. The complete title for this index is "Index of Change in Prices of Goods and Services

Purchased by City Wage Earner and Clerical Worker Families." The title clearly indicates the limitations of the measure. Information concerning wholesale prices, prices in farm areas, or prices for other than moderate-income families cannot be found in this particular index.

The Consumer Price Index had its beginning during World War I. During this period prices were rising rapidly, and such an index was needed for use in negotiating wage contracts, especially in the shipbuilding industry. The weights used in calculating this series were at first based on family expenditures between 1917 and 1919. In 1935 the Bureau revised the weights to correspond with family expenditures between 1934 and 1936. Weights were adjusted during World War II so that they would represent more correctly this period in which shortages and rationing were commonplace. After the war, the Bureau again adjusted the weights used so that postwar changes in spending patterns would be better represented. Another adjustment was made in 1953 in order that weights would represent family expenditures between 1951–1952. These illustrations provide an excellent indication of the extensive work done by the Bureau in compiling index numbers. Every attempt is made to make each series an "up-to-date" measure. Each revision of weights, such as the comprehensive revision in 1953, requires about 3–4 years of work on the part of the Bureau.

The present base period used in the Consumer Price Index is the period 1957–1959. The indexes prior to this date have been recalculated by the Bureau on the new base so that they are comparable. A sample of about 300 items is used in the calculation of the index, which is a weighted average of price relatives. Evidence of the wide use of this index number is found in the quantity of labor-management contracts designating it as the measure to be used for wage adjustments under the contract.

The wages of about 4 million workers are partly governed by this index. An indication of its importance to labor and management is the statement made by the Commissioner of Labor Statistics, Mr. Ewan Clague, that "...each point increase in the index amounts to about $160 million in wages for the union contracts, and perhaps $20 million more for the voluntary arrangements by the employer...."[3]

Wholesale Price Index

Another widely used index published by the Bureau is the Wholesale Price Index. This is the oldest continuous index published by the Bureau, and it is published both monthly and weekly. A quite condensed daily index based on the prices of 22 commodities is also published.

The monthly index uses the period 1957–1959 as its base and covers

[3] Ewan Clague, Commissioner of Labor Statistics, U.S. Department of Labor, "The Consumer Price Index in the Current Price Situation." Speech made to the Milwaukee Chapter of the Controllers Institute of America, Milwaukee, Wis., April 8, 1958, p. 13.

about 5000 separate price quotations and about 2000 commodities. No attempt is made to make the weekly index a continuous series, because when the monthly index becomes available it supersedes all of the weekly indexes for that particular month.

This index is calculated by the Average of Weighted Relatives method; the weights used are the total transactions reported in the 1957 Census of Manufactures. This series is designed to show price changes for all commodities sold in primary markets in the United States. The word "wholesale" means sales in large lots and does not mean the prices paid by wholesalers or jobbers. The term "primary markets" refers to the first important commercial transaction of a particular commodity, which is the one used in constructing the index.

The Wholesale Price Index serves many different purposes. It is often used in the periodic adjustment of long-term purchase or rental agreements because it serves as a proper measure for indicating the changing purchasing power of the dollar—except with regard to retail prices, where the Consumer Price Index is used. It also is used as an indicator of general economic change.

Index of Industrial Production

The outstanding quantity index number in this country is the Federal Reserve Index of Industrial Production. It also is calculated by the Average of Weighted Relatives method and is based on the period 1957–1959. This series is intended to measure physical output.

SUGGESTED READINGS

Fisher, I. *The Making of Index Numbers*. Boston: Houghton Mifflin Company, 1922.

Lewis, E. V. *Statistical Analysis, Ideas and Methods*. Englewood Cliffs, N. J.: D. Van Nostrand Company, Inc., 1963, chaps. 22-24.

Mills, F. C. *Introduction to Statistics*. New York: Holt, Rinehart and Winston, Inc., 1956, chap. 13.

Mitchell, W. C. *Bulletin 284*. Washington, D.C.: Bureau of Labor Statistics.

Riggleman, J. R., and I. N. Frisbee. *Business Statistics*. New York: McGraw-Hill Book Company, Inc., 1951, chap. 13.

Spurr, W. A., L. S. Kellogg, and J. H. Smith. *Business and Economic Statistics*. Homewood, Ill.: Richard D. Irwin, Inc., 1954, chaps. 12 and 13.

QUESTIONS

1. (a) "The purpose determines the type of index number to use." Explain.
   (b) How can an Average of Relatives Index number based on 1930 be shifted to a 1950 base?

2. Present two reasons for base shifting.
3. What should be considered in selecting a base year?
4. The concept of the arithmetic mean is important in constructing a good index number. Explain.
5. An index number is a special type of average. Discuss.
6. Besides providing a measure of relative change, index numbers perform two additional services. What are they?
7. List the steps involved in calculating a price index by the Relative of Aggregates method.
8. Indicate some of the decisions that depend on the definition of the purpose of the index number.
9. List the steps involved in calculating a price index by the Average of Relatives method.
10. Information pertaining to a firm may be presented in the form of index numbers that permit the firm to keep confidential the size of dollars sales, profits, and the like. Explain.
11. Why is it true that commodities whose physical characteristics are uniform from market to market and year to year are preferable in index-number construction?
12. Sampling techniques are important to agencies concerned with the construction of general index numbers. Why?
13. List the steps involved in constructing a quantity index by the Relative of Weighted Aggregates method.
14. Why are commodities weighted in obtaining an index number?
15. There is no such thing as an unweighted index number. Discuss.
16. Usually weights are kept constant, even though they will be inaccurate for most of the period covered by the index number. Why?
17. Why is it unlikely that a private firm will undertake the preparation of a wholesale price index?
18. List the steps involved in constructing a price index by the Average of Weighted Relatives method.
19. Because of the lack of "normality" in recent years, the average values for a group of years are usually used as the base period in current index numbers. Discuss.
20. The choice of a suitable base period is at best a temporary solution. Why?
21. Discuss the wisdom of the popularity of the arithmetic mean in index-number construction.
22. The constant change in the weights used by the Bureau of Labor Statistics in calculating the Consumer Price Index has increased rather than decreased the usefulness of this index number. Explain.
23. Would it be wise for American women to adopt the habit of examining the Wholesale Price Index each month so that they might do the family food shopping more intelligently?

24. Which one of the four basic methods of index-number construction is involved in the calculation of the Wholesale Price Index?

25. Decide whether the following statements are true or false and present your reasoning:
    (a) The Consumer Price Index can be used to measure changes in total family spending.
    (b) The Consumer Price Index is designed to measure the average change in the prices of goods and services bought by city wage-earner and clerical-worker families.
    (c) The Consumer Price Index measures the changes in family spending that result from changes in the family's standards of living.

26. Are the following statements true or false? Present your reasoning:
    (a) The Wholesale Price Index is an excellent measure of the general purchasing power of the dollar.
    (b) The Wholesale Price Index is designed to provide a continuous monthly series showing price changes for all commodities sold in primary markets in the United States.
    (c) The Wholesale Price Index measures prices paid by industrial consumers.

PROBLEMS

1. From the following information calculate
   (a) The unweighted Average of Relatives Price Index for 1964, using 1955 as the base year
   (b) The Relative of Weighted Aggregates Price Index for 1964, using 1955 as the base year and using base-year weights

	Price		Quantity	
	1955	1964	1955	1964
Commodity				
A	$ 2.50	$ 2.00	400,000 ft.	450,000 ft.
B	.80	.60	250,000 yds.	300,000 yds.
C	24.00	20.80	750,000 lbs.	900,000 lbs.

2. (a) Using the data below, calculate the Average of Weighted Relatives Price Index for 1958, using 1950 as the base year and base-year weights.

	Price		Quantity exchanged	
	1950	1958	1950	1958
Commodity				
Coal	$18.00	$24.00	50,000 tons	60,000 tons
Oil	.10	.12	20,000,000 gal.	25,600,000 gal.
Wood	1.50	2.00	1,500,000 bu.	2,000,000 bu.

    (b) Exactly what does this index mean?

    (c) Discuss briefly the major problems of index-number construction.

3. From the following data (1938 = 100) calculate

    (a) The Average of Weighted Relatives Price Index for each year using base-year weights

    (b) The Relative of Weighted Aggregates Price Index for each year, using base-year weights

		Price			Quantity (millions)		
	Unit	*1938*	*1948*	*1958*	*1938*	*1948*	*1958*
Commodity							
A	pound	$ .30	$ .40	$ .20	125	105	75
B	peck	.90	1.00	.60	65	100	50
C	gallon	3.50	4.00	2.50	40	12	15

4. Assume that in 1958 new commodities enter the market and it is desirable to construct an index number including these new commodities yet continuous with the index numbers calculated in question 3 above. The new index number is 100 in 1958 and 120 in 1959.

    (a) Shift the answers found in 3 (a) above to the new base year.

    (b) Shift the answers found in 3 (b) above to the new base year.

5. Using the following data and 1954 as the base year, compute the price index for 1964 by (a) the Average of Weighted Relatives method with base-year weights, (b) the Relative of Aggregates method.

CHILDREN'S COST OF LIVING INDEX

	1954 Price	*1954* Quantity weekly	*1964* Price	*1964* Quantity weekly
Popsicles	5¢	5	7¢	8
Comic books	20¢	2	25¢	4
Cones	7¢	3	10¢	4
Candy	1¢	6	2¢	7

6. The average cost of the farm price-support program from 1932–1939 was $280 million a year. From 1950–1956 the annual average was approximately $857 million. "In terms of constant (1956) dollars the average based on deflation by the consumer's price index would be $548 million for the 1932–1939 period and $880 million for the 1950–1956 period." (SOURCE: *Toward a Realistic Farm Program,* Committee for Economic Development, December 1957, pp. 18–19.) Using the above information, explain the reason for deflating values such as these.

7. (a) "According to the information below, in 1956 in Boston consumer prices were .9 percent higher than they were for the entire United States." Discuss the correctness of this statement.

    (b) Shift the base of these index numbers to 1951.

	U.S. Consumer Price Index	Consumer Price Index for Boston
1920	85.7	89.1
1930	71.4	74.8
1940	59.9	61.7
1945	76.9	77.3
1950	102.8	103.2
1951	111.0	110.0
1952	113.5	112.4
1953	114.4	112.7
1954	114.8	113.2
1955	114.5	113.7
1956	116.2	117.1

Source: U.S. Department of Labor, Bureau of Labor Statistics.

8. (a) Compute an index of average weekly wages for certain industries, using the following data, by the Relative of Weighted Aggregates method with 1950 as the base year and using base-year weights.

(b) What additional information might be gained by calculating the wage index by the Average of Weighted Relatives method?

(c) Even though additional information might be gained by using the Average of Weighted Relatives method, the Relative of Weighted Aggregates method would be more likely to be used. Why?

AVERAGE WEEKLY GROSS EARNINGS IN CERTAIN INDUSTRIES, 1948–1956

	1948	1950	1952	1954	1956
Contract construction	$68.25	$73.73	$87.85	$93.98	$101.83
Automobiles	61.86	73.25	82.82	88.91	94.71
Food and kindred products	51.11	55.29	63.23	68.47	75.03
Textile mill products	45.59	48.95	53.18	52.09	57.57
Leather and leather products	41.66	44.56	50.69	50.92	56.02

Source: U.S. Department of Labor, Bureau of Labor Statistics.

SEASONALLY ADJUSTED AVERAGE MONTHLY EMPLOYMENT IN CERTAIN INDUSTRIES, 1948–1956
(in thousands)

	1948	1950	1952	1954	1956
Contract construction	2169	2333	2634	2593	2993
Automobiles	655	702	644	624	652
Food and kindred products	1187	1143	1137	1102	1105
Textile mill products	1280	1200	1101	976	966
Leather and leather products	367	353	343	331	341

Source: U.S. Department of Labor, Bureau of Labor Statistics.

9. (a) Using the data presented in problem 8, prepare a quantity index by the Average of Relatives method with 1950 as the base year.

   (b) Do the data presented give an indication of the reason why the relatives for some of the industries considered moved in a different direction from that of the relatives for the "contract-construction" industry?

10. (a) Plot both index numbers on a chart.

	1929	1934	1939	1944	1949	1954	1956
Consumer Price Index (1947–1949 = 100)	73.3	57.2	59.4	75.2	101.8	114.8	116.2
Mfg. Production Worker Employment Index (1947–1949 = 100)	68.3	55.1	66.2	118.1	93.8	101.8	106.7

   (b) The purchasing power of the dollar as measured by consumer prices is the reciprocal of the Consumer Price Index. Calculate the purchasing-power index for the years given.

11. Using the data presented below, calculate the
    (a) Relative of Aggregates Price Index
    (b) Average of Relatives Price Index
    (c) Relative of Weighted Aggregates Price Index
    (d) Average of Weighted Relatives Price Index
    Use 1958 as the base year, and use base-year weights.

		Price		Quantity (millions)	
	Unit	1958	1963	1958	1963
Commodity					
Wheat	bu.	.50	.60	20	25
Potatoes	peck	.40	.30	10	20
Tomatoes	lb.	.20	.50	100	80

12. Two series of index numbers, one series representing the cost of living and the other representing the prices of agricultural commodities, are presented below.

	1948	1953	1958	1963
Index				
Cost of living	100	95	105	170
Farm prices	140	100	120	180

   (a) Which series shows the greatest relative increase?
   (b) If you were representing agricultural interests, how would you organize the data so that you most advantageously present your

argument for increased farm supports? Bear in mind that, although statistically unsound and perhaps even unethical, each series can be put on a different base year. Thus this question can be answered by putting each series on a different base year (making for a meaningless comparison), as well as by picking the most advantageous common base year.

CHAPTER TWELVE

Time-Series Trend

When quantitative data are arranged in the order of their occurrence, the resulting statistical series is called a *time series*. Monthly records of industrial production in the United States, annual birth-rate figures for the entire world, state reports on weekly unemployment, and records of the daily sales of tooth paste in a corner drugstore are all examples. Each has the common characteristic of enumerating magnitudes that vary with the passage of time.

Time series are influenced by a variety of forces. Some of these forces are continuously effective, others make themselves felt at recurring intervals, and still others are nonrecurring or random in nature. The job of the investigator is first to break down or decompose the data and study each of these influences in isolation. Then, armed with a fuller understanding of the nature of the forces at work, he can analyze their combined interactions. Such a study is known as *time-series analysis*.

THE IMPORTANCE OF TIME-SERIES ANALYSIS

Time-series analysis is important to both the businessman and the economist. It enables them not only to develop a more adequate understanding of the past and present but also to foresee the future more clearly. For the businessman to evaluate the current position of his firm he must know the manner in which his costs and prices have been behaving and whether production and sales objectives are being realized. He should be aware of how his firm's performance compares with that of his immediate competitors, the rest of the industry, and the economy as a whole. It is essential also that he have fairly precise ideas regarding future sales prospects. If expansion is in the offing, more personnel will be required, entailing not only the hiring of workers but also training periods of varying lengths. Should enlarged sales volume necessitate the construction of new facilities, this need must be anticipated far enough in advance to allow for the completion of the work. Expansion poses financial problems as well as production problems. If more goods are going to be sold, larger inventories will have to be carried, the volume of accounts receivable will rise, and outlays for current operations will necessarily be increased. Hence the investment in working capital will have to grow. Additions to fixed facilities often involve tying up substantial sums for long periods of time. The skillful executive in analyzing these needs must rely in whole or in part on time-series analysis.

It is not enough to forecast pleasant or desirable events. Should declining sales be in prospect, early and adequate forecasts may enable management to prepare the firm to withstand the strain. Such preparations may involve building financial reserves, curtailing expensive and unprofitable operations, or reducing fixed commitments. In some fortunate situations it may even be possible for the firm to forestall or offset the impending difficulty. At the present time various companies are diversifying their operations for the purpose of minimizing the total impact of declining sales in any one product line. The Procter and Gamble Company, on the other hand, has been able to eliminate most of the seasonal variation in its operations by altering its techniques of distribution. Nevertheless, all such compensatory or preventive measures are based on the type of understanding of the problem that time-series analysis provides.

The economist also relies very heavily on time-series analysis. It is of particular use in the study of economic fluctuations, which has commanded so much attention in recent years. An excellent example is found in the investigations of the National Bureau of Economic Research, which has analyzed the cyclical behavior of approximately 1000 specific time series representative of particular industries and processes in the economy. Other studies of this problem, although usually less comprehensive, have been equally dependent on time-series analysis. When the interrelation of variables, such as Federal Reserve Discount Rates and the volume of bank credit, are being examined, time-series analysis frequently can be very helpful.

The forecaster of general economic movements, like the businessman predicting the sales of an individual enterprise, must rely to a great extent on his interpretations of historical data organized into time series. Further, many forecasting techniques are based on the projection of past behavior into future, either with or without significant modifications. In view of the fact that most programs of economic stabilization depend on adequate warning of impending difficulties, the significance of time-series analysis in this area is indeed great. Although only a few examples have been cited, it should be evident that the study of the behavior of time series is of central importance to both the businessman in running a firm and the economist in attempting to understand or predict the operation of our business system.

ELEMENTS OF TIME-SERIES VARIATION

The variation of time series is usually broken down into four component elements: secular trend, seasonal variation, cyclical variation, and random or irregular influences.

The Secular Trend

The secular trend is the long-term movement of the series, reflecting continuous growth, stagnation, or decline. In Figure 12-1, where the data both for total employment in nonagricultural establishments and for

FIGURE 12–1. *Employment in Nonagricultural Establishments*

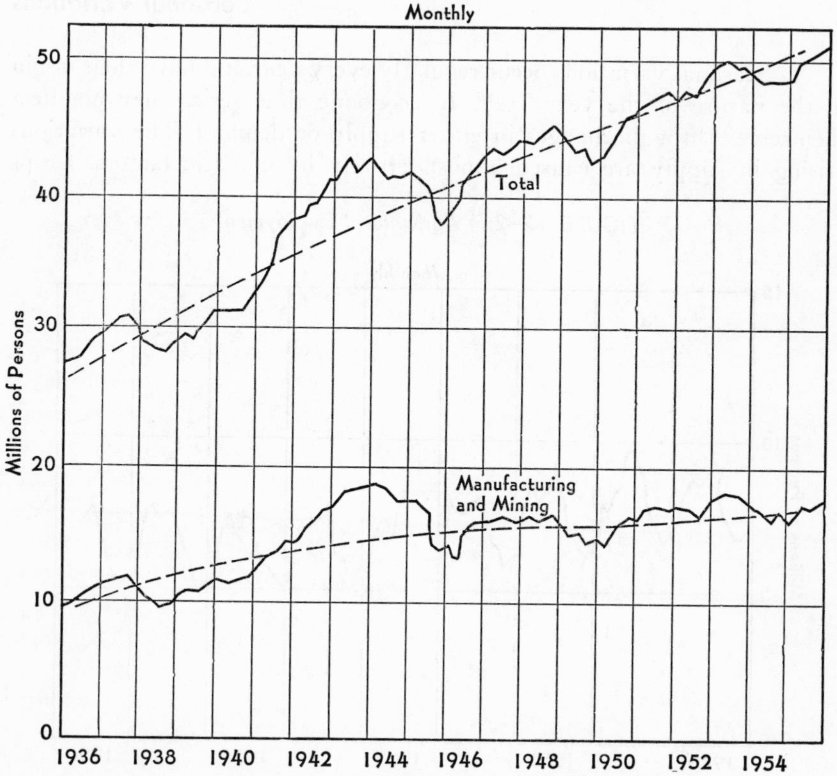

SOURCE: Board of Governors of the Federal Reserve System.

employment in manufacturing and mining alone are plotted, it is evident that despite the numerous fluctuations of each series there is a general sweep or trend in both types of employments. These trends are suggested by the dashed lines. The trend is the result of whatever fundamental forces shape the long-term development of the series in question. For example, the trend of total output in the economy as a whole is based on such factors as the state of technology, the size of the population, the proportion of population normally employed, the supply of capital equipment and natural resources, and the effectiveness of the manner in which production is organized. In the United States this trend has been rising at a rate of approximately 3 percent per year for many years. The elements underlying secular trend are embedded in the social, economic, and political institutions of the community, which, although by no means immutable, change but slowly. Consequently, trends usually are slow and continuous movements rarely subject to sudden alteration. Although the actual values of the series may vary considerably from the trend because of the influence of other elements, the trend is nonetheless operative in determining their values.

Seasonal Variations

Seasonal variations occur regularly every year and have their origin in the nature of the year itself. In economic time series they manifest themselves through changes in either supply or demand. The variations arising in supply are caused almost entirely by climatic factors. Crops

FIGURE 12–2.   Agricultural Employment

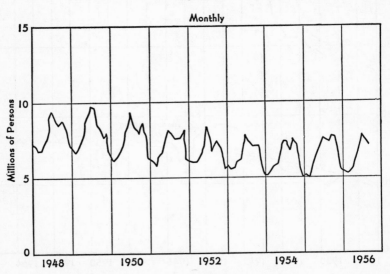

SOURCE: Board of Governors of the Federal Reserve System.

can be harvested only at certain times of the year, many avenues of transportation are open only during limited periods, and certain types of construction can be undertaken only when weather conditions are favorable. Variations in demand, on the other hand, may have their origin either in weather or custom. The demand for such goods as light-weight clothing, cool drinks, and air-conditioning equipment expands during the summer because of climatic factors, whereas the demand for gifts during the Christmas season or for fashionable clothing immediately before Easter has its source in the customs of the community. Nevertheless, whether the variations make themselves felt through changes in supply or in demand, or whether they are caused by climate or custom, they recur in a regular and predictable manner each year. Figure 12-2 illustrates the highly seasonal behavior of agricultural employment.

Cyclical Variations

If both the secular trend and the pattern of seasonal variation are known, it might be expected that the actual value of the data would approximate a figure representing these two forces. However, this approximation usually does not occur. Typically, the real magnitudes of the data will either exceed or fall short of the value that trend and seasonal considerations would lead one to expect. At times such deviations are the result of noncurrent or random factors. More often, however, the variations recur, even though not periodically, and they reflect basic institutional influences in the economy. These repeating variations, persisting longer than a year, are called cycles. In Figure 12-3 the cyclical fluctuations in the data for industrial production are readily apparent. Peaks occur in 1948, 1951, 1953, and 1955, but troughs can be noted in 1949, 1952, and 1954.

Most familiar is the cycle of general business that is envisioned as continuously moving through four phases. Depression is followed by recovery, which in turn develops into prosperity. When prosperity has run its course it gives way to recession, and this leads once again to depression. Because the business cycle is general, it influences most economic time series. Few businesses prosper during depression, and most concerns enjoy better than normal results during prosperity. Nevertheless, many industries exhibit patterns of cyclical behavior that at times are considerably different from the cycle of general business. The construction industry for many years has been going through cycles averaging approximately 18 years in length. The automobile, textile, and electrical-appliances industries have in recent years manifested behavior substantially at variance with that of the general cycle. For example, in 1956, when total activity was achieving a record high, automobile production dropped sharply. However, this lack of conformity of individual series in no way

FIGURE 12–3.   Industrial Production

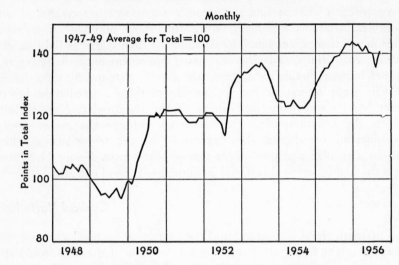

SOURCE: Board of Governors of the Federal Reserve System.

reduces the value of cycle analysis either for the particular industry or for the economy as a whole.

Irregular or Random Factors

Irregular or random factors give rise to nonrecurring variations that cannot be explained as either secular, seasonal, or cyclic in nature. They may stem from several sources. Natural catastrophes such as floods, droughts, or earthquakes may be responsible. Sudden changes in demand or very rapid technological progress may also be included in this category, as well as would wars and other international disturbances that exert profound influences. In Figure 12-1, a substantial bulge in nonagricultural employment during the years of World War II is the result of that irregular element. Developments on the political scene such as the passage or repeal of tax or labor legislation must certainly make themselves felt. The common denominator of every random factor is that it does not come about as a result of the ordinary operation of the business system and does not recur in any meaningful manner.

Problems of Classification

Although it is a simple matter to classify the factors affecting time series into these four groups for analytical purposes, the actual application of the classification frequently presents serious problems. Seasonal variations are no means always so uniform in amplitude and timing that their identification can be made with certainty. Consequently, the investigator is often hard put to distinguish seasonal influences from cyclical or random factors. Long and severe cycles may, to some observers, appear to be changes in the direction of the secular trend. During the great depression of the 1930's, for example, many leading economists interpreted the existing conditions, not as a cyclical depression, but as "secular stagnation."

Another difficulty arises because the four components of time-series data are not mutually independent of one another. An exceedingly severe seasonal may aggravate or even precipitate a change in the cyclical movement. Conversely, the cyclical influence may seriously affect the seasonal. A very rapidly rising trend virtually eliminates seasonal and cyclical variations, especially if this rise is so rapid that it dictates capacity operations. On the other hand, a firm that has greatly expanded facilities by reinvesting the profits of an unusually high prosperity will probably experience a permanently higher trend of sales, although another firm that had to sell plant and equipment to maintain solvency during depression will have its sales trend depressed. Thus the cycle can affect trend. Random elements can alter any of the other components: the development of cold-storage facilities has greatly reduced the seasonality of the consumption of many foods; the creation of the Federal Reserve System altered the pattern of behavior of credit over the cycle; and the Eighteenth Amendment obviously changed the trend of consumption of alcoholic beverages in the United States.

Finally, the fourfold breakdown of time-series data when applied to general economic conditions has frequently been challenged on analytical grounds. Bratt sees, not one trend, but two: a primary trend representing the long-term growth of productive capacity, and the drift away from it, which he calls secondary trend.[1] Schumpeter developed an even more detailed breakdown by identifying three cyclical components: the 3-year Kitchin cycle, the 10-year Juglar cycle, and the 50-year Kondratieff cycle.[2] The divergence of opinion among eminent scholars indicates clearly that the fourfold breakdown is mere approximation, convenient to employ but frequently subject to modification.

Mathematical Statement of the Composition of Time Series

The combined influence of the components of time series is often represented by the following equation:

$$O = T \times S \times C \times I$$

[1] Elmer C. Bratt, *Business Cycles and Forecasting* (Homewood, Ill.: Richard D. Irwin, Inc., 1952).

[2] J. A. Schumpeter, *Business Cycles* (New York: McGraw-Hill Book Company, Inc., 1939).

Here O denotes the original data, T the secular trend, S the seasonal variation, C the cyclical movement, and I the irregular or random element. If this formula is employed, the seasonal, cyclical, and random items are not viewed as absolute amounts but rather as relative influences. Thus a seasonal index of 106 percent would mean that the actual value is 6 percent higher than it otherwise would be because of seasonal influences. Although the relation of the components may not always be of this kind, it is sufficiently typical to be employed in the analysis of most elementary problems.

METHODS OF MEASURING TREND

Before proceeding with an attempt to measure secular trend it is advisable to check and, if necessary, edit the data. Should the purpose of the investigation be to measure the physical volume of industrial production, data presenting the value of industrial output in current dollars would require correction to eliminate the influence of rising price levels. Also it is essential that all the items of data employed for trend computation should be comparable—that is, they should be measuring the same thing in the same way. If data for the first years of the industrial output series were drawn primarily from durable producer-goods industries but items for the latter years emphasized consumer-goods production more heavily, comparability would obviously be lacking. Once the data have been edited, they should be plotted on a graph in order to facilitate visualization of the general sweep of the series.

Manual Trend-Fitting

In some series the drift of the data is so clear that a freehand line can easily be drawn to represent the secular trend. However, although the over-all direction of the trend may be discernible, it is usually difficult to determine the precise or even approximate location of the trend line in this manner. Under such circumstances those not highly skilled in freehand trend-fitting will find it necessary to resort to some form of mathematical computation. Nevertheless, a specialist of long experience who is familiar with the institutional setting, history, and behavior of the series may well be able manually to fit a trend superior to one derived by mathematical means.

Moving Averages

The moving-averages method of measuring trend is based on the idea that, if the values of the series for a sufficient period of time are averaged, the influence of shorter term fluctuations will be eliminated.

At a minimum this period should equal the length of a single business cycle, and preferably it should encompass several cycles. In this way the influence of the cycle will presumably be averaged out of the data. Seasonal variations create no problem because in most instances annual data are employed in trend computations.[3]

A moving average is computed by adding the values for some number of years both before and after to the value for the year for which the average is being obtained and then dividing by the total number of years included. In Table 12-1, the 3-year moving average for 1951, 662, was found by adding the values for 1950 and 1952 to the value for 1951 and dividing the total, 1987, by 3. The 1952 average is derived when the sum of the values for 1951, 1952, and 1953 is divided by 3. Thus, each year

Table 12-1. THREE-YEAR MOVING AVERAGE OF THE SALES OF GASOLINE
The Standard Oil Company of New Jersey

	Thousands of barrels per day	3-year moving total	3-year moving average
1950	597		
1951	664	1987	662
1952	726	2154	718
1953	764	2288	763
1954	798	2418	806
1955	856	2548	849
1956	894		

SOURCE: 1956 *Annual Report*, The Standard Oil Company of New Jersey.

the earliest year is dropped and the next later year is added. The 3-year moving average computed in this manner for the sales of gasoline by The Standard Oil Company of New Jersey is shown by the dashed line in Figure 12-4. It should be noted that it does smooth out the more extreme variations of the data. Were a 5-year moving average to be computed for 1952, the two preceding year values, 597 and 664, and the two succeeding year values, 764 and 798, would be added to 726, the 1952 figure, and the total, 3549, divided by 5. This would yield a 5-year moving average of 710.

The computation becomes somewhat more complex when an even number of years is employed in the moving average. Here, obviously, the same number of years before and after the given year cannot be included. As a result, the moving average has a mid-point that lies between

[3] Even when monthly or quarterly data are used, a moving average covering several years would eliminate seasonal influences.

two years and consequently represents no one year. This problem is resolved by computing two moving averages, the first containing an even
number of years including one more year before the given year, and the
second containing one more year after. These two moving averages themselves are then averaged. For example, to compute a 4-year moving average
of gasoline sales by Standard Oil for 1952, the values of 1950 through
1953 are averaged by dividing the 4-year total, 2751, by 4; the result is 688.
Then the values for 1951 through 1954, which total 2952, are averaged;
the result is a second 4-year moving average of 738. These two averages are
then averaged; the result is the centered 4-year moving average for 1952
of 713.

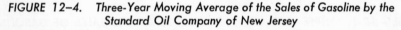

FIGURE 12–4.   Three-Year Moving Average of the Sales of Gasoline by the
Standard Oil Company of New Jersey

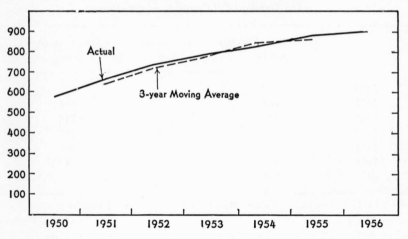

The moving-averages method has the advantages of being easily
understood and of minimizing the influence of extreme items. However,
it possesses several shortcomings that reduce its usefulness for many
purposes. (1) A moving average, by its very nature, can never be brought
up to date. Consequently, it can be of little value for current-period analysis
or for projections. (2) Although it seeks to eliminate cyclical influences
by employing averaging periods that are multiples of the length of the
cycle, this effort is frustrated by the fact that cycles are by no means
uniform in duration. Although a very long averaging period minimizes
this problem, it causes the average to lag by long periods and renders
it more difficult to compute. (3) When cyclical fluctuations are irregular
in their amplitudes, the cyclical variation would not be eliminated even
by a moving average whose period coincides with that of the cycle. (4)

Finally, when the trend situation is not linear (a straight line), the moving average lies either above or below the true sweep of the data. Consequently, the moving average is appropriate for trend computation only when (1) the purpose of the investigation does not call for current analysis or forecasting, (2) the trend is linear, and (3) the cyclical variations are regular both in period and amplitudes. Unfortunately, these conditions are encountered very infrequently.

Fitting Least Squares Lines

The values for secular trend may be determined by mathematical means. What is sought is a line of best fit, one that represents the movements of the data most satisfactorily. A so-called least squares line is often considered to be such a line because of two properties that it possesses. First, the sum of the squares of the deviations of the actual values from it is less than from any other line of the same shape, and, second, the sum of the deviations, when deviations above the trend are given positive signs and deviations below negative, is zero. These characteristics should already be familiar because they are also properties of the arithmetic mean. Consequently, a least squares line may be thought of as an average line in the same way that the mean is often viewed as an average single value.

The sum of the squared deviations from a least squares straight line are less than from any other straight line, and those from a least squares second-degree parabola less than from any other second-degree parabola that might be fitted to the data.[4] However, the same conclusion cannot be reached when curves of different shapes are compared. The sum of the squared deviations from a parabola, other than a least squares parabola, might be less than those from a least squares straight line. The indication would then be that a parabola is a better description of trend than a straight line is. Finally, the least squares method does not indicate what kind of trend line should be fitted; this decision must be made by the investigator. However, once the decision has been made, it gives formulas for lines of that type that will best fit the data.

The formula for a straight-line trend can most simply be expressed as

$$Y_c = a + bX$$

Y_c is the ordinate or numerical value of the trend,[5] a represents the ordinate of the trend at the middle of the time period from which trend is computed and for which X is assigned the value of 0, b is the amount by which the trend rises or falls with the passage of each unit of time, and X is the number of units of time each given year lies away from the middle

[4] A parabola is a curved rather than a straight line.
[5] Y_c means the calculated value of Y.

of the period. (See also Chapter 10.) Thus a trend formula of $Y_c = 10 + 3X$ would mean that at the origin (middle of the period when this method is used) the trend ordinate would be 10. It would also mean that with the passage of each period of time the trend will increase by 3. At the end of 3 years, for example, the trend value would be 19.

Table 12-2. COMPUTATION OF LEAST SQUARES STRAIGHT-LINE TREND SALES
OF GASOLINE
The Standard Oil Company of New Jersey
(Odd Number of Years)

| | Thousands of barrels per day | | | | |
	Y	X	X²	XY	Y_c
1950	597	−3	9	−1791	613
1951	664	−2	4	−1328	661
1952	726	−1	1	− 726	709
1953	764	0	0	0	757
1954	798	+1	1	798	805
1955	856	+2	4	1712	853
1956	894	+3	9	2682	901
Totals	5299	0	28	1347	

$$a = \Sigma Y/N \quad = 5299/7 \ = 757$$
$$b = \Sigma XY/\Sigma X^2 = 1347/28 = 48$$

The values of a and b for a least squares straight-line trend are found by solving the following equations:

$$a = \Sigma Y/N$$
$$b = \Sigma XY/\Sigma X^2$$

Here the Y values are the actual values of the series for the period used in the computation, N the number of values included, and the X values are those assigned to each time period. Thus in Table 12-2, where the trend of gasoline sales is computed, ΣY, the sum of the Y values, comes to 5299. When this sum is divided by N, in this example 7, the value of a is found to be 757. The value of b is calculated by dividing the sum of the XY's (1347) by the sum of the X^2's (28). This yields the b value of 48. It should be pointed out that when this method of calculation is employed the origin is assumed to lie at the middle of the series. In Table 12-2, the year 1953 is the middle year and is assigned the zero X value. Years before 1953 have negative X values, and years after 1953 have positive X values.

The ordinates of the trend are computed by substituting in the trend equation. This procedure involves multiplying the X value for the year by b and adding this figure to a. In the gasoline sales example the value for 1953 is, of course, 757, because X is 0. For 1954, when X is 1, 48 (1 × 48) is added to 757 to give 805. For 1956, 3 times 48 is added to 757 to give 901. For years prior to 1953, the multiples of b are subtracted from a. The trend of gasoline sales by Standard Oil is indicated by the dashed line in Figure 12-5.

FIGURE 12–5.   Least Squares Straight-Line Trend Sales of Gasoline by the
                Standard Oil Company of New Jersey

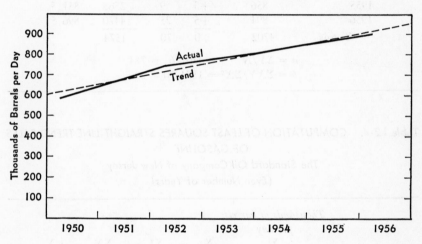

If there should be an even number of years in the period used for trend computation, there will be no middle year. The exact center of the series will fall between 2 years, at midnight on December 31. This difficulty is overcome by having X represent periods of 6 months rather than a year. Because the value of any year is assumed to lie at the middle of the year, the value for the first of the 2 middle years is −1 and the second +1. This value indicates that the middle of the first of these 2 years is 6 months before the center of the series and that the middle of the second comes 6 months after. In Table 12-3, trend is computed by using an even number of years. Consequently, the value of −1 and +1 is assigned to 1953 and 1954, respectively. Because the period designated by X is now only 6 months, the passage of a year causes a change of 2 in X. Thus the value of 1954 is +1 and the value of 1955 is +3. The values

Table 12-3. COMPUTATION OF LEAST SQUARES STRAIGHT-LINE TREND SALES
OF GASOLINE
The Standard Oil Company of New Jersey
(Even Number of Years)

	Thousands of barrels per day Y	X	X²	XY	Y_c
1951	664	−5	25	−3320	671.5
1952	726	−3	9	−2178	716.5
1953	764	−1	1	− 764	761.5
1954	798	+1	1	798	806.5
1955	856	+3	9	2568	851.5
1956	894	+5	25	4470	896.5
Totals	4702	0	70	1574	

$$a = \Sigma Y/N \quad = 4702/6 \ = 784$$
$$b = \Sigma XY/\Sigma X^2 = 1574/70 = 22.5$$

Table 12-4. COMPUTATION OF LEAST SQUARES STRAIGHT-LINE TREND SALES
OF GASOLINE
The Standard Oil Company of New Jersey
(Even Number of Years)

	Thousands of barrels per day Y	X	X²	XY	Y_c
1951	664	−2.5	6.25	−1660	671.5
1952	726	−1.5	2.25	−1089	716.5
1953	764	− .5	.25	− 382	761.5
1954	798	+ .5	.25	+ 399	806.5
1955	856	+1.5	2.25	+1284	851.5
1956	894	+2.5	6.25	+2235	896.5
Totals	4702	0	17.50	787	

$$a = \Sigma Y/N \quad = 4702/6 \ = 784$$
$$b = \Sigma XY/\Sigma X^2 = 787/17.50 = 45$$

for a and b are computed in exactly the same manner as before. It should be noted that b will be a smaller figure because it represents the change occurring in 6 months rather than a year. The ordinates are again computed by substituting X values in the trend equation.[6]

Another technique of handling the computation of trend using an even number of years is to assign the first of the 2 middle years the X value of $-.5$ and the second $+.5$. Earlier years will be -1.5, -2.5, and so on, and later years $+1.5$, $+2.5$, and so on. The advantage of this method is that the value of b remains the annual increment of change rather than becomes the 6-month increment, as in the method above. It should be noted in Table 12-4 that b is 45 when this second method is used, which is exactly twice the 22.5 obtained with the first technique.

Conversion of Annual Trend Values to Monthly Values

Usually annual figures are employed in trend computations. Nevertheless, it is sometimes desirable to obtain monthly trend ordinates. In converting straight-line trends from an annual to a monthly basis, two situations must be clearly distinguished. For series such as sales, production, or earnings, the annual figure is the total of the monthly figures. Here it is necessary to divide both a and b by 12 to reduce them to monthly levels. In other words, on the average, monthly sales or production is one-twelfth of the annual total. The b value must then be divided by 12 once again in order to convert from annual to monthly increments. The reason is that series such as sales or production change on the average only one twelfth as much during a month as during a year. Thus b is divided by 144. Should X in the trend-line equation represent only 6 months, b is divided by 72 instead of 144. If the annual figures are not compiled by totaling monthly data, as is the situation with series reporting prices, inventories, or employment, a remains unchanged and b is divided by 12 to convert from annual to monthly increments. If X represents 6 months, the latter division will be by 6.

If the investigator knows in advance that monthly trend ordinates will be required, much of the difficulty in converting the values to a monthly basis can be avoided by using data expressed as monthly averages. Then the only correction required to convert to monthly increments, would be to divide b by 12.

[6] The technique of trend computation that has been presented shortens the labor of computation by choosing the middle year as the origin. This method causes the values of the sum of the X's to be zero. Had some other year been chosen, the values of a and b could have been obtained by solving the following two equations simultaneously:

$$\Sigma Y = Na + b\Sigma X$$
$$\Sigma XY = a\Sigma X + b\Sigma X^2$$

*Fitting
a Geometric Straight Line*

The straight-line trend, which has just been discussed, changes by constant amounts each year, and for this reason is called an *arithmetic* straight-line trend. Such a pattern of variation is characteristic of many series. However, several other patterns are also frequently encountered. One of the most important of these, which will suffice here as the only detailed example of more complex trend patterns, is found where series seem to change by a constant percentage rather than by a constant absolute amount each year. When such a series is plotted on an arithmetic grid, a curve results; on a semilogarithmic grid it appears as a straight line. Under these conditions a *geometric* straight-line trend is appropriate. The formula for such a line is

$$\log Y_c = a + bX$$

Its meaning is that the value of the series at the origin is successively multiplied by the antilog of b; in other words, there is a constant percentage of change.

The method of computation is essentially the same as that employed in the arithmetic straight-line trend except that logarithms of the Y, a, and b values are employed. The formulas are

$$a = (\Sigma \log Y)/N$$
$$b = (\Sigma X \log Y)/\Sigma X^2$$

Table 12-5 illustrates the computations involved in fitting a geometric straight line to the data on gasoline sales. When the antilogs of the $\log Y_c$ values are plotted, together with the original Y values, on an arithmetic grid, a curvilinear trend will result.

Several other types of trend situations are by no means unusual. The sweep of the data may indicate that a smooth curve would best indicate trend. Here a second-degree parabola could be appropriate. Such a curve would have a formula of the following type:

$$Y_c = a + bX + cX^2$$

On the other hand, some series pass through periods of slow growth followed by rapid expansion, after which the rate of growth slows down once more. An industry passing from a stage of experimentation to one of exploitation and finally into a period of stability or saturation illustrates this pattern. Such a trend pattern is best described by a mathematical line called a Gompertz curve. Although no attempt will be made to illustrate the computation of the more complex lines, it is important to realize that they are available and to utilize them should the situation warrant.

Table 12-5.   COMPUTATION OF A GEOMETRIC STRAIGHT-LINE TREND SALES
OF GASOLINE

The Standard Oil Company of New Jersey

| | Sales (thousands of barrels per day) | | | | | | |
	Y	log Y	X	X²	X log Y	log Y_c	Y_c
1950	597	2.7760	−3	9	−8.3280	2.7911	618
1951	664	2.8222	−2	4	−5.6444	2.8192	660
1952	726	2.8609	−1	1	−2.8609	2.8473	704
1953	764	2.8831	0	0	0	2.8754	751
1954	798	2.9020	1	1	2.9020	2.9035	801
1955	856	2.9325	2	4	5.8650	2.9316	854
1956	894	2.9513	3	9	8.8539	2.9597	911
Totals		20.1280	0	28	.7876		

$$a = \Sigma \log Y / N = 20.1280/7 = 2.8754$$
$$b = \Sigma X \log Y / \Sigma X^2 = .7876/28 = .0281$$

The trend equation is $\log Y_c = 2.8754 + .0281\ X$

SELECTION OF THE TYPE
OF CURVE TO BE FITTED

There are many curves that can be fitted to time-series data. The more complex the curve, the more nearly it will approach the points of the series. In fact, if enough constants are included in the equation for the least squares line, it can be made to pass through each actual observation. Such a curve would be of little value because it would not be describing trend, which is the general movement of the series, but rather depicting every variation. The actual choice cannot be made on grounds of minimizing deviations or other mathematical criteria, but rather must reflect the informed judgment of the investigator. The type of trend chosen should have characteristics that correspond to the known or expected characteristics of the series. It should, if possible, be in line with corroborating evidence from other sources. It should minimize the influence of random or cyclical factors that are not indicative of secular movements. The procedure of selecting the type of curve to be fitted can be summarized as follows:

1. Examine the plotted data to see if a general movement exists.
2. Decide which curve or curves could reasonably be fitted to the data.

3. Compare the characteristics of each type of curve considered with the characteristics of the series and other supporting information.

4. Fit the curve that best describes the sweep of the data.

A word of caution is necessary at this point. Some curves that would adequately fit past observations cannot be used for projections because at higher values of X they act in a manner inconsistent with the expected behavior of the series. Consequently, a different type of curve may have to be fitted for a forecasting investigation than would be used for an historical study. Also, should a change occur in the fundamental forces affecting the data during the observed period, one type of curve may well have to be fitted to the first part of the series and a different one employed for the remainder.

CHOICE OF THE TREND PERIOD

In order to simplify the discussion of trend computation, the numerical examples in this chapter have been based on periods of only 6 or 7 years. However, whenever possible, the period should be longer. Over a long span of years the fundamental forces underlying trend have an opportunity to manifest themselves more clearly. The longer the period, the less the trend values will be distorted by cyclical or random influences. For example, a trend computed from the data gathered in the 1930's would in most instances be far too low, and figures from either the 1920's or 1950's alone would probably be too high. The period employed should encompass a number of business cycles and should begin and end in such a way that distortion is avoided. This purpose can be accomplished by using a period that starts and finishes either in prosperity or depression, or by beginning during recovery and ending during recession. It would also be acceptable to begin in recession and end in recovery. In this way there would be no concentrations of prosperous or depressed data at certain points in the period that might distort the slope of the trend. To begin the period in prosperity and end in depression, for example, would cause an upward slope to be less than the sweep of the data justifies.

THE EXTRAPOLATION OF TREND

Trend analysis may be employed to forecast future levels of time-series data. This process, called extrapolation, merely requires the extension of the trend to cover future periods. By substituting in the trend-equation values of X for the dates for which forecasts are desired, the ordinates for those dates can be obtained. For example, the trend of daily gasoline sales computed in Table 12-2 may be extended to 1970 by assigning X the value of 17. When the equation $Y_c = 757 + 48(17)$ is solved, the ordinate is found to be 1573. Care must be taken in interpreting such a forecast. First, this is a forecast of trend only. Actual values may be expected to diverge from it because of cyclical and random factors. Second, the forecast has meaning only if the same basic influences that shaped the trend in the past can be expected to be controlling in the future. Thus extrapolation implicitly assumes that the institutional pattern will be quite stable. All too frequently economic and business forecasts based on the extrapolation of past trends go far wide of the mark because significant changes in conditions governing the values of the data cannot be or are not properly anticipated. Many predictions of the level of production between 1956 and 1960 made during the late 1940's have already proved to be incorrect for this reason. In other instances institutional changes that have occurred in the recent past are ignored or assigned little weight when trends based on more remote periods are extended into the future. That such procedure leads to erroneous forecasts is by no means surprising. Finally, the type of curve employed must not only properly describe the past movement of the data but also be capable of sensible extrapolation. As was pointed out above, the extrapolation of some trends, especially the more complex curves, may yield results that are essentially meaningless.

SUGGESTED READINGS

Bratt, E. C. *Business Cycles and Forecasting.* Homewood, Ill.: Richard D. Irwin, Inc., 1953, chap. 3.

Chou, Y. *Applied Business and Economic Statistics.* New York: Holt, Rinehart and Winston, Inc., 1963, chaps. 16, 17.

Croxton, F. E., and D. J. Cowden. *Applied General Statistics* (2d ed.). Englewood Cliffs, N.J.: Prentice-Hall, Inc., 1955, chaps. 12 and 13.

Mills, F. C. *Introduction to Statistics.* New York: Holt, Rinehart and Winston, Inc., 1956, chap. 10.

Neiswanger, W. A. *Elementary Statistical Methods* (rev. ed.). New York: The Macmillan Company, 1956, chap. 15.

QUESTIONS

1. In what ways do time series differ from other arrangements of statistical data?
2. Explain each of the types of forces influencing the movement of time-series data.
3. Are the elements of time-series variation entirely independent of one another?

4. What is meant by the equation $O = T \times S \times C \times I$?

5. It is sometimes necessary to make corrections in the stated values of the data before proceeding with a time-series analysis. Why?

6. A moving average can never be brought up to date. Do you agree?

7. When a moving average for an even number of years is computed, the average must be centered. Explain.

8. Under what conditions can a moving-average trend be employed satisfactorily?

9. In the formula for a straight line, $Y_c = a + bX$, what are the specific meanings of a and b?

10. What is meant by a least squares line? How is it similar to the arithmetic mean?

11. The statistician for the Cincinnati Metals Company was considering the problem of selecting a period of years to be used in computing the secular trend of the firm's sales. An assistant had suggested two periods, one beginning in 1933 and ending in 1949, the other starting in 1952 and terminating in 1957. Which would you choose?

12. The sales of the Marshhorn Mining Machine Company had been increasing approximately 5 percent per year for the last 20 years. When a secular trend of sales was to be computed, the treasurer suggested that an arithmetic straight-line trend be fitted to the data. The comptroller, on the other hand, argued that a geometric straight line would be more appropriate. Which official's position is most acceptable? Could they both be wrong?

13. What is meant by extrapolation of trend? On what underlying assumption is this procedure based?

14. In fitting a curve to represent secular trend, it is usually wise to select a type of line whose equation can most easily be computed. Comment on this approach.

15. If the trend of a company's sales is $Y_c = 1,350,000 + 250,000X$, where X represents a period of 1 year and has a value of 0 in 1950, a sales forecast of $8,000,000 in 1962 is quite reasonable. Is this statement true?

16. Are the statements below true, false, or a combination of truth and falsehood?

(a) Preferably the period used in computing secular trend should begin in a period of recession and end during prosperity. In this way the basic growth of our economy will be given an ample opportunity to manifest itself fully.

(b) The least squares straight line is essentially the same as the arithmetic mean.

(c) One outstanding advantage of the moving-average trend line is that it enables the investigator to avoid choosing among the various mathematical lines that might be fitted to the data.

(d) Moving-average trend lines cannot be used directly in the preparation of forecasts. As a consequence, the moving average is used primarily in studying past situations.

(e) Secular-trend measurements are supposed to depict the basic sweep of the series over the years rather than temporary fluctuations that occur within any one year or over a short period of years.

(f) The extrapolation of secular trend constitutes a very useful tool for forecasting future values of economic time series. Although this technique cannot provide estimates of the influence of seasonal or cyclical elements, if the type of line selected properly describes the past behavior of the series the projection of the trend element itself must necessarily be correct.

(g) Arithmetic straight-line trends indicate constant percentage growth or decline, whereas logarithmic (that is, geometric) straight-line trends depict constant absolute amounts of change.

(h) A mathematically fitted curve, even though mechanically precise, in one sense still reflects the judgment of the investigator.

17. The sales manager of the Bentham-Wirtheimeyer Glass Company received two requests for estimates of sales 5 years hence. One came from the treasurer, who was preparing a long-range financial projection. He desired the sales projection so that he could estimate the amount of funds that would be tied up in inventory and accounts receivable. The amount of these items ordinarily fluctuates with the volume of sales. The other request came from the physical facilities planning committee of the Board of Directors. Their interest was occasioned by the fact that plans were being prepared for future plant expansion. After considering these requests, the sales manager finally decided that two projections rather than one were required. In one situation the influence of changing price level, he felt, should be removed; in the other it should not. In addition, one estimate probably should be on the high side, but the other should be as accurate as possible.

(a) Why should price-level changes be removed in one projection and not in the other?

(b) Which estimate should be somewhat high and why?

18. The sales of the Bentham-Wirtheimeyer Glass Company for the twelve years since its organization were as follows:

	Sales		Sales
1948	$1,200,000	1954	$3,280,000
1949	1,320,000	1955	3,940,000
1950	1,580,000	1956	4,730,000
1951	1,900,000	1957	5,770,000
1952	2,280,000	1958	6,920,000
1953	2,740,000	1959	8,400,000

In preparing his sales projection without price-level corrections, the sales manager was faced with two problems. First, should the entire period since 1948 be employed in the trend computation, or would some part thereof be preferable? Second, what type of trend measurement should be used?

(a) What trend period do you suggest?

(b) Evalute the following types of trend lines for use in this sales projection: (1) moving average, (2) least squares arithmetic straight line, (3), geometric straight line.

(Plot data in preparing your answer.)

19. In early 1958 the McGregor Sports Products Company became a subsidiary of the Brunswick-Balke Collender Company. It was felt that this merger would strengthen the position of both concerns in the sporting-goods field. Nevertheless, the consolidated statements of Brunswick-Balke after this merger were no longer comparable with those issued before.

Assuming that you were employed by an investment analyst to prepare a projection of the sales trend for the combined company, how would you proceed?

PROBLEMS

1. The sales of Mamouth Industries for the years 1950 through 1956 are listed below:

	Sales (thousands of dollars)
1950	112
1951	120
1952	124
1953	134
1954	125
1955	139
1956	143

(a) Plot the sales data.

(b) Compute secular trend using a 3-year moving average.

(c) Plot this trend and comment on its limitations.

(d) Compute and plot a least squares arithmetic straight-line trend.

(e) Compute and plot a geometric straight-line trend.

(f) Which of the three trend lines do you feel most nearly describes the basic movement of the data?

2. Using the equation for a least squares arithmetic straight line computed

in problem 1, predict the volume of sales in 1970 and in 2000. How good are these forecasts?

3. Using the data in problem 1 but omitting the value for 1950, compute the equation of a least squares arithmetic straight-line trend.

4. The Avon Machine Company estimates that it requires 1000 square feet of factory floor space for each 100 machines manufactured per year. At present the company's plant has 100,000 square feet of space. Current production is running at about 8000 units per year. The trend equation that used the year 10 years in the past as the 0 value for X is $Y_c = 5000 + 300X$.

    (a) How soon will an addition to plant be required?

    (b) Assuming that additions are contemplated only every 5 years, how many additional feet of floor space should be added at that time?

5. The number of workers employed by the McAideen-Springer Tool Company and the average hourly wage for a period of 11 years are listed below.

	No. of workers	Average hourly wage
1949	973	$1.91
1950	982	1.95
1951	991	1.96
1952	999	1.98
1953	1010	2.00
1954	1018	2.02
1955	1028	2.04
1956	1035	2.06
1957	1045	2.08
1958	1054	2.11
1959	1060	2.11

    (a) Compute a least squares arithmetic straight-line trend for the number of workers employed by the company.

    (b) Compute a least squares arithmetic straight-line trend for the average hourly wage.

    (c) Forecast the number of employees that you expect the firm to hire in 1970.

    (d) What average hourly wage would you expect in 1967?

    (e) Predict total weekly pay roll in 1965. Assume that all employees work 40 hours per week.

    (f) What are the limitations of these estimates?

6. The profits per share of the Wicksteed-Ashley Mercury Mining Company for the period from 1952 through 1958 are as follows:

	Profit per share
1953	$1.10
1953	1.16
1954	1.22
1955	1.28
1956	1.35
1957	1.42
1958	1.49

(a) Compute a geometric straight-line trend.

(b) Estimate profits per share in 1961.

7.

	Monthly average for production of steel (tons)
1960	1
1961	2
1962	5
1963	3
1964	4

(a) Determine the trend equation for the above time series, employing a least squares arithmetic straight line.

(b) Determine the trend equation, employing a least squares geometric (or logarithmic) straight line.

(c) Which of the two lines just derived is the line of best fit? This question can be answered by comparing the (1) sum of the squared deviations of actual production from the trend value of production estimated from the arithmetic line with (2) the sum of the squared deviations of actual production from the trend value of production estimated from the geometric straight line by taking the antilogs of the log Y_c values.

(d) Employing the equation derived in question (a), above, estimate the trend value in 1966.

8. In a study of its sales, a motor company obtained the following equation for the least squares trend:

$$Y_c = 1600 + 200X \text{ (origin, 1954; } X \text{ units, 1 year; } Y \text{, total num-}$$
ber of units sold annually)

The company, with physical facilities to produce only 3,600 units a year, believes that it is reasonable to assume that, at least for the next decade, the trend will continue as before.

(a) What is the average annual increase in the number of units sold?

(b) By what year will the company's expected sales have equaled its present physical capacity?

(c) Estimate the annual sales for 1969. How much in excess of the company's present physical capacity is this estimated value?

9. Compute the trend values for the following by fitting an arithmetic straight line by the method of least squares.

ALUMINUM PRODUCTION
(thousands of tons)

1958	30
1959	44
1960	50
1961	42
1962	51
1963	68
1964	65

10. Applying a 4-year moving average to the following data, what is the trend value for 1960?

	Output
1958	90
1959	91
1960	95
1961	97
1962	107
1963	110
1964	125

11. The sales of the Jersey Co. for the years 1952 through 1958 are listed below. Compute the secular trend by using a 3-year moving average.

Jones Company
Sales
(thousands of dollars)

1952	18
1953	20
1954	21
1955	25
1956	24
1957	26
1958	35

Measuring Seasonal Variations

Seasonal variations are those rhythmic changes in time-series data that occur regularly each year. As was pointed out in the last chapter, they have their origin in climatic or institutional factors that affect either supply or demand, or both. It is important that these variations be measured accurately for three reasons. First, and probably most important, the investigator frequently wants to eliminate the seasonal influence from the data he is studying. In business-cycle analysis, for example, it is essential that a mere seasonal downturn should not be identified as some more fundamental and serious economic change. Second, a precise knowledge of the pattern of seasonal variation aids in planning future operations. Accurate estimates of seasonal increases in sales enable a firm's buyers to have adequate inventories on hand when needed, and at the same time these estimates inform the financial officers concerning the amount of additional money that will be tied up in receivables and inventory. Finally, the thorough understanding of the seasonal pattern, which precise measurement provides, is of use to those who are trying to remove the cause of seasonals or are attempting to mitigate the problem by diversification, offsetting opposing seasonal patterns, or some other means.

PRELIMINARY EDITING

Before proceeding with the techniques of measuring seasonal variations, it is advisable to check the data and, if necessary, make revisions needed to remove unwanted influences. This study is essential because months are uniform neither in the number of calendar days nor in the number of working days they contain. February values are frequently less than those of March because February usually has 3 fewer days and because both Washington's and Lincoln's birthdays fall during this month. The number of working days in 30- and 31-day months also varies, depending on the number of week-end days falling in these months. If the series is one that describes a level, such as the volume of business inventories or of bank deposits, the values are not influenced by the number of calendar or working days during the month, and consequently no editing is required. If, on the other hand, the monthly value is a total of daily quantities—production and sales figures are examples—it is affected thereby. Should the investigation concern itself with the total only, no editing is needed. The sales forecast for February, for instance, should be influenced by the fact that February has fewer days. If, on the other hand, attention centers on the rate of sales or production, corrections are necessary. Lower February figures occasioned by calendar- or working-day differences are not indicative of seasonal or other significant differences. Such unwanted variations can be eliminated by stating the data on a working-day or calendar-day basis or by applying certain correctional factors.[1]

THE PROBLEM OF ISOLATING SEASONAL VARIATIONS

In the preceding chapter it was pointed out that the actual values of time-series data are influenced by trend, cyclical, and irregular or random factors in addition to seasonal elements. The formula $O = T \times C \times S \times I$ was employed to describe this relation. The problem of isolating the seasonal variation then becomes one of eliminating T, C, and I. An index based on a single year's monthly values obviously cannot eliminate these three elements because none of the other elements is removed. When the monthly values over a period of years are averaged, the resulting index, computed by expressing the average value for each month as a percentage of the average value of all the months, is somewhat superior but still inadequate. Rising trend would continue to cause values in later months of the year to be higher than those at the beginning of the year, and unless the period used in computing the index exactly conformed to one or a number of exceedingly uniform business cycles, cyclical influences also would remain.

THE RATIO-TO-TREND METHOD

When the ratio-to-trend method is employed, each monthly value is expressed as a percentage of the trend ordinate for that month. Because a

---

[1] When data are converted to a working- or calendar-day basis, the total value for the month is divided by the number of working or calendar days. Hence variations caused by different numbers of working or calendar days are removed.

Table 13-1.   COMPUTATION OF RATIOS TO TREND FOR PRODUCTION
The Ajax Company
(1962–1964)

	Production (thousands) 1	Trend (thousands) 2	Ratio to trend 3
1962			
Jan.	120	101.0	119
Feb.	115	102.7	112
Mar.	110	104.4	105
Apr.	100	106.0	94
May	90	107.7	84
June	80	109.4	73
July	90	111.0	81
Aug.	100	112.7	89
Sept.	110	114.4	96
Oct.	120	116.0	103
Nov.	130	117.7	110
Dec.	140	119.4	117
1963			
Jan.	150	121.0	124
Feb.	140	122.7	114
Mar.	130	124.4	105
Apr.	120	126.0	95
May	110	127.7	86
June	100	129.4	77
July	110	131.0	84
Aug.	120	132.7	90
Sept.	130	134.4	97
Oct.	140	136.0	103
Nov.	150	137.7	109
Dec.	160	139.4	115
1964			
Jan.	170	141.0	121
Feb.	160	142.7	112
Mar.	150	144.4	104
Apr.	140	146.0	96
May	130	147.7	88
June	120	149.4	80
July	130	151.0	86
Aug.	140	152.7	92
Sept.	150	154.4	97
Oct.	160	156.0	103
Nov.	170	157.7	108
Dec.	170	159.4	107

number of years is included in the computation, several ratios (percentage values) are available for each of the 12 months. The ratios for each individual month are then averaged in order to arrive at the typical value for the month. The problem of determining which average should be used as a typical value will be considered in a later section of the chapter. In the examples of the ratio-to-trend and ratio-to-the-moving-average methods, the arithmetic mean is employed; the median is used in the explanation of the link-relative technique.

The example of the ratio-to-trend method, presented in Tables 13-1 and 13-2, is abbreviated by including only 3 years in the computation and simplified by rounding the ratios to the nearest percentage. In column 1 of Table 13-1 the actual production figures of the Ajax Company are

Table 13-2. COMPUTATION OF SEASONAL INDEX FOR PRODUCTION BY AVERAGING RATIOS TO TREND

The Ajax Company

(1962–1964)

	Jan.	Feb.	Mar.	Apr.	May	June	July	Aug.	Sept.	Oct.	Nov.	Dec.
1962	119	112	105	94	84	73	81	89	96	103	110	117
1963	124	114	105	95	86	77	84	90	97	103	109	115
1964	121	112	104	96	88	80	86	92	97	103	108	107
Total	364	338	314	285	258	230	251	271	290	309	327	339
Average	121	113	105	95	86	77	84	90	97	103	109	113
Index leveled	121.7	113.7	105.6	95.6	86.5	77.4	84.5	90.5	97.6	103.6	109.6	113.7

presented; in column 2 the trend ordinates are listed. The ratios to trend in column 3 were found by dividing the column 1 values by the figures in column 2. Because 3 years are used in the computation, there are three ratios to trend for each month. These are listed in Table 13-2, together with their arithmetic means. These means are close approximations of the typical seasonal values.

Adjusting Seasonal Indexes to Total 1200 Percent

The total of the means of the ratios to trend comes to only 1193, and consequently the average of these 12 typical seasonals amounts to 99.4 percent. From this statement one might conclude that because of seasonal influences over the years the actual values amount to only 99.4 percent of (or lie .6 percent below) the value that otherwise would have been realized. Such an interpretation would be entirely incorrect. The values failed to average exactly 100 percent solely because of mechanical elements in the computation. Averages either above or below 100 percent are not indicative of over-all depressing or elevating seasonal influences. Although such influences may in some situations exist, their magnitude is conjectural and could not be shown in the seasonal index. The whole idea of seasonal variation is that at times during the year this influence depresses and at other times raises the values of the series. An index below 100 for a given month indicates depressing seasonal influence, whereas indexes above 100 show that seasonal factors are inflating the values. An index of 100 is interpreted as meaning that seasonal factors are neutral, neither elevating nor reducing the value. Over the year seasonal influences necessarily cancel out, the increases being offset by the decreases. Consequently, the seasonal indexes should average 100 and total 1200. The technique of adjusting them so that they will meet this requirement is quite simple. Each index is merely divided by the average of the 12 indexes. In the example, each index is divided by .994; thus the values are sufficiently increased to make them total 1200. If the average were above 100, this process would reduce the total to 1200.

Appraisal of the Ratio-to-Trend Method

The ratio-to-trend method presumably isolates the seasonal factor in the following manner. Trend is eliminated when the ratios are computed. In effect,

$$(T \times C \times R \times S)/T = C \times S \times I$$

Random elements are supposed to disappear when the ratios are averaged. A careful selection of the period of years used in the computation is expected to cause the influences of prosperity and depression to offset each other and thus remove the cycle. For series that are not subject to pronounced cyclical or random influences and for which trend can be computed accurately, this method may suffice. However, in many instances it is impossible to eliminate cyclical influence through a judicious selection of the right period, either because no such period exists or because the necessary data are not conveniently available. Erratic elements that occur frequently and are of a significant order of magnitude will not always average out. In addition, if trend has been incorrectly computed, the ratios will be affected. The great merit of the ratio-to-trend method is that it is simple to compute and easy to understand.

THE RATIO-TO-THE-MOVING-AVERAGE METHOD

A 12-month moving average exactly encompasses an entire year. Consequently, it should not be influenced to any great extent by seasonal

Table 13-3. COMPUTATION OF RATIOS TO TWELVE-MONTH CENTERED
MOVING AVERAGE FOR PRODUCTION
The Ajax Company
(1962–1964)

	Production (thousands) 1	12-month moving total 2	12-month moving average 3	Centered 12-month moving average 4	Ratio to moving average 5
1961					
July	70				
Aug.	80				
Sept.	90				
Oct.	100				
Nov.	110				
Dec.	120				
1962					
		1185	98.8		
Jan.	120			99.6	120.5
		1205	100.4		
Feb.	115			101.2	113.6
		1225	102.1		
Mar.	110			130.0	106.8
		1245	103.8		
Apr.	100			104.6	95.6
		1265	105.4		
May	90			106.2	84.7
		1285	107.1		
June	80			108.0	74.1
		1305	108.8		
July	90			110.0	81.8
		1335	111.3		
Aug.	100			112.3	89.0
		1360	113.3		
Sept.	110			114.2	96 3
		1380	115.0		
Oct.	120			115.8	103.6
		1400	116.7		
Nov.	130			117.5	110.6
		1420	118.3		
Dec.	140			119.2	117.4

Table 13-3 (cont.)

	Production (thousands) 1	12-month moving total 2	12-month moving average 3	Centered 12-month moving average 4	Ratio to moving average 5
1963					
		1440	120.0		
Jan.	150			120.8	124.2
		1460	121.7		
Feb.	140			122.5	114.3
		1480	123.3		
Mar.	130			124.2	104.7
		1500	125.0		
Apr.	120			125.8	95.4
		1520	126.7		
May	110			127.5	86.3
		1540	128.3		
June	100			129.2	77.4
		1560	130.0		
July	110			130.8	84.1
		1580	131.7		
Aug.	120			132.5	90.6
		1600	133.3		
Sept.	130			134.2	96.9
		1620	135.0		
Oct.	140			135.8	103.1
		1640	136.7		
Nov.	150			137.5	109.1
		1660	138.3		
Dec.	160			139.2	114.9
1964					
		1680	140.0		
Jan.	170			140.8	120.7
		1700	141.7		
Feb.	160			142.5	112.3
		1720	143.3		
Mar.	150			144.2	104.0
		1740	145.0		
Apr.	140			145.8	96.0
		1760	146.7		

Table 13-3 (cont.)

	Production (thousands) 1	12-month moving total 2	12-month moving average 3	Centered 12-month moving average 4	Ratio to moving average 5
May	130			148.0	87.8
		1780	148.3		
June	120			148.8	80.6
		1790	149.2		
July	130			150.0	86.7
		1810	150.8		
Aug.	140			151.6	92.3
		1830	152.5		
Sept.	150			153.4	97.8
		1850	154.2		
Oct.	160			155.0	103.2
		1870	155.8		
Nov.	170			156.6	108.6
		1890	157.5		
Dec.	170			158.4	107.3
1965					
		1910	159.2		
Jan.	190				
Feb.	180				
Mar.	170				
Apr.	160				
May	150				
June	140				

or short-term irregular elements. As a result, the 12-month moving average can be considered to represent the influences of cycle and trend, $C \times T$. If the actual value for any month is divided by the 12-month moving average centered to that month, presumably cycle and trend are removed. This may be represented by the following expression:

$$(T \times C \times S \times I)/(T \times C) = S \times I$$

Thus the ratio to the moving average, from which this method gets its name, represents irregular and seasonal influences. If the ratios for each month over a period of years are then averaged, most random influences

Table 13-4. COMPUTATION OF SEASONAL INDEX BY AVERAGING RATIO TO THE MOVING AVERAGE FOR PRODUCTION

The Ajax Company

(1962–1964)

	Jan.	Feb.	Mar.	Apr.	May	June	July	Aug.	Sept.	Oct.	Nov.	Dec.	Average
1962	120.5	113.6	106.8	95.6	84.7	74.1	81.8	89.0	96.3	103.6	110.6	117.4	
1963	124.2	114.3	104.7	95.4	86.3	77.4	84.1	90.6	96.9	103.1	109.1	114.9	
1964	120.7	112.3	104.0	96.0	87.8	80.6	86.7	92.3	97.8	103.2	108.6	107.3	
Total	365.4	340.2	315.5	287.0	258.8	232.1	252.6	271.9	291.0	309.9	328.3	339.6	
Avg.	121.8	113.4	105.2	95.7	86.3	77.4	84.2	90.6	97.0	103.3	109.4	113.2	99.8
Seasonal	122.0	113.6	105.4	95.9	86.5	77.6	84.4	90.8	97.2	103.5	109.6	113.4	100

will usually be eliminated. Hence, in effect,

$$(S \times I)/I = S$$

The illustration in Table 13-3 should make the techniques of computation clear. This example, like the one employed to explain the ratio-to-trend method, will be abbreviated by including only 3 years in the computation. However, in order to make the centering process entirely clear, the figures will be carried out to the tenth of a percent rather than rounding to the nearest percent.

A 12-month moving average is computed by averaging the values for 12 successive months. In Table 13-3 the first 12-month moving average of 98.8 is found by adding the values from July 1961 through June 1962 and dividing by 12. The next moving average of 100.41 is computed by averaging the values from August 1961 through July 1962. Thus in each successive month the earliest monthly value is dropped from the average and a later month is added. The periods for which these 12-month moving averages are computed have mid-points that fall between two months. The July 1961–June 1962 period has its center at 12 A.M. January 1, 1962 (or 12 P.M. December 31, 1961) and the August 1961–July 1962 at 12 A.M. February 1, 1962. Although these values cannot represent any one particular month, when they themselves are averaged they center at the middle of a month and therefore serve as a value for a month. Thus, when the value of 98.8 for January 1, 1962, is averaged with the February 1 value of 100.4, the resulting figure 99.6 is centered at January 15, and satisfactorily represents that January.

In Table 13-3 the 12-month moving averages are found in column 3 and the centered averages in column 4. Next, the actual value for the month is divided by the centered 12-month moving average; the quotient is the ratio to the moving average which is found in column 5. The three ratios for each month are then averaged. In Table 13-4 the arithmetic mean is employed. Although the 12 averages are close approximations of the typical seasonal indexes, they require adjustment because they total 1197.5 instead of 1200. The technique of adjustment is exactly the same as that employed in the discussion of the ratio-to-trend method. Each average is then divided by the average of the averages, 99.8. In this way the total is increased to 1200.

THE MEDIAN LINK-RELATIVE METHOD

Another technique for computing seasonal indexes that is highly regarded by many statisticians is the median link-relative method. It is based on expressing the value for each month as a percentage of the previous month. The use of these month-to-month comparisons eliminates the need for trend calculations and reduces cyclical influences to a minimum. Months within each phase of the cycle are compared with other months in the same phase. Distortions occasioned by cyclical changes during a single month are usually slight because the amount of cyclical change over so short a period is usually insignificant. Random influences, again, are presumably removed by averaging.

The computation of the seasonal index by the median link-relative method is somewhat more complicated than the methods already presented. The example that follows is abbreviated and simplified by using data from only 3 years and rounding to the nearest percent. Five steps are involved.

Step 1: Compute Link Relatives for Each Month. Link relatives are computed by dividing the value for each month by the value of the month before. In computing the link relatives for the production of the Ajax Company, the actual production figures found in column 1 of Table 13-1 were employed. The link relative of 100 for January 1962 was obtained by dividing 120, the actual production figure for January, by 120, the figure for December 1961. The February link relative of 96 was found by dividing 115, the February production, by the 120 figure for January. The link relatives for all the months included in the computation are recorded in Table 13-5.

Step 2: Find the Median. There will be as many link relatives for each month as there are years included in the computation. As a result, the problem of averaging appears once again. As the name suggests, when this method is employed the median is customarily selected. The medians for each month are found on the line so labeled in Table 13-5.

Step 3: Compute the Chain Relative. Each of the median link relatives expresses the typical value for the month as a percentage of the previous month. As a result, because there are 12 different bases for the 12 link relatives, it is necessary to convert them to a common base. This conversion is done by arbitrarily assigning January the value of 100 and expressing all other months as a percentage of January. The relatives when converted to this form are known as *chain relatives*. The chain relative for February is found by multiplying the 100 value for January by the median link relative for February, which is 94. This process gives the chain relative of 94 also. The chain relative for March is found by multiplying the chain relative for February, 94, by the median link relative of 94 for March, which gives 88. The April chain relative of 81 was computed by multiplying the March chain relative of 88 by the April median link relative of 92. Thus the chain relative for each month is found by multiplying the chain relative of the previous month by the median link relative of the month in question.

Table 13-5. COMPUTATION OF THE SEASONAL INDEX BY THE MEDIAN LINK-RELATIVE METHOD, PRODUCTION
The Ajax Company
(1962–1965)

	Jan.	Feb.	Mar.	Apr.	May	June	July	Aug.	Sept.	Oct.	Nov.	Dec.	Jan.
1962	100	96	96	91	90	89	112	111	110	109	108	108	108
1963	107	93	93	92	92	91	110	109	108	108	107	107	107
1964	106	94	94	93	93	92	108	108	107	107	106	100	100
Median	106	94	94	92	92	91	110	109	108	108	107	107	107
Chain relative	100	94	88	81	75	68	75	82	89	96	103	110	117
Adjusted relative	100	92.6	85.2	76.8	69.4	61	66.6	72.2	77.8	83.4	89	94.6	100
Seasonal index	124	115	106	95	86	76	82	90	96	103	110	117	

Step 4: Adjust the Chain Relatives to Remove Trend and Cycle. At this point it is usually necessary to adjust the chain relatives in order to remove the trend and cyclical influences still present in the data. The chain relative for January, which is computed by multiplying the December chain relative by the January median link relative, comes to 117. This is 17 points above the arbitrarily assigned original chain relative of 100 for this month. Consequently, the 17 point increase is attributable to other than seasonal factors, and must be removed. If it can safely be assumed that the 17-point increase was spread evenly over the year, this distortion can easily be eliminated by subtracting $\frac{1}{12}$ of 17 from February, $\frac{2}{12}$ from March, $\frac{3}{12}$ from April, and so on. In this way the second January value is reduced to 100 and the intervening chain relatives are appropriately adjusted. Had the trend been downward, the adjustment would have required successive additions. If the increase that necessitates the adjustment cannot reasonably be assumed to have occurred in equal monthly amounts, more complex adjustments, which are beyond the scope of this volume, are required.

Step 5: Adjust the Chain Relatives to Average 100 and Total 1200. In discussing the ratio-to-trend method, it was emphasized that it is highly desirable for the indexes to average 100 and total 1200. The same line of reasoning applies with equal force here. The total of the adjusted chain relatives comes to only 968.6 and the average is only 80.7. This correction is easily made by dividing each adjusted chain relative by the average value of 80.7 percent or .807. The chain relatives adjusted in this way for the second time constitute the seasonal indexes.

SELECTING THE PERIOD

In order to abbreviate and simplify the examples in this chapter, a period of only 3 years was employed to compute the seasonal indexes. In actual fact, however, it is usually both desirable and necessary to include many more years. A seasonal index based on a short period is often unduly affected by conditions prevailing during one phase of the business cycle or by powerful random influences. The period should encompass at least one and, if possible, several business cycles. The long span of years offers greater likelihood that irregular and cyclical forces will cancel out or at least have their influence minimized. Ten years is often viewed as a practical minimum. Nevertheless, the period should not be lengthened at the expense of comparability. If it encompasses years during which different seasonal forces were operative, the index is of little value. Care should also be taken to have the period begin and end at the same phase of the business cycle in order to avoid distortions that could result if more years of prosperity than of depression were included.

AVERAGE IN COMPUTING
SEASONALS

In each of the methods described, the individual monthly values were averaged in order to eliminate random influences and any remaining cyclical elements. In two of these examples the average selected was the arithmetic mean, and in the third, the median. This naturally poses the question of the relative merits of these or other averages for the purpose at hand. Because the mean is affected by every item in the series, it should be used when the number of years is large. However, when the period is shorter the use of the mean is not recommended because extreme items, occasioned by the very random or cyclical factors that the calculation is designed to eliminate, distort its value. The median, on the other hand, is a positional average. As such it is not affected in any way by extreme values, but it may be unduly influenced by the inclusion or exclusion of a year or two in the calculation. A positional mean avoids the disadvantages of both the mean and the median. It is computed by taking the arithmetic mean of the central items in the series. Suppose the following are the arrayed ratios to the moving average for March:

$$
\begin{array}{c}
81 \\
86 \\
\underline{92} \\
96 \\
96 \\
97 \\
99 \\
99 \\
\underline{100} \\
104 \\
106 \\
113
\end{array}
$$

In this instance the arithmetic mean of the middle six items would be employed as the seasonal index. It is obvious that extreme items cannot influence this value and that detail of position alone is not significant.

CHANGING SEASONALS

The pattern of seasonal variations does not always remain unchanged. Sometimes significant events occur that immediately have pronounced effects on the way in which a series fluctuates during the year.

Moving the time of the introduction of new models of automobiles from early spring to late fall, the alteration of distribution channels by Procter and Gamble, and the development of commercially feasible techniques for freezing food—are all examples of events that altered the patterns of seasonal variation of certain time series. Because changes of this sort involve basic alterations in the institutional framework influencing the series, it is best to employ different seasonal indexes for the periods before and after the change. Should the seasonal change slowly, more complex indexes may be constructed to reflect such variation. If, for example, the seasonal variation is becoming more pronounced, this tendency can be measured and projected. Least square lines and manually fitted curves are frequently employed for this purpose. Although these techniques will not be explored further in this elementary treatment, the student should be aware of their existence and should employ them if the occasion demands. Above all, a seasonal index should not be used merely because it is available, when it is known that fundamental changes in the pattern of seasonal variation have occurred since the index was computed.

ELIMINATING
SEASONAL INFLUENCES

The seasonal influences may be removed from time-series data by dividing the actual values for each month by the seasonal index. This

Table 13-6. ADJUSTMENT OF PRODUCTION DATA FOR
SEASONAL VARIATION
The Ajax Company
(1962)

	Production	Seasonal index	Adjusted production
Jan.	120	122.0	98
Feb.	115	13.6	101
Mar.	110	105.6	104
Apr.	100	95.9	104
May	90	86.5	104
June	80	77.6	103
July	90	84.4	107
Aug.	100	90.8	110
Sept.	110	97.2	113
Oct.	120	103.5	116
Nov.	130	109.6	119
Dec.	140	113.4	123

adjustment may be symbolically expressed as follows:

$$(T \times S \times C \times I)/S = T \times C \times I$$

Such adjustments are frequently made for series that manifest significant seasonals when these series are being studied for other characteristics. Table 13-6 demonstrates the removal of the seasonal influence from the production of the Ajax Company for 1962.

SEASONAL INDEXES AND PLANNING

The seasonal index may be very helpful in planning sales or production for specific periods. For example, if a firm expects to sell $24,000,000 worth of goods during the forthcoming year, average monthly sales of $2,000,000 are anticipated. If, however, the volume of sales is subject to seasonal fluctuation, the actual monthly values will deviate significantly from this average. Should the seasonal index for March be 110, the firm can expect sales of $2,200,000 during that month; in comparison, an index of 80 for August would lead them to anticipate sales of only $1,600,000.

Forecasts for future periods are frequently made by combining what is known about both trend and seasonal elements. First, the trend ordinate for a given month is computed. Then this ordinate is multiplied by the seasonal index for that month. For example, if the equation for the trend of a company's sales is $Y_c = 60,000 + 500X$, where X represents 1 month and has a value of 0 in December 1958, and the seasonal index for May is 90, the sales for May 1960 may be estimated in the following way. In May 1960 the value of X will be $+ 17$ and the trend ordinate will therefore be 68,500. When this figure is multiplied by .90, the estimated sales are found to be $61,650. Although this type of forecast necessarily ignores cyclical and random influences, it frequently can be very useful. As will be noted in the following chapter, this product of trend and seasonal is frequently viewed as statistical "normal."

SUGGESTED READING

Greenwald, W. I. *Statistics for Economics.* Columbus, Ohio: Charles E. Merrill Books, Inc. 1963, chap. 9.
Lewis, E. E. *Methods of Statistical Analysis in Economics and Business.* Boston: Houghton Mifflin Company, 1953, chap. 11.
Mills, F. C. *Introduction to Statistics.* New York: Holt, Rinehart and Winston, Inc., 1956, chap. 11.
Neiswanger, W. A. *Elementary Statistical Methods* (rev. ed.). New York: The Macmillan Company, 1957, chap. 16.

1. The president of the Marsch Company felt that the year 1948 was typical of the normal pattern of operations for his firm. As a result, when the problem of constructing an index of the seasonal variations in sales arose, he instructed the comptroller to use 1948 data only. The sales figure for each month was to be expressed as a percentage of the average monthly value for that year. Comment on this procedure.

2. In some years Easter falls in March; in others it comes in April. How does this fact complicate the job of the statistician who is constructing or using a seasonal index? For what types of data would no difficulties arise?

3. List the causes of seasonality in the sales of athletic equipment.

4. A seasonal index of 140 for March means that because of seasonal factors the March value will be 40 percent above the monthly average for the year. Do you agree?

5. What are the principal weaknesses of the ratio-to-trend method of computing the seasonal index? What is its principal merit?

6. Why must monthly seasonal indexes be adjusted so that they total 1200?

7. How are trend and cyclical influences removed when the ratio-to-the-moving-average technique of computing seasonal indexes is employed?

8. What purpose is served when the ratios to the moving average for each month for several years are averaged?

9. Why is a positional mean frequently employed in averaging ratios to the moving average?

10. If the basic conditions influencing the series under study are known to have changed recently, can the seasonal indexes computed in the more remote past still be employed?

11. List three examples of changes in the pattern of seasonal variations that occurred suddenly and three that came about gradually.

12. How may seasonal influences be removed from time-series data? What assumptions underlie the method you suggest?

13. In the late spring of 1958 the sales manager of the Evanstone Tractor Company became engaged in a controversy with the comptroller over whether sales had really increased during the last two months. The comptroller contended that greater dollar volume during this period could be more than explained by seasonal factors. The sales manager thought otherwise. Sales had risen from $1,250,000 in April to $1,300,000 in May and $1,320,000 in June. The seasonal index for April was 100, May 110, and June 99. Whose view would you support?

14. Are the following statements true or false?
    (a) Seasonal indexes are used almost exclusively to facilitate the removal of seasonal influences from the data under study.
    (b) When the basic factors causing the pattern of seasonal variation remain unchanged, seasonal indexes computed in the past may be employed with confidence, but if these factors themselves undergo change, the indexes must be corrected or abandoned entirely.
    (c) If the sales trend ordinate for November 1970 is $2,007,000 and the seasonal index for that month is 90, sales of $2,230,000 can be expected at that time.
    (d) Seasonal influences change as climatic conditions vary, but for no other reason.
    (e) The pay-as-you-go system of income tax collection now employed in the United States reduces the seasonality of Treasury receipts.
    (f) Custom plays a larger role in the seasonality of department store sales than in that of industrial production.
    (g) It would be worth while to eliminate most seasonal variation if this were possible.

PROBLEMS

1. The quarterly sales figures for the Mancheon Company for the years 1954 through 1958 are listed below. Construct the quarterly seasonal indexes, using the ratio-to-the-moving-average method. Here it will be necessary to compute a centered 4-quarter moving average.

1954		1955	
1st — $45,000		1st — $42,000	
2nd — $64,000		2nd — $62,000	
3rd — $52,000		3rd — $54,000	
4th — $85,000		4th — $81,000	
1956		1957	
1st — $35,000		1st — $50,000	
2nd — $54,000		2nd — $67,000	
3rd — $56,000		3rd — $74,000	
4th — $85,000		4th — $96,000	

1958
1st — $45,000
2nd — $63,000
3rd — $80,000
4th — $100,000

2. Adjust the following series for seasonal variation:

The Ritz Company
Actual sales

(*thousands*), 1957		*Seasonal indexes*	
Jan.	260	Jan.	90
Feb.	250	Feb.	80
Mar.	280	Mar.	90
Apr.	320	Apr.	130
May	260	May	120
June	240	June	90
July	230	July	70
Aug.	240	Aug.	70
Sept.	270	Sept.	90
Oct.	280	Oct.	100
Nov.	360	Nov.	120
Dec.	400	Dec.	150

3. The secular trend of sales for the Jones Department Store is accurately described by the equation $Y_c = 120,000 + 1000X$, where X represents a period of 1 month and has a value of 0 in December 1957. The seasonal indexes for the company's sales are as follows:

Jan.	100	Apr.	120	July	75	Oct.	95
Feb.	80	May	115	Aug.	70	Nov.	120
Mar.	90	June	95	Sept.	90	Dec.	150

Ignoring cyclical and random influences, forecast sales for (a) February 1959, (b) May 1962, (c) December 1970.

4. The seasonally adjusted figures for total employment in non-agricultural establishments as reported by the Bureau of Labor Statistics for the period from February 1957 through January 1958 are listed below.

Feb.	1957	52,577,000	Aug.	1957	52,844,000
Mar.		52,547,000	Sept.		52,662,000
Apr.		52,593,000	Oct.		52,469,000
May		52,698,000	Nov.		52,218,000
June		52,773,000	Dec.		51,980,000
July		52,815,000	Jan.	1958	51,756,000

The unadjusted figures for the same period were as follows:

Feb.	1957	51,704,000	Aug.	1957	52,891,000
Mar.		51,919,000	Sept.		53,152,000
Apr.		52,270,000	Oct.		53,043,000
May		52,482,000	Nov.		52,789,000
June		52,881,000	Dec.		53,084,000
July		52,605,000	Jan.	1958	50,987,000

Determine the seasonal indexes employed in adjusting this data.

5. The working-capital requirements of the Cincinnati Metals Company have been subject to seasonal fluctuations. At the same time, a steady secular advance can be noted. In order to evaluate comprehensively future working-capital needs, the treasurer calculated a straight-line trend and the seasonal indexes. The trend equation is $Y_c = 150,000 + 2000X$, where X represents a period of 1 month and has a value of 0 in January 1959. The seasonal indexes are as follows:

Jan.	90	July	120
Feb.	80	Aug.	100
Mar.	80	Sept.	80
Apr.	100	Oct.	100
May	120	Nov.	110
June	130	Dec.	90

   (a) Prepare a schedule of estimated working-capital requirements for 1960.
   (b) What factors could cause these estimates to be incorrect?
   (c) What might be done to compensate for inaccuracies as they become apparent?
   (d) Would you as a banker have any interest in estimates of this type?

6. Sales of Company A in March 1963 were $343,440, and in December 1963 were $272,000. Thus there was a decline of 20 percent from March to December. The monthly trend values of the sales of Company A are given below for the year 1963. The index of seasonal variation in sales is also given.

Company A

Monthly trend values (thousands of dollars)		Index of seasonal variation	
	Value		Index
January	299	January	102
February	300	February	104
March	301	March	106
April	302	April	110
May	303	May	120
June	304	June	115
July	305	July	100
August	306	August	90
September	307	September	85
October	308	October	98
November	309	November	90
December	310	December	80

   (a) Adjust the sales of March and December for seasonal variation and for secular trend.

(b) What, according to the adjusted figures, happened to sales between March and December?

(c) How can you account for this change?

7. The equation for the trend of the ABC Company's sales is $Y_e = 40,000 + 400X$, where X represents 1 month and has a value of 0 in June 1959. The seasonal index, in part, is presented below:

March	April	May	June	July	August	September
95	105	110	130	135	115	90

Assuming that random and cyclical influences can be neglected, give the sales estimate for September 1964.

8. On the basis of past experience, you (a manufacturer) expect to sell 36,000 pairs of shoes in the coming year. Your personnel manager, in order to plan vacations, needs to know how many workers will be required for the month of June. A close competitor has compiled a seasonal index for shoe sales; this (available to you) is presented, in part, below:

March	April	May	June	July	August
95	105	110	95	90	88

It takes a period of 1 month to manufacture shoes. One worker is required for every 10 pairs of shoes produced. How many workers are required for the month of June?

9. Following are the "link relatives" derived from a series of figures. Finish finding the seasonal index by the median-link-relative method.

	QUARTER			
	I	II	III	IV
1960		80	110	60
1961	140	75	130	64
1962	160	85	125	66
1963	140	82	126	76
1964	112	76	120	77

Measuring
Cyclical Movements

The term "cycle" refers to the recurrent variations in time series that usually last longer than a year and are regular neither in amplitude nor in length. Although the 23 cycles of general business in the United States between 1854 and 1949 averaged 49 months in duration, individual cycles differed greatly. The shortest lasted only 29 months, contrasted with the longest, which persisted for 99 months. Wesley C. Mitchell, one of the foremost students of this phenomenon, defined the cycle as follows:

> Business cycles are a type of fluctuation found in the aggregate economic activity of nations that organize their work mainly in business enterprises: a cycle consists of expansions occurring at about the same time in many economic activities, followed by similarly general recessions, contractions, and revivals which merge into the expansion phase of the next cycle: this sequence of changes is recurrent but not periodic: in duration business cycles vary from more than one year to ten or twelve years: they are not divisible into shorter cycles of similar character with amplitudes approximating their own.[1]

Most cycles in economic or business data conform roughly to the pattern of the cycle of general business. This fact is not surprising, because the over-all level of activity has an influence on almost all parts of the economy. However, some series exhibit substantially different and independent patterns of behavior that reflect institutional arrangements and conditions peculiar to the series in question.[2]

[1] Wesley C. Mitchell, *Business Cycles: The Problem and Its Settings* (New York: National Bureau of Economic Research, 1927), p. 468.

[2] Series that vary inversely with the level of general business—unemployment and business failures, for example— are really varying with the general cycle. This inverse behavior reflects the particular nature of the series, such as business failures, or the way in which data are stated. Thus unemployment varies inversely because employment varies directly.

THE RESIDUAL METHOD
OF MEASURING CYCLES

Because cyclical variations are so irregular, it would be impossible to construct meaningful typical cycle indexes or curves similar to those that have been developed for trends and seasonals. This fact, however, does not preclude presentation of cycle data that can facilitate analysis and interpretation. As trend and seasonal factors, in addition to cyclical forces, are affecting the original data, the elimination of either or both of these influences may aid in the isolation of the cycle. Sometimes the removal of

Table 14-1. ANNUAL INDUSTRIAL PRODUCTION IN THE UNITED STATES
Adjustment for Trend
(1950–1956)

	Index of industrial production (1947–1949 = 100)	Trend ordinate	Production adjusted for trend (1 ÷ 2)
	1	2	3
1950	112	113.9	98.2
1951	120	118.6	101.2
1952	124	123.3	100.6
1953	134	128	104.6
1954	125	132.7	94.2
1955	139	137.4	101.2
1956	143	142.1	100.6

seasonal influences alone may be sufficient, particularly when the line of division between trend and cycle is not clear and as a result the elimination of trend would necessarily be based on highly arbitrary assumptions.

The technique of adjusting for seasonal variation, discussed in the preceding chapter, merely requires dividing the actual value for each month by the seasonal index. Similarly, trend may be removed by dividing the actual values by the ordinates of the trend. In Table 14-1 this solution is shown for the data on industrial production in the United States. Because the data in Table 14-1 are annual values, no seasonal variations are present. The elimination of trend presumably leaves values that represent only cyclical and irregular influences. Therefore

$$(T \times C \times I)/T = C \times I$$

Observe that the adjusted value that results is expressed as percentages of the trend ordinates. Thus the figure of 101.2 for 1951 means 101.2 percent of the trend value for that year.

If monthly data are employed, both trend and seasonal influences can be removed by dividing the actual values by the trend ordinate multiplied by the seasonal index for the month. Symbolically, this may be expressed as

$$(T \times S \times C \times I)/(T \times S) = C \times I$$

If seasonally adjusted figures are available, division of such figures by trend ordinates accomplishes the same purpose. In either situation the adjusted values are really percentages of trend times seasonal.

Trend ordinates for annual data and the product of trend and seasonal ($T \times S$) for monthly data are often considered *normal*. In such circumstances normal means a value that represents persistent and regularly recurrent influences. This method then expresses cyclical and irregular variation as percentages of *normal*.

Limitations of the Residual Method

If the trend ordinates perfectly depicted the pattern of secular change and if the seasonal index exactly reflected seasonal influences, the residual method would leave values reflecting only cyclical and irregular influences. Because such perfection is rarely encountered, the computed values almost always contain some trend and seasonal elements. This condition will be more or less serious depending on how well or poorly the trend line and the seasonal index represent secular and seasonal forces. If a straight-line trend is employed to describe an essentially curvilinear secular movement, figures presumably adjusted for trend will be grossly distorted. The distortion would also occur if the seasonal index were not descriptive of the seasonal pattern at the time in question. Thus the residual method is based on the assumption that trend and seasonal can be accurately measured and therefore be removed at least in large part.

Comparing Cyclical Variations

Some series vary much more widely than do others. Agricultural prices, for example, fluctuate to a substantially greater extent than does the output of agricultural commodities; on the other hand, the sales of machine tools are much more volatile than the sales of nondurable consumer goods. For some purposes the absolute amplitude of fluctuation may be most significant. Thus when the problem of unemployment is being considered the magnitude of sales variation is critical because it is usually very influential in determining the number of workers who will be laid off. For other purposes, such as forecasting, a slight variation of a very stable series may be of greater import than a wide swing of highly volatile data. With respect to durable goods, changes of small percentage magnitudes in the demand for the services of these goods frequently bring about sharp variations in the demand for durable goods themselves. Hence proper evaluation of the significance of the first change, even though small in absolute magnitude, may enable the analyst to forecast the second.

Comparison of the fluctuations of series whose amplitudes differ may sometimes be facilitated in the following manner. First, the cycle data are converted into deviations from normal, by subtracting 100 from the indexes. The deviations are then expressed as a percentage of the standard deviation of the series. Thus individual deviations are related to the typical deviations of the same series, thereby making comparisons between different series more meaningful. For example, if one series exhibited a deviation of −10 percent and another showed a variation of −30 percent, it might at first glance be concluded that the condition in the second series was the more significant. However, if the standard deviation of the first series were only 5 and that of the second were 30, the change in the first series would be twice its standard deviation and that of the second would equal only its standard deviation. This would be indicative of a more unusual variation in the first series, even though the absolute magnitude of that variation was smaller.

THE NATIONAL BUREAU METHOD

The National Bureau of Economic Research has developed a different method of analyzing cyclical variations, which it has used in the study of approximately 1000 specific time series. This method, which is of value in analyzing past cycles only, seeks to determine, first, the particular characteristics of each individual series, and, second, the degree of conformity of these series to the general business cycle. Although the data, preferably monthly, which are analyzed usually are adjusted for seasonal variations, trend influences are not removed in the conventional manner. It is felt that secular changes, occurring during the cycle, affect cycles to such an extent that an attempt to eliminate them would be unwise. National Bureau investigators can take the presence of intracycle trend elements into account in their analyses. How the influence of trend between cycles is removed will be shown below.

Specific Cycles

The procedure employed in studying any individual series is as follows. First, the series is examined in order to determine the peaks and troughs of its variations. This step makes possible the location of the beginning and ending of every individual cycle of the series. National Bureau analysts view each cycle as beginning and ending in a trough. When these turning points have been determined, the items in the series during each cycle are averaged. The individual values in the series are then divided by this cycle average so that they are expressed as a percentage of the cycle average. The values so stated are called "specific-cycle relatives." Because each cycle begins in a trough, the relatives will necessarily start below the cycle average of 100 percent and rise continuously until the peak has been reached, at which point values considerably in excess of 100 will be encountered. Thereafter they will fall steadily as the series approaches its terminal trough. In the absence of very rapidly rising trend, values in the area of the terminal trough will also lie below the cycle average of 100 percent. Different trend levels during different cycles cannot influence these relatives because they are in every instance percentages of their own particular cycle average; however, the effect of rising or falling trend during each cycle remains.

Next, each cycle is broken into nine periods, called stages, and the specific-cycle relatives for the months during each stage are averaged to derive the *standing* at that stage. The standing for Stage I, the initial trough, is found by averaging the specific-cycle relatives of the 3 months centered on that trough. Stage V is the peak, and its standing is measured by the average of the 3 months centered on the peak. An average of the relatives for the 3 months centered on the terminal trough gives the standing for Stage IX. The period between Stage I and Stage V, regardless of length, is divided into three equal parts, which become Stages II, III, and IV. The period between Stage V and Stage IX is also divided into three equal parts, and they become Stages VI, VII, and VIII. The standings at each of these stages are determined by averaging the specific-cycle relatives of the months during each stage. The length of the stages during the rising phase of the cycle usually varies from that of the stages during the declining phase, because the periods of expansion and contraction are usually not of exactly the same duration. As a result, the number of months in these stages may vary between the periods of expansion and of contraction. In addition, the number of months in Stages II through IV and VI through VIII may vary from cycle to cycle because the lengths of the periods from trough to peak and peak to trough may, and usually do, differ.

The series of standings at each of the nine stages of a cycle gives the specific-cycle pattern for that cycle. This pattern is of interest and frequently is plotted and studied. Needless to say, these individual cycle patterns of a number of cycles are by no means uniform. To eliminate peculiar variations of individual cycles, the standings for each stage of a number of cycles are averaged. In Figure 14-1 the average standing for each stage is plotted at the middle of that stage. When these points are then joined by the dashed line, the pattern of the typical specific cycle for coke becomes apparent. The dispersion of the actual relatives

FIGURE 14–1

Sample Chart of Cyclical Patterns

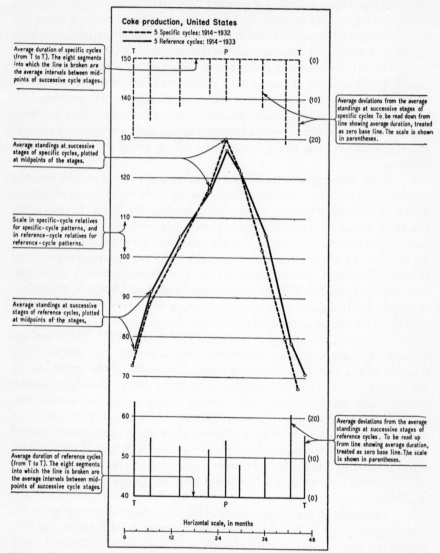

SOURCE: Arthur F. Burns and Wesley C. Mitchell, *Measuring Business Cycles* (New York: National Bureau of Economic Research, 1946), p. 35.

from these averages is measured by the average deviation, which is indicated in Figure 14-1 by the length of the vertical dashed bar over the middle of each stage.

Reference Cycles

In order to determine the relation of a specific series to the general cycle, a procedure very similar to the one presented above is employed.

Table 14-2. MONTHLY REFERENCE DATES OF THE BUSINESS CYCLE IN THE UNITED STATES

Monthly reference dates		
Initial trough	*Peak*	*Terminal trough*
Dec. 1854	June 1857	Dec. 1858
Dec. 1858	Oct. 1860	June 1861
June 1861	Apr. 1865	Dec. 1867
Dec. 1867	June 1869	Dec. 1870
Dec. 1870	Oct. 1873	Mar. 1879
Mar. 1879	Mar. 1882	May 1885
May 1885	Mar. 1887	Apr. 1888
Apr. 1888	July 1890	May 1891
May 1891	Jan. 1893	June 1894
June 1894	Dec. 1895	June 1897
June 1897	June 1899	Dec. 1900
Dec. 1900	Sept. 1902	Aug. 1904
Aug. 1904	May 1907	June 1908
June 1908	June 1910	Jan. 1912
Jan. 1912	Jan. 1913	Dec. 1914
Dec. 1914	Aug. 1918	Apr. 1919
Apr. 1919	Jan. 1920	Sept. 1921
Sept. 1921	May 1923	July 1924
July 1924	Oct. 1926	Dec. 1927
Dec. 1927	June 1929	Mar. 1933
Mar. 1933	May 1937	May 1938
May 1938	Feb. 1945	Oct. 1945
Oct. 1945	Nov. 1948	Oct. 1949

Source: National Bureau of Economic Research.

It differs only in that it uses the timing of the general business cycle rather than that of the specific cycle. First, exact timing of the cycles of general business are marked off. Table 14-2 gives the monthly reference dates of the general cycle since 1854. In marking off these cycles, National Bureau analysts did not limit themselves to an examination of economic time series, but also consulted many other sources and types of material. The monthly values of the series under study for the period of each *general business cycle* are then averaged, and then expressed as percentages of this average. Thus they become "reference-cycle relatives." The standings of the reference-cycle relatives for nine stages of the general cycle are determined. Again Stage I is the initial trough, and Stage IX the terminal trough. Stages II, III, and IV represent an equal division of the period between Stages I and V, and Stages VI, VII, and VIII represent an equal division of the period between Stages V and IX. When this method is followed for a substantial period, the standings for each stage for several cycles are available and may be averaged. These averages describe the typical reference-cycle pattern. In Figure 14-1 the average reference-cycle pattern for coke production in the United States is indicated by the solid black line that joins the plotted average standings at each of the nine stages. The average deviations of the standing at each stage are also computed for the reference cycle and are indicated by the length of the solid vertical lines at the bottom of Figure 14-1.

In Figure 14-1 the reference-cycle pattern does not conform exactly to the average specific cycle for coke. The explanation is that the coke series does not have precisely the same timing as the general business cycle. If it did, identical monthly data would be employed in computing the standings at every stage of every cycle, and the specific cycle and the reference cycle would coincide. However, the cycle averages used in converting the absolute values into relatives differed because of the timing difference, as did the exact location of the nine cycle stages for which standings were computed. Nevertheless, the two patterns do not diverge significantly, an indication that the coke series follows the general business cycle very closely. A specific cycle varying considerably from the reference cycle may indicate a lagging or leading relation. A *leading series* is one that reaches its turning points—peaks and troughs—before similar turns occur in general business. A *lagging series* turns after the general cycle. Because leads and lag may have great significance in business-cycle forecasting, the National Bureau is interested in both the consistency of this type of behavior by individual series and the length of period of lead or lag.

Although the National Bureau method of cycle analysis may seem more complicated and cumbersome than the residual technique, it has proved to be the simplest and most accurate way of comparing the cyclical variations of individual series with those of general business. In addition, it is free of errors that might be introduced were secular trend improperly estimated. The latter advantage is indeed significant when series whose trend patterns are not clear are under analysis. Its principal shortcoming is found in the fact that, because no cycle can be studied in this way until it is completed, the method cannot be applied to current data.

FORECASTING
THE BUSINESS CYCLE

The analysis of leading series offers one of the most promising avenues to cycle forecasting. Presumably, all that would be necessary in order
to predict a change in general business would be to observe a turn in a series
that invariably leads the cycle of general business. Unfortunately, no
single series of economic data is sufficiently reliable. As an approach to this
type of forecasting, Geoffrey Moore selected eight series which possessed
significant leading characteristics in that they led most consistently and by
reasonably long and uniform periods and at the same time conformed
closely to the general cycle. The behavior of these series in this regard
up to 1938 is presented in Table 14-3.

Table 14-3. TIMING OF LEAD SERIES
(to 1938)

	Peak			Troughs		
	Total no.	*No. leading*	*Average lead*	*Total no.*	*No. leading*	*Average lead*
Series						
Liabilities of business failures inverted —Dun's	14	11	10.5	16	14	7.5
Industrial stock Prices—Dow Jones	11	8	6.0	11	8	7.2
New orders, durable goods	25	21	6.9	30	24	4.7
Residential building contracts	5	4	6.2	6	5	4.5
Commercial and industrial building contracts, floor space —F. W. Dodge	5	4	5.2	6	4	1.7
Weekly hours mfg. —BLS	4	3	3.8	5	3	2.6
New incorporations —Dun's	20	12	2.5	20	15	3.5
Index of spot market prices—BLS	11	7	2.6	11	8	3.2

Source: Adapted from Geoffrey H. Moore, *Statistical Indicators of Cyclical Revivals
and Recessions* (New York: National Bureau of Economic Research, 1950).

Another technique that currently seems quite promising is based on the fact that at all times most series are either expanding or contracting. During periods of general expansion the number of economic time series whose values are expanding usually exceeds the number contracting; during general contraction the opposite is true. At turning points the number of series expanding or contracting is approximately equal. Consequently,

FIGURE 14–2.   Percentage of Series Undergoing Cyclical Expansion
Moore's Sample of Well-Conforming Series
(1885–1939)

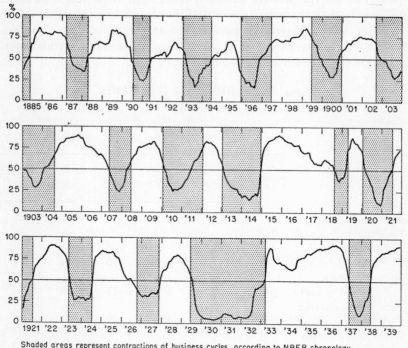

Shaded areas represent contractions of business cycles, according to NBER chronology.

SOURCE: Arthur F. Burns, *New Facts on Business Cycles* (New York: National Bureau of Economic Research, 1950), p. 12.

before the end of expansion the percentage of series expanding necessarily declines toward the 50-percent level, and before the trough the percentage of series expanding must begin to rise toward this same figure. As a result, the series that expresses the percentage of series expanding is inherently a consistently leading series. Figure 14-2 clearly demonstrates that this characteristic has been true of every cycle since 1885.

The two methods of forecasting described above rely on historical comparisons and assume that relations which existed in the past will persist in the future. Another technique that has gained considerable support in recent years attempts to forecast on the basis of a thorough understanding of currently operative forces. Favorable and unfavorable factors are enumerated, evaluated, and interrelated in making the prediction. Assumptions are made concerning the levels of government expenditures and taxation. Rates of population growth are projected, the status of productivity is estimated, and technological factors are anticipated. When these and many other and diverse elements are finally integrated, an over-all forecast is forthcoming. This approach is known as crosscut analysis, or model building. When it is used to predict Gross National Product, each of the expenditure streams that in combination comprise GNP is separately analyzed and a value projected. Thus individual forecasts would be prepared for domestic-consumption expenditures, domestic investment, and the like. After they have been edited for mutual consistency, the forecasts of the components of GNP are combined into a prediction of GNP itself.

SUGGESTED READINGS

Bratt, E. C. *Business Cycles and Forecasting*. Homewood, Ill.: Richard D. Irwin, Inc., 1953, chap. 4.

Burns, A. F., and W. C. Mitchell. *Measuring Business Cycles*. New York: National Bureau of Economic Research, Inc., 1946, chap. 1.

Greenwald, W. I. *Statistics for Economics*. Columbus, Ohio: Charles E. Merrill Books, Inc., 1963, chaps. 11, 12.

Mills, F. C. *Introduction to Statistics*. New York: Holt, Rinehart and Winston, Inc., 1956, chap. 12.

Schumpeter, J. A. *Business Cycle*. New York: McGraw-Hill Book Company, Inc., 1939, chap. 5.

QUESTIONS

1. What is a business cycle?
2. How can cyclical influences be isolated from the other elements causing variations in time-series data?
3. On what assumptions is the residual method based? Are these assumptions usually realized in actual practice?
4. Statistical normal for annual data is merely secular trend; in contrast, for monthly data it is the product of trend and seasonal. Explain.
5. Monthly production data for the Recktly Notion Company in 1958 are listed below:

Jan.	134,326	July	139,174
Feb.	136,721	Aug.	139,232
Mar.	137,524	Sept.	139,471
Apr.	138,297	Oct.	142,650
May	138,163	Nov.	149,780
June	138,208	Dec.	151,643

(a) Is the conclusion that the firm is experiencing a period of cyclical rise justified?

(b) What other forces could explain the variations apparent in these figures?

6. If the estimate of secular trend is too high, how will results obtained from the use of the residual technique be distorted?

7. In what way may the comparison of cyclical fluctuations in two or more series that differ in amplitude be facilitated?

8. How does the National Bureau mark off the individual cycles in specific series?

9. Why does the National Bureau method eliminate trend between cycles but not during cycles?

10. How are the nine periods of the reference cycle determined?

11. In what ways do specific cycles differ from reference cycles?

12. What is gained by comparing specific cycles and reference cycles?

13. What is a leading series? How may leading series be employed to advantage in economic forecasting?

14. The liabilities of business failures and industrial stock prices usually lead the cycle of general business. Explain the reason for this behavior.

15. Explain two general approaches to economic forecasting.

16. Explain why accurate forecasts of the business cycle would be of great value to management.

17. Are the following statements true, false, or a combination of truth and falsehood?

(a) The National Bureau method of measuring business cycles does not attempt to remove all trend influences. Only the intercycle trend is presumably taken out.

(b) It is sometimes difficult to distinguish cyclical from irregular elements. As a result, occasionally a random event is viewed as a cyclical force.

(c) The pattern of most business cycles is regular and uniform. This fact makes it possible, once the current position in the cycle is known, to forecast with little difficulty the onset of later stages.

(d) Reference cycles indicate the way in which the particular series behaved at the critical periods of the general business cycle. Through their use the lagging or leading attributes of the series can be determined.

(e) If trend has been improperly measured so that it rises too slowly, the use of the residual method will cause the data to appear to be more and more cyclically inflated as time passes.

(f) It is often advisable to use seasonally adjusted data when studying the cycle so that seasonal and cyclical changes are not confused.

(g) Government that is committed to maintaining the level of income and employment must have some advance knowledge of cyclical turns if its actions are to be effective.

PROBLEMS

1. Adjust the following series, showing the production of the Markright Company, to remove the influence of trend and seasonal elements.

	Production	Trend ordinate
Jan.	180,000	200,000
Feb.	185,000	201,000
Mar.	192,000	202,000
Apr.	198,000	203,000
May	206,000	204,000
June	193,000	205,000
July	160,000	206,000
Aug.	145,000	207,000
Sept.	120,000	208,000
Oct.	125,000	209,000
Nov.	150,000	210,000
Dec.	165,000	211,000

Seasonal index

Jan.	80	July	100
Feb.	90	Aug.	90
Mar.	100	Sept.	80
Apr.	110	Oct.	90
May	120	Nov.	110
June	110	Dec.	120

(a) In what phase of the production cycle do the months listed above probably fall?

(b) During what month or months were irregular or random influences most active?

2. In January of 1958 the sales of the Renton Products Company amounted to $263,000. Seven months before they were $242,000. The trend ordinates for January 1958 and June 1957 were $250,000 and $244,000, respectively. The seasonal index for June is 80 and January 92. Had business really improved over the period in question?

3. The Johnson Company in 1958 had sales of $375,000 compared with a sales trend value of $250,000. The Weston Company realized sales of $1,687,500 compared with a trend of $1,125,000. Which company turned in the best relative performance?

4. Interpret Figure 14-3 with respect to the following points.

(a) Is the Railroad Freight Ton-Miles series a leading or a lagging series? If so, at what points does it lead or lag?

FIGURE 14-3.   Patterns of Reference and Specific Cycles in
Railroad Freight Ton-Miles in the United States, 1904–1949

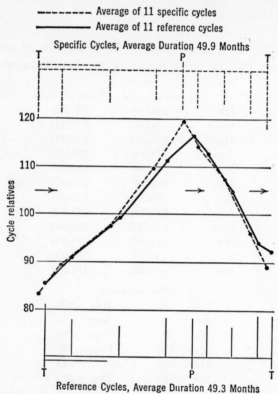

SOURCE: National Bureau of Economic Research.

The nine black dots connected by lines of dashes in the
specific cycle pattern and by solid lines in the reference
cycle pattern mark the average standings of freight ton-
miles in cycle relatives at the nine stages into which
specific and reference cycles are divided.

(b) What evidence of secular trend do you observe?

(c) Which phase of the cycle was longest? Which was shortest?

5. In the first part of 1959 the president of the Gadsen Microwave Company was faced with the problem of evaluating certain key executives.
Up until the time that the current sales manager took over in 1956,
the trend of sales could appropriately be expressed as $Y_e = 5,000,000 +
100,000X$, where X represents a period of 1 year and had a value of
0 in 1950. Sales for 1958, which have just been reported, amounted to
$6,000,000. From trade sources the president had learned that com-

petitors in 1958 did about 35 percent more business than in 1950. What would be your evaluation of the sales manager?

6. For the following data, express cyclical and irregular variation as percentages of *normal*.

Company A, 1964

	Sales (thousands of dollars)	Trend ordinate	Seasonal index
Jan.	12	11	80
Feb.	18	14	90
March	15	17	105
April	25	20	110
May	20	23	105

Arithmetic and
Algebraic Techniques

RATIOS

Comparisons are often made between two magnitudes by dividing one by the other. The resulting value is known as the ratio of the two magnitudes. For example, one of the most widely used ratios in financial analysis—the current or working-capital ratio—is computed by dividing total current assets by total current liabilities. This ratio relation is frequently verbally stated as the ratio of current assets to current liabilities. Because this type of statement is commonplace, it should be emphasized that the first mentioned of the magnitudes is divided by the second. In reality "current assets to current liabilities" means current assets divided by current liabilities. Thus the word "to" is merely an abbreviation of "divided by."

The use of ratios is widespread. In the area of financial analysis mentioned above, great reliance is placed on this technique. Dun & Bradstreet, the largest credit-rating service, bases its evaluation of a firm's credit standing in large part on the results obtained from 14 ratios. Throughout the study of statistics, ratios will be employed again and again. For example, in analyzing seasonal variations, ratios to a moving average will be used, but in testing hypotheses, certain critical ratios will be examined. A special form of ratio that is particularly useful in business is the compound ratio. In such a ratio both the numerator and the denominator are themselves ratios. For example, in this manner the profit-to-sales ratios for individual firms might be compared with the average profit-to-sales ratio for the entire industry. Here the denominator ratio would be the industry figure that would remain stable while the individual firm figure in the numerator varied.

The great advantage of the use of ratios is that they constitute a simple way of comparing the relative size of different magnitudes. It is clear that the relation of 15,612,324 to 5,204,108 can be much more easily understood when expressed in ratio form as 3 to 1. However, it is important to note that the ratio indicates only relative size and that it obscures the absolute levels of the values and the magnitude of the difference between them. Thus the ratio 3 to 1 gives no indication that the variables are in the orders of magnitude of 15 and 5 million, respectively, or that the difference between them approximates 10 million.

PERCENTAGES

When ratios are multiplied by 100 they are converted thereby into percentages. Thus a ratio of 2 to 1 can be alternately expressed as 200 percent. This expression must be interpreted as meaning that the value of the first magnitude is 200 percent or twice that of the second. Percentages are very frequently employed in relation to changes; care must be taken to interpret these percentage results correctly. If the price of a low-cost automobile increased from $2000 in 1954 to $2500 in 1958, the latter price would be 125 percent of the former. This percentage is computed by dividing 2000 into 2500 and multiplying the resulting figure, 1.25, by 100. An alternate statement would be that the price in 1958 was 25-percent higher than in 1954. A frequent error is to misconstrue such figures to mean either that price in 1958 was 25 percent of 1954 or that by 1958 it had increased by 125 percent. Several other sources of error or misinterpretation in use of percentages deserve mention.

Percentage of Change

The percentage of change is computed by dividing the value before the change into the amount of change. Thus if the price of a car increases from $2000 to $2500, the original price of $2000 is divided into the amount of change, $500, and the result multiplied by 100 to arrive at an answer of a 25-percent increase. Were price then to fall from $2500 to $2000, the change of $500 would be expressed as a percentage of $2500, or a decline of 20 percent. The percentages of change in these two examples are not directly comparable, because each is computed from a different base. If an attempt to average them were made, an erroneous conclusion could easily be reached. Thus the average of $+25$ percent and -20 percent might seem to be $+2.5$ percent, which could be taken to indicate a 2½-percent increase in the price of the car. Actually, the price, after the two changes, has returned to the original value. Successive changes of the same absolute amount, here $500, produce a larger percentage of increase, 25 percent, than of decrease, 20 percent, because the increase is computed on the smaller base, $2000.

Another example may serve further to clarify this point. Suppose the price of the car is once again originally $2000 and that price first increases 20 percent and then decreases by 20 percent. The 20-percent increase would bring the price to $2400. The decrease of 20 percent based on the $2400 price would amount to $480 and would bring the final price down to $1920, which is lower than the original price of $2000. Thus successive increases and decreases of the same percentage amounts will depress the final value below the starting figure.

The amount of possible percentage increase is not limited; however, this characteristic is often not true of percentage decline. Because the values of most economic and business data such as sales, wages, and costs cannot become negative, their minimum possible value is 0. A decrease from any positive figure to 0 is a decline of 100 percent. Percentages of decline greater than 100 percent cannot occur with such data and would indicate error. Should the price of a car be reduced from $2000 to $800, the amount of decline would be 150 percent of the final price. Nevertheless, percentage of decrease must be figured as a percentage of the original price from which the reduction was made; in this illustration there would be a drop of only 60 percent. Some data such as profits can assume negative values; as a result, percentages of decline greater than 100 percent sometimes occur. If a firm earned a profit of $10,000 in one year and sustained a $5000 loss the next, the total decline in profit would be $15,000, or 150 percent of the original profit figure.

Distortions Caused by Small Bases

When percentages of growth in sales or profits are reported, the reader is often surprised to find apparently phenomenal performances exhibited by unknown or little known firms. Such percentages can usually be explained by the very small bases on which these increases were computed. If a small firm's profits grow from $1000 to $10,000, they show a 900-percent increase, whereas an expansion of earnings in a large and established concern from $5,000,000 to $7,000,000 represents only a 40-percent rise. Although the very high percentage increase in the first example has been computed correctly, caution should be taken in the interpretation of these figures. Obviously, a conclusion that the management of the smaller firm was much more efficient could not be justified. Further, the two percentages of increase should not be averaged and the resulting 470 percent considered typical of the increase in profits of the two firms.

Percentages and Magnitudes

Percentages indicate relative magnitudes only; therefore no inference should be drawn from them regarding absolute amounts. If one firm earns 10 percent on its investment and another nets only 6 percent, a comparison between profit rates alone is justified. There is no basis for concluding that the amount of the profit of the firm earning 10 percent is greater than that of the firm netting 6 percent. The total amount of profit is determined by both rate of return and the size of the investment, and no conclusions regarding total profit are justified unless both of these elements are known. Similarly, even though wage rates increase 20 percent in community A and 30 percent in community B during the same period of time, it still is impossible to determine which community pays the higher wages until the wage level from which these increases took place is considered.

Percent Changes in Precentages

In June of 1954 the Board of Governors of the Federal Reserve System reduced the legally required reserves on time deposits from 6 percent to 5 percent. How much had the reserve requirement changed? When measured as a percentage of deposits, the change is 1 percent. However, here the point at issue is the relative change in the amount of reserves that must be maintained. Consequently, because, before the change, reserves of 6 percent of deposits were required, a reduction by 1 percent of deposits amounts to a reduction of 16⅔ percent in the amount of reserves. This illustrates the need for carefully defining the base when computing percentage change in percentages.

SOLVING SIMPLE EQUATIONS

Seven types of simple equations involving one unknown will be considered.

1. A simple equation involving one unknown may be stated as

$$aX = b$$

Here X designates the unknown and a and b represent any two numbers. It will be recalled that if the same operation is applied to both sides of an equation the equality remains. Thus the same amount can be added to or subtracted from both sides and they remain equal. Similarly, both sides may be multiplied or divided by the same number or raised to the same power without disturbing the equality. This simple equation is solved by dividing both sides by a.

Thus
$$\frac{aX}{a} = \frac{b}{a}$$

Hence
$$X = \frac{b}{a}$$

If a and b are given numerical values of 5 and 10, respectively, the equation may be written as follows:
$$5X = 10$$

This expression is solved by dividing both sides by 5:
$$\frac{5X}{5} = \frac{10}{5} = 2$$
$$X = 2$$

2. When the equation is stated as
$$\frac{X}{a} = b$$

it is solved by multiplying both sides by a.

Thus
$$\frac{Xa}{a} = ba$$

Hence
$$X = ba$$

Again, if we give a and b the values of 5 and 10, the equation is stated as
$$\frac{X}{5} = 10$$

and is solved as follows:
$$\frac{X \times 5}{5} = 10 \times 5 = 50$$
$$X = 50$$

3. When the equation is stated as
$$\frac{a}{X} = b$$

it is solved by first multiplying both sides by X and then dividing both by b:
$$\frac{aX}{bX} = \frac{bX}{b}$$

Hence
$$X = \frac{a}{b}$$

With values of 5 and 10 for a and b, this equation is written

$$\frac{5}{X} = 10$$

and solved by multiplying both sides by X and dividing both by 10:

$$\frac{5X}{10X} = \frac{10X}{10}$$

$$X = \frac{5}{10} = \frac{1}{2}$$

4. The equation

$$X - a = b$$

is solved by adding a to both sides:

$$X - a + a = b + a$$

Hence $X = b + a$

With a and b assuming the numerical value of 5 and **10,**

$$X - 5 + 5 = 10 + 5$$
$$X = 15$$

5. The equation

$$X + a = b$$

is solved by subtracting a from both sides:

$$X + a - a = b - a$$

Hence $X = b - a$

With a and b once again being 5 and 10,

$$X + 5 - 5 = 10 - 5$$
$$X = 5$$

6. When the equation takes the form

$$X^2 = a$$

it is solved by taking the square root of both sides:

$$\sqrt{X^2} = X = \sqrt{a}$$

If a were 25, X would be 5.

7. The equation

$$\sqrt{X} = a$$

is solved by squaring both sides:

$$\sqrt{X} \cdot \sqrt{X} = X = a^2$$

If a were 25, X would be 625.

These seven expressions illustrate several simple forms that an equation in one unknown may take. It should be evident that the elements of more than one of these examples may be found in any given equation. Thus the equation

$$\sqrt{X} - 5 = 10$$

requires first that 5 be added to both sides and then that they be squared:

$$\sqrt{X} - 5 + 5 = 10 + 5$$
$$\sqrt{X} = 15$$
$$(\sqrt{X})^2 = 15^2$$
$$X = 225$$

Although this discussion by no means covers all the possible types of equations involving one unknown, let alone equations that include several unknowns, it reviews the principles needed in elementary statistics.

LOGARITHMS

The use of logarithms greatly simplifies many of the more complex arithmetic operations required in statistical computations. Multiplication, division, extracting roots, and raising to powers may be carried out quickly and easily in this manner.

The logarithm of a number is the exponent or power to which 10 must be raised in order to give that number. Because 10^2 equals 100, 2.0 is the logarithm of 100. Similarly, 10^3 equals 1000, and consequently 3.0 is the logarithm of 1000. Because every positive number can be expressed as a power of 10, every positive number has a logarithm. For numbers that are integral powers of 10 (for example, 10, 100, 1000, 10,000, and so on), the logarithms will be the whole numbers. When the number is other than an integral power of 10, the logarithm will contain a fraction. The logarithm of 50, for example, is 1.69897.

Two parts of every logarithm should be distinguished. The whole number lying to the left of the decimal point is known as the *characteristic*. It determines the range between integral powers of 10 within which the number falls. Thus, because the logarithm of 10 is 1 and that of 100 is 2, a characteristic of 1 indicates that the number lies between 10 and 100. The part of the logarithm lying to the right of the decimal point is called the *mantissa*. It is determined by the figures in the number whose logarithm is being found. The mantissa of .69897 represents the digits 5000 and was found by referring to the table of five-place logarithms in Appendix Table I. The entire procedure used to find the logarithm of 50 is carried out in the following manner. First look up the mantissa corresponding to the digits

5000, which is .69897. Then, because it is known that 50 lies between 10 and 100, the characteristic of 1 is assigned, giving the complete logarithm of 1.69897. Mantissas are always found by referring to the table of logarithms, whereas characteristics are determined by finding the integral powers of 10 between which the number falls. Stated differently, the mantissa is determined by the digits in the number; the characteristic locates the decimal point.

Determining the Characteristic

The characteristic of any number is determined by the number of places to the right or left of the decimal point the first (farthest to the left) digit of the number falls. Because the logarithm of 1 is 0, numbers between 1 and 10 have a characteristic of 0. For each additional place to the left of the decimal point that the first digit falls, the characteristic mounts by 1. Thus, to find the characteristic of whole numbers, subtract 1 from the number of places to the left of the decimal point that the first digit falls. The characteristic of numbers between 10 and 100 is 1, between 100 and 1000 is 2, between 1000 and 10,000 is 3, and so on. Decimal fractions—numbers between 0 and 1—have negative characteristics. The number of places to the right of the decimal point that must be counted before the first digit is encountered determines the negative characteristic. Thus, for numbers between .1 and 1, the characteristic is −1; between .01 and .1 it is −2; and the like. Uusually these negative characteristics are expressed indirectly. The decimal fraction .5 would have a characteristic of −1. However, the logarithm of .5 is written 9.69897 − 10. The −1 here is expressed as 9 followed by −10.

Examples of Finding Logarithms

(a) Find the log of 7360. By referring to the five-place logarithm table the mantissa for the digits 7360 is found to be .86688. Because the first digit lies four places to the left of the decimal point, the characteristic is 3. Thus the log of 7360 is 3.86688.

(b) Find the log of 4.25. The mantissa corresponding to the digits 425 is .62839. Because 4.25 lies between 1 and 10, the characteristic is 0. Hence the log of 4.25 is 0.62839.

(c) Find the log of .08190. Here the mantissa for the digits 819 is .91328. Since the first digit falls two places to the right of the decimal point, the characteristic is −2. The log of .08190 is expressed as 8.91328 − 10.

Interpolation

If instead of finding the log of 7360 an attempt had been made to determine the log of 7365.5, a complication would have been encountered. The table provides mantissas corresponding to the digits 7365 and 7366 but not for values lying between. The mantissa of 7365 is .86717 and of 7366 is .86723. As 7365.5 lies halfway between 7365 and 7366, it is permissible to assume that the mantissa will lie halfway between .86717 and .86723, and as the difference between these two is 6, really .00006, the amount to be added to the lower figure is 3. Thus the mantissa of 7365.5 is .86720. This process of estimation is known as interpolation. This same result can be achieved by adding the amount shown in the proportionate parts at the right-hand side of the table.

Finding Antilogarithms

The antilogarithm is the number that corresponds to a logarithm. Because 3.86688 is the logarithm of 7360, then 7360 is the antilogarithm of 3.86688. If the logarithm is known, the antilog can be quickly found. The digits are found by locating the mantissa in the log table and determining the numbers with which it is associated. The characteristic indicates the location of the decimal point. The antilog of 1.99612 is found in the following manner. By referring to the log table the mantissa of .99612 is found to represent the digits 9911. The characteristic of 1 indicates that the first digit is two places to the left of the decimal point. Hence the antilog of 1.99612 is 99.12. If the antilog of 1.64700 is desired, a complication arises because a mantissa of .64700 cannot be located in the log table. The closest values that can be found there are .64699 and .64709, representing the digits 4436 and 4437, respectively. Again interpolation is required. As .64700 lies one-tenth of the way between .64699 and .64709, the antilog can be assumed to lie .1 of the way between 4436 and 4437. Thus the digits in the antilog are 44361. When the characteristic is used to locate the decimal point, the antilog of 1.64700 is found to be 44.361.

Multiplication with the Use of Logarithms

The sum of the logarithms of two numbers gives the logarithm of their product. When 10, whose log is 1, is multiplied by 100, whose log is 2, the sum of 1 plus 2 (that is, 3) is the log of the answer. This can be explained as follows:

$$10^1 \times 10^2 = (10) \times (10 \times 10) = 10 \times 10 \times 10 = 10^3 = 1000$$

EXAMPLE: Multiply 25 by 600.

Log   25 = 1.39794
Log 600 = 2.77815
Add   4.17609

Antilog 4.17609 = 15,000

Division by Using Logarithms

Division is accomplished by subtracting logarithms. When the log of the divisor is subtracted from the log of the dividend, the log of the quotient is obtained. The division of 10,000 by 100 is accomplished as follows:

$$10^4 \div 10^2 = 10^{4-2} = 10^2$$

This may be illustrated in the following manner:

$$10^4/10^2 = (10 \times 10 \times 10 \times 10)/(10 \times 10) = 10 \times 10 = 10^2 = 100$$

EXAMPLE: Divide 725 by 25.

$$
\begin{aligned}
\text{Log } 725 &= 2.86034 \\
\text{Log } 25 &= \underline{1.39794} \\
\text{Subtract} & 1.46240 \\
\text{Antilog } 1.46240 &= 29
\end{aligned}
$$

Extracting Roots with Logarithms

To find the log of the root of a number, divide its logarithm by the index of the root desired. Hence, to take the square root, divide the log by 2, a cube root divide by 3, and so on.

EXAMPLE: Find the square root of 625.

$$
\begin{aligned}
\text{Log } 625 &= 2.79588 \\
2.79588/2 &= 1.39794 \\
\text{Antilog} 1.39794 &= 25
\end{aligned}
$$

Raising to Powers with Logarithms

To find the logarithm of a power of a number, multiply its logarithm by the index of that power. To square, multiply by 2; to cube, by 3; and so on.

EXAMPLE: Find the cube of 10.

$$
\begin{aligned}
\text{Log } 10 &= 1.0 \\
3 \text{ Log } 10 &= 3.0 \\
\text{Antilog } 3.0 &= 1000
\end{aligned}
$$

The Slide Rule

When a slide rule is employed, logarithmic computations can be made in a mechanical manner. In its usual form this device consists of four scales, two of which are located on the frame of the rule and the other

FIGURE A-2. *Slide Rule Open*

FIGURE A-1. *Slide Rule Closed*

two on the slide. On each scale the numbers are plotted at the position of their logarithms. The top two scales are identical and each contains two cycles from 1 to 1. The bottom two scales are also identical but twice as large as the top, and each contains but one cycle. Some slide rules have an additional K scale. This type of slide rule is illustrated in Figure A-1.

Multiplication, an operation that is in reality the adding of logarithms, is accomplished by setting the 1 on the sliding scale directly above (or below) one of the numbers being multiplied. Then, when the other number is located on the sliding scale, the product of the two numbers is found immediately below (or above) on the fixed scale. Although the bottom two scales are usually employed for this purpose, the top pair could serve equally well. Figure A-2 illustrates the multiplication of 2 times 4. The 1 on the sliding scale is set directly above 2 on the fixed scale. Reading out to 4 on the slide, we find it directly above 8, the product of 2 and 4. Division is accomplished in a similar manner. When the divisor on the sliding scale is placed directly above the dividend on the fixed scale, the quotient will be found on the fixed scale directly below 1 on the slide. Figure A-2 also illustrates the division of 8 by 4. When 4 on the slide is set directly above 8 on the frame, the quotient 2 is found on the fixed scale directly below 1 on the slide.

Since two logarithmic cycles are calibrated on the top scales as opposed to only one on the bottom, numbers at the same physical locations on the top scales are necessarily the squares of the numbers on the bottom scales. Hence, to find the square root of a number, locate it on the top scale and read directly below on the bottom scale. To square a number, locate it on the bottom scale and read directly above on the top scale. Although slide-rule computations are not entirely accurate, they are satisfactory for most statistical purposes, especially when the data themselves are only estimates. It is necessary merely that the slide-rule readings be accurate to the number of significant figures (as explained below) in whatever item of data employed in the computation contains the fewest significant figures.

FINDING SQUARE ROOTS

In the preceding section the derivation of square roots by the use of logarithms was explained. Should logarithmic tables be unavailable or should the use of logarithms seem cumbersome, two other methods of finding square roots are available.

Tables of Squares and Square Roots

Appendix Table III gives squares and square roots. In order to find the square root of any three-digit number, it is necessary only to locate the number in the table and read across to the square-root column. Care must be taken in determining the square roots of numbers larger or smaller than those in the table. Caution is necessary because the square root of 10 times any given number contains digits different from the square root of the number itself. Thus, although the square root of 9 is 3, the square root of 90 is 9.4868330. On the other hand, the square root of 900 is 30. The square root of a number that is 100 times a number found in the table has the same digits as those in the square root of the number itself. If the number is 10 times the number in the table, the digits would be different. These digits can also be located in the table. For example, the square root of 900 is 30, of 90,000 is 300, of 9,000,000 is 3000, but the square root of 9000 is 94.86, of 900,000 is 948.6, and so on.

The Longhand Technique

Step 1. Separate the number into groups of two digits. Begin at the decimal point.

Step 2. Find the largest square in the group farthest to the left.

Step 3. Record the square root of this figure as the first digit of the square root of the number.

Step 4. Subtract the square from the first group.

Step 5. Bring down the next group to the right of the remainder.

Step 6. Divide this figure, omitting the last digit, by twice the part of the square root already determined. Tentatively add the quotient to the square root.

Step 7. Insert the tentatively obtained second digit of the root as the rightmost digit of the divisor. Then multiply the divisor by the tentatively obtained second digit of the root. If the product is less than the previous remainder, the tentatively obtained second digit has been confirmed. If the product is greater, reduce the tentative digit by 1 and multiply again.

Step 8. Subtract the product from the remainder, bring down the next group of two digits, double the two confirmed digits of the root, and again make the trial division.

Step 9. Continue this process of doubling the part of the root already determined and using it as a trial division until the entire square root is found.

EXAMPLE: Find the square root of 625.

$$
\begin{array}{r}
2\ 5 \\
\text{Divided into groups} \quad \sqrt{6'25} \\
\text{Largest square} \qquad\qquad 4 \\
\hline
45\ \big|\ 2\ 25 \\
2\ 25 \\
\hline
\end{array}
$$

$$
\begin{array}{r}
Square\ Root = 25 \\
5+ \\
4\ \big|\ 22
\end{array}
$$

EXAMPLE: Find the square root of 549081.

```
              7  4  1
            ┌─────────
          √ │54'90'81       Square Root = 7 4 1
            │49                           ─────────
   ─────────────────
      144 │ 5 90                     · 4+
          │ 5 76              ──────────
   ─────────────────         14 │ 59
     1481 │ 14 81                 56
          │ 14 81
```

SIGNIFICANT FIGURES
AND ROUNDING

If a town votes a monthly pension of $50 to each person over 65, and if by count it is determined that there are 19 persons of that age group living in the town, the town treasurer could expect to make pension payments of exactly $3250 each month (assuming all pensions are accepted). If, on the other hand, the typical individual eats 4 pounds of meat per week and there are about 2000 people in the community, meat dealers could not reasonably anticipate a weekly meat consumption of exactly 8000 pounds. The figures in the first example are called *integers*. They are definite and exact amounts, in this example determined by the ordinance enacting the pension and physical count of persons. Consequently, precise computations can be made. In the second example the figures are based on measurements and estimates that are not entirely exact. As a result, conclusions cannot and should not be stated with the same precision as in the first instance.

Significant Figures

The investigator should know how accurate his estimates are. For instance, the estimate of meat consumption of 4 pounds per week may be accurate to the nearest pound. Hence the figure 4 pounds may mean any actual value from 3.50 pounds to 4.50 pounds. Here there is but one significant figure. If the estimate were accurate to the nearest tenth of a pound, the actual values could lie between 3.95 and 4.05 pounds. Here there would be two significant figures. Frequently this measurement would be written 4.0 in order to indicate the degree of precision. The size of the magnitude is of no importance in determining the number of significant figures. Thus 4,000,000,000 may contain only one significant figure, though 2.93 may contain three. The nine zeros in the large number merely serve to locate the decimal point.

Rounding in Multiplication and Division

If 2, which is assumed to be accurate to one significant figure, is multiplied by the integer 11, a numerical answer of 22 will result. However, 2 means any value between 1.5 and 2.5, and as a result the actual product could lie anywhere between 16.5 and 27.5. Consequently, there is only one significant figure in the product. The principle here is that when estimates or measurements are employed in multiplication or division, there can be no more significant figures in the answer than in that figure employed in the computation which contains the smallest number of significant figures. Therefore answers should be rounded to the closest significant figure. In the above example, 22 should be rounded to 20 because there can be only one significant figure in the answer. In rounding, amounts of less than 5 are dropped. Thus, in rounding 22 to one significant figure, the second 2 is dropped and the rounded value is 20. When the amount of the digit to be rounded out exceeds 5, it is rounded to the higher significant figure. Hence 27 would be rounded to 30.

EXAMPLES OF ROUNDING:
   (a)   373 rounded to two significant figures is   370
   (b)   4,563 rounded to one significant figure is   5,000
   (c) .037926 rounded to four significant figure is .03793
   (d)   4.04 rounded to two significant figures is   4.0

Rounding 4.5 to one significant figure presents a problem. Because it lies equidistant between 4 and 5, to which of these numbers should it be rounded? Usual practice is to round to the nearest even digit. Hence 4.5 would be rounded to 4.

Rounding in Addition and Subtraction

When numbers that are significant to a different number of decimal places are added or subtracted, the answer is significant only to the place of the least accurate figure. To express this idea another way, figures in the answer that lie to the right of the last significant figure of any of the numbers in the computation are not significant and should be rounded out. For example, assume that 62,500 significant to three figures is added to 311, which is also significant to three figures:

$$
\begin{array}{r}
62{,}500 \\
311 \\
\hline
62{,}811
\end{array}
$$

The last significant figure in 62,500 is the 5. The two zeros merely serve to locate the decimal point. As a result, the 11 in the sum lies to the right of the 5 and is not significant. Therefore 62,811 should be rounded to 62,800.

Indication of Significance

In an honest investigation the number of significant figures is indicated by the number of figures given in the statement. Thus 25, 1.1, .0023, and .010 would each indicate two significant figures, and 312,000, .00302, and 3.01 would indicate three. A problem arises only with numbers like 2000. Are the three zeros merely used to locate the decimal, leaving only one significant figure, or is the degree of accuracy great, because up to four figures might be significant? Sometimes the source of the data will place a dot over the last significant figure. Thus 2000 indicates three significant figures.

QUESTIONS

1. Why are ratios useful in the analysis of business problems?
2. Give an example of a compound ratio.
3. How is a ratio converted into a percentage?
4. When percentage change is computed, what difficulties may arise?
5. If the sales of the Family Food Market rose 20 percent in January, 10 percent in February, and 5 percent in March, sales in March were 35 percent more than in December. Do you agree?
6. During 1955 the profits of the Highline Department Store amounted to $2,000,000. The following year they increased 25 percent. In 1957, however, owing to higher costs and lower prices, profits fell 20 percent. Despite this decrease, the treasurer claimed they still were ahead of 1955. Do you agree with his reasoning?
7. In 1957 the amount of unemployment in Meadville rose 400 percent. Is this increase indicative of a serious worsening in the economic conditions of the area?
8. A business executive claimed that both the costs and the profits of his firm had declined about 150 percent during the preceding 6-month period. His statement was challenged by a listener who alleged that a decline of more than 100 percent could not occur. Do you feel this criticism is justified?
9. Explain five ratios encountered in your studies of economics and business that have indicated performance over time, and five that indicate conditions at a given point of time.
10. In November 1957 the Board of Governors of the Federal Reserve System approved the reduction of Reserve Bank discount rates from $3\frac{1}{2}$ to 3 percent. Despite the decrease of only $\frac{1}{2}$ percent how do you account for great significance that was attached to this move?
11. Why bother to round numbers?
12. Are the following statements true, false, or a combination of truth and falsehood?

(a) Ratios are very useful in making comparisons between magnitudes but at the same time obscure the absolute values of the items being compared.

(b) The product of 2.00 and 3.716 contains four significant figures.

(c) The sum of 2,170,000 and 19,000 should be correctly stated as 2,190,000.

(d) Great care must be taken when percentages of change are compared. Erroneous conclusions are often obtained when the percentage changes are computed on different bases.

(e) To multiply numbers, add their logarithms and find the antilog of the sum.

(f) If the national income expressed in current dollars increased 10 percent, real income per capita has risen 10 percent.

13. How does an integer differ from a measurement?

14. To how many places is the integer 4 significant?

15. On what mathematical principle is the ordinary slide rule constructed?

PROBLEMS

1.

Ford Motor Company
CONSOLIDATED BALANCE SHEETS
December 31, 1957–1956

Assets

Current assets	1957	1956
Cash............................	$ 77,464,184	$ 96,660,982
Marketable securities...............	187,690,273	118,470,322
Receivables.......................	151,506,750	134,920,275
Inventories.......................	653,594,572	597,493,385
Prepaid expenses..................	21,071,991	19,631,691
Total current assets............	1,091,327,770	967,176,655
Investments and noncurrent receivables		
Investments in unconsolidated subsidiaries...................	96,677,599	88,764,385
Other investments................	12,786,603	12,294,798
Total investments and noncurrent receivables...............	109,464,202	101,059,183
Property, plant, and equipment		
Property, plant, and equipment, at cost	2,623,265,125	2,335,389,331
Less accumulated depreciation........	780,968,098	649,323,712
Net property, plant, and equipment...	1,842,297,027	1,686,065,619
Deferred charges......................	71,383,323	38,333,461
Total assets...................	$ 3,114,472,322	$ 2,792,634,918

Liabilities, Reserves, and Capital

Current liabilities	1957	1956
Accounts payable and accrued liabilities......................	$ 572,184,174	$ 683,104,172
United States income taxes, 1957—$317,220,840 and 1956—$278,842,901, net of United States Government securities.....	84,048,437	.....
Total current liabilities..........	656,232,611	683,104,172
4 Percent promissory notes due Nov. 1, 1976	250,000,000	58,615,000
Other liabilities and reserves		
Supplemental compensation awards...	16,288,038	16,386,726
Supplemental compensation reserve...	30,478,139	30,060,520
Reserves for other specific purposes...	12,000,000	16,987,924
Total other liabilities and reserves	58,766,177	63,435,170
Capital		
Capital stock.......................	272,427,850	270,068,475
Capital account in excess of par value of stock.......................	279,638,639	272,088,639
Earnings retained for use in the business.......................	1,597,407,045	1,445,323,462
Total capital......................	2,149,473,534	1,987,480,576
Total liabilities, reserves, and capital...................	$ 3,114,462,322	$ 2,792,634,918

SOURCE: *1957 Annual Report*, Ford Motor Company.

(a) Compute the following ratios for both 1956 and 1957: current ratio; quick-asset ratio; debt-equity ratio.
(b) Compute the percentage change from 1956 to 1957 in total assets; current assets; capital; net working capital.
(c) Express each of the following as a percentage of total assets in 1957: current assets; net property, plant, and equipment; current liabilities.
2. Convert the following ratios to percentages: (a) 3 to 2, (b) 5 to 3, (c) 2 to 6, (d) 8 to 5.
3. Convert the following percentages to the simplest possible ratios: (a) 200 percent, (b) 133 percent, (c) 25 percent, (d) 60.
4. Compute the percentage change in the situations below:
(a) Employment increases from 45 million to 60 million.
(b) Sales decline from $80,000 to $50,000.
(c) Profits of $10,000 in 1956 fall to losses of $10,000 in 1957.
(d) Bad-debt losses rose from 4 percent to 5 percent of credit sales.

5. Solve the following equations:

(a) $3A = 9$ (e) $3/x = 5$ (i) $\sqrt{y} + 3 = 8$
(b) $x - 4 = 8$ (f) $y + 10 = 4$ (j) $B^2 = A$
(c) $B - 3 = C$ (g) $M^2 = 2$ (k) $x^2/2 = y$
(d) $x/4 = 2$ (h) $\sqrt{x} = 5$ (l) $6/\sqrt{x} = 3$

6. Determine the solutions of the word problems below:

(a) The sales of tooth paste in the Rite Price Drug Store amounted to $76.00 during February of 1957. This figure represents an increase of 20 percent over January of the same year. What was the dollar amount of tooth-paste sales during January?

(b) The number of employees of the Standard Manufacturing Company fell 20 short of three times the number hired by the Excellsior Company. Excellsior employed 1240 men. How many men did Standard employ?

(c) If a carload of goods weighs 9 tons plus the weight of one half of a carload, how much does a carload and a half weigh?

(d) In the Ajax Company, managerial costs rise with the square root of sales. When sales were $1,000,000 per year, these costs amounted to $25,000. Should sales rise to $4,000,000, what level managerial cost could be expected?

7. Find the logarithms of the following numbers:

(a) 101   (e) .000601
(b) 6,320,000   (f) 8.033
(c) .762   (g) 10,000
(d) 1.00   (h) 0

8. Find the antilogarithms of the figures below:

(a) 1.0294   (d) 2.7782
(b) 10.7324   (e) 0.7408
(c) $8.8762 - 10$ (f) 3.6028

9. Multiply the following, using logarithms:

(a) 10×100 (c) $.0012 \times 3.0$
(b) 621×325 (d) 0×10

10. Divide by means of logarithms:

(a) $100 \div 5$ (c) $625 \div 25$
(b) $1094 \div 15$ (d) $60 \div .003$

11. Extract the square root of the following by means of logarithms:

(a) 81   (c) 19,900
(b) .0037   (d) 6225

12. Square the numbers below, using logarithms:

(a) 83   (c) .031
(b) 602   (d) 628

13. Make the computations called for in problems 9, 10, 11, and 12 by means of a slide rule.

14. Find the values called for in problems 11 and 12 by using the table of squares and square roots.

15. How many significant figures does each of these numbers contain?
    (a) 1.00062   (e) 21.0
    (b) .003   (f) 27,000,000
    (c) 367,000   (g) 201.2
    (d) 3000   (h) 6.0

16. Express the product or quotient with the appropriate number of significant figures. Unless there is a specification to the contrary, each value is a measurement.
    (a) 6231.01 × 3.1   (e) 2463 × 2 (2 is an integer)
    (b) 22 ÷ 2   (f) 25.37 × 5
    (c) 62.0 × 4.00   (g) 100 ÷ 3 (3 is an integer)
    (d) 21.3 ÷ .0003   (h) 321 × 652 (both numbers are integers)

17. Express the sum or remainder with the proper number of significant figures. Unless otherwise specified, each number is a measurement.
    (a) 62,100.   (b) 63.2501   (c) 62 (both numbers
          35.   are integers)
    Add 5283.4   Subtract 2.   Add 91

Tables

Appendix Table I

Common Logarithms (Five-Place) of the Natural Numbers 1 to 10,000

N	Log	N	Log	N	Log	N	Log	N	Log
0	—	20	1.30 103	40	1.60 206	60	1.77 815	80	1.90 309
1	0.00 000	21	1.32 222	41	1.61 278	61	1.78 533	81	1.90 849
2	0.30 103	22	1.34 242	42	1.62 325	62	1.79 239	82	1.91 381
3	0.47 712	23	1.36 173	43	1.63 347	63	1.79 934	83	1.91 908
4	0.60 206	24	1.38 021	44	1.64 345	64	1.80 618	84	1.92 428
5	0.69 897	25	1.39 794	45	1.65 321	65	1.81 291	85	1.92 942
6	0.77 815	26	1.41 497	46	1.66 276	66	1.81 954	86	1.93 450
7	0.84 510	27	1.43 136	47	1.67 210	67	1.82 607	87	1.93 952
8	0.90 309	28	1.44 716	48	1.68 124	68	1.83 251	88	1.94 448
9	0.95 424	29	1.46 240	49	1.69 020	69	1.83 885	89	1.94 939
10	1.00 000	30	1.47 712	50	1.69 897	70	1.84 510	90	1.95 424
11	1.04 139	31	1.49 136	51	1.70 757	71	1.85 126	91	1.95 904
12	1.07 918	32	1.50 515	52	1.71 600	72	1.85 733	92	1.96 379
13	1.11 394	33	1.51 851	53	1.72 428	73	1.86 332	93	1.96 848
14	1.14 613	34	1.53 148	54	1.73 239	74	1.86 923	94	1.97 313
15	1.17 609	35	1.54 407	55	1.74 036	75	1.87 506	95	1.97 772
16	1.20 412	36	1.55 630	56	1.74 819	76	1.88 081	96	1.98 227
17	1.23 045	37	1.56 820	57	1.75 587	77	1.88 649	97	1.98 677
18	1.25 527	38	1.57 978	58	1.76 343	78	1.89 209	98	1.99 123
19	1.27 875	39	1.59 106	59	1.77 085	79	1.89 763	99	1.99 564
20	1.30 103	40	1.60 206	60	1.77 815	80	1.90 309	100	2.00 000

Common Logarithms (Five-Place) of the Natural Numbers 1 to 10,000

N	0	1	2	3	4	5	6	7	8	9
100	00 000	043	087	130	173	217	260	303	346	389
101	00 432	475	518	561	604	647	689	732	775	817
102	00 860	903	945	988	*030	*072	*115	*157	*199	*242
103	01 284	326	368	410	452	494	536	578	620	662
104	01 703	745	787	828	870	912	953	995	*036	*078
105	02 119	160	202	243	284	325	366	407	449	490
106	02 531	572	612	653	694	735	776	816	857	898
107	02 938	979	*019	*060	*100	*141	*181	*222	*262	*302
108	03 342	383	423	463	503	543	583	623	663	703
109	03 743	782	822	862	902	941	981	*021	*060	*100
110	04 139	179	218	258	297	336	376	415	454	493
111	04 532	571	610	650	689	727	766	805	844	883
112	04 922	961	999	*038	*077	*115	*154	*192	*231	*269
113	05 308	346	385	423	461	500	538	576	614	652
114	05 690	729	767	805	843	881	918	956	994	*032
115	06 070	108	145	183	221	258	296	333	371	408
116	06 446	483	521	558	595	633	670	707	744	781
117	06 819	856	893	930	967	*004	*041	*078	*115	*151
118	07 188	225	262	298	335	372	408	445	482	518
119	07 555	591	628	664	700	737	773	809	846	882
120	07 918	954	990	*027	*063	*099	*135	*171	*207	*243
121	08 279	314	350	386	422	458	493	529	565	600
122	08 636	672	707	743	778	814	849	884	920	955
123	08 991	*026	*061	*096	*132	*167	*202	*237	*272	*307
124	09 342	377	412	447	482	517	552	587	621	656
125	09 691	726	760	795	830	864	899	934	968	*003
126	10 037	072	106	140	175	209	243	278	312	346
127	10 380	415	449	483	517	551	585	619	653	687
128	10 721	755	789	823	857	890	924	958	992	*025
129	11 059	093	126	160	193	227	261	294	327	361
130	11 394	428	461	494	528	561	594	628	661	694
131	11 727	760	793	826	860	893	926	959	992	*024
132	12 057	090	123	156	189	222	254	287	320	352
133	12 385	418	450	483	516	548	581	613	646	678
134	12 710	743	775	808	840	872	905	937	969	*001
135	13 033	066	098	130	162	194	226	258	290	322
136	13 354	386	418	450	481	513	545	577	609	640
137	13 672	704	735	767	799	830	862	893	925	956
138	13 988	*019	*051	*082	*114	*145	*176	*208	*239	*270
139	14 301	333	364	395	426	457	489	520	551	582
140	14 613	644	675	706	737	768	799	829	860	891
141	14 922	953	983	*014	*045	*076	*106	*137	*168	*198
142	15 229	259	290	320	351	381	412	442	473	503
143	15 534	564	594	625	655	685	715	746	776	806
144	15 836	866	897	927	957	987	*017	*047	*077	*107
145	16 137	167	197	227	256	286	316	346	376	406
146	16 435	465	495	524	554	584	613	643	673	702
147	16 732	761	791	820	850	879	909	938	967	997
148	17 026	056	085	114	143	173	202	231	260	289
149	17 319	348	377	406	435	464	493	522	551	580
150	17 609	638	667	696	725	754	782	811	840	869
N	0	1	2	3	4	5	6	7	8	9

Prop. Parts

	44	43	42
1	4.4	4.3	4.2
2	8.8	8.6	8.4
3	13.2	12.9	12.6
4	17.6	17.2	16.8
5	22.0	21.5	21.0
6	26.4	25.8	25.2
7	30.8	30.1	29.4
8	35.2	34.4	33.6
9	39.6	38.7	37.8

	41	40	39
1	4.1	4.0	3.9
2	8.2	8.0	7.8
3	12.3	12.0	11.7
4	16.4	16.0	15.6
5	20.5	20.0	19.5
6	24.6	24.0	23.4
7	28.7	28.0	27.3
8	32.8	32.0	31.2
9	36.9	36.0	35.1

	38	37	36
1	3.8	3.7	3.6
2	7.6	7.4	7.2
3	11.4	11.1	10.8
4	15.2	14.8	14.4
5	19.0	18.5	18.0
6	22.8	22.2	21.6
7	26.6	25.9	25.2
8	30.4	29.6	28.8
9	34.2	33.3	32.4

	35	34	33
1	3.5	3.4	3.3
2	7.0	6.8	6.6
3	10.5	10.2	9.9
4	14.0	13.6	13.2
5	17.5	17.0	16.5
6	21.0	20.4	19.8
7	24.5	23.8	23.1
8	28.0	27.2	26.4
9	31.5	30.6	29.7

	32	31	30
1	3.2	3.1	3.0
2	6.4	6.2	6.0
3	9.6	9.3	9.0
4	12.8	12.4	12.0
5	16.0	15.5	15.0
6	19.2	18.6	18.0
7	22.4	21.7	21.0
8	25.6	24.8	24.0
9	28.8	27.9	27.0

Common Logarithms (Five-Place) of the Natural Numbers 1 to 10,000

N	0	1	2	3	4	5	6	7	8	9
150	17 609	638	667	696	725	754	782	811	840	869
151	17 898	926	955	984	*013	*041	*070	*099	*127	*156
152	18 184	213	241	270	298	327	355	384	412	441
153	18 469	498	526	554	583	611	639	667	696	724
154	18 752	780	808	837	865	893	921	949	977	*005
155	19 033	061	089	117	145	173	201	229	257	285
156	19 312	340	368	396	424	451	479	507	535	562
157	19 590	618	645	673	700	728	756	783	811	838
158	19 866	893	921	948	976	*003	*030	*058	*085	*112
159	20 140	167	194	222	249	276	303	330	358	385
160	20 412	439	466	493	520	548	575	602	629	656
161	20 683	710	737	763	790	817	844	871	898	925
162	20 952	978	*005	*032	*059	*085	*112	*139	*165	*192
163	21 219	245	272	299	325	352	378	405	431	458
164	21 484	511	537	564	590	617	643	669	696	722
165	21 748	775	801	827	854	880	906	932	958	985
166	22 011	037	063	089	115	141	167	194	220	246
167	22 272	298	324	350	376	401	427	453	479	505
168	22 531	557	583	608	634	660	686	712	737	763
169	22 789	814	840	866	891	917	943	968	994	*019
170	23 045	070	096	121	147	172	198	223	249	274
171	23 300	325	350	376	401	426	452	477	502	528
172	23 553	578	603	629	654	679	704	729	754	779
173	23 805	830	855	880	905	930	955	980	*005	*030
174	24 055	080	105	130	155	180	204	229	254	279
175	24 304	329	353	378	403	428	452	477	502	527
176	24 551	576	601	625	650	674	699	724	748	773
177	24 797	822	846	871	895	920	944	969	993	*018
178	25 042	066	091	115	139	164	188	212	237	261
179	25 285	310	334	358	382	406	431	455	479	503
180	25 527	551	575	600	624	648	672	696	720	744
181	25 768	792	816	840	864	888	912	935	959	983
182	26 007	031	055	079	102	126	150	174	198	221
183	26 245	269	293	316	340	364	387	411	435	458
184	26 482	505	529	553	576	600	623	647	670	694
185	26 717	741	764	788	811	834	858	881	905	928
186	26 951	975	998	*021	*045	*068	*091	*114	*138	*161
187	27 184	207	231	254	277	300	323	346	370	393
188	27 416	439	462	485	508	531	554	577	600	623
189	27 646	669	692	715	738	761	784	807	830	852
190	27 875	898	921	944	967	989	*012	*035	*058	*081
191	28 103	126	149	171	194	217	240	262	285	307
192	28 330	353	375	398	421	443	466	488	511	533
193	28 556	578	601	623	646	668	691	713	735	758
194	28 780	803	825	847	870	892	914	937	959	981
195	29 003	026	048	070	092	115	137	159	181	203
196	29 226	248	270	292	314	336	358	380	403	425
197	29 447	469	491	513	535	557	579	601	623	645
198	29 667	688	710	732	754	776	798	820	842	863
199	29 885	907	929	951	973	994	*016	*038	*060	*081
200	30 103	125	146	168	190	211	233	255	276	298

Prop. Parts

	29	28
1	2.9	2.8
2	5.8	5.6
3	8.7	8.4
4	11.6	11.2
5	14.5	14.0
6	17.4	16.8
7	20.3	19.6
8	23.2	22.4
9	26.1	25.2

	27	26
1	2.7	2.6
2	5.4	5.2
3	8.1	7.8
4	10.8	10.4
5	13.5	13.0
6	16.2	15.6
7	18.9	18.2
8	21.6	20.8
9	24.3	23.4

	25
1	2.5
2	5.0
3	7.5
4	10.0
5	12.5
6	15.0
7	17.5
8	20.0
9	22.5

	24	23
1	2.4	2.3
2	4.8	4.6
3	7.2	6.9
4	9.6	9.2
5	12.0	11.5
6	14.4	13.8
7	16.8	16.1
8	19.2	18.4
9	21.6	20.7

	22	21
1	2.2	2.1
2	4.4	4.2
3	6.6	6.3
4	8.8	8.4
5	11.0	10.5
6	13.2	12.6
7	15.4	14.7
8	17.6	16.8
9	19.8	18.9

Common Logarithms (Five-Place) of the Natural Numbers 1 to 10,000

N	0	1	2	3	4	5	6	7	8	9
200	30 103	125	146	168	190	211	233	255	276	298
201	30 320	341	363	384	406	428	449	471	492	514
202	30 535	557	578	600	621	643	664	685	707	728
203	30 750	771	792	814	835	856	878	899	920	942
204	30 963	984	*006	*027	*048	*069	*091	*112	*133	*154
205	31 175	197	218	239	260	281	302	323	345	366
206	31 387	408	429	450	471	492	513	534	555	576
207	31 597	618	639	660	681	702	723	744	765	785
208	31 806	827	848	869	890	911	931	952	973	994
209	32 015	035	056	077	098	118	139	160	181	201
210	32 222	243	263	284	305	325	346	366	387	408
211	32 428	449	469	490	510	531	552	572	593	613
212	32 634	654	675	695	715	736	756	777	797	818
213	32 838	858	879	899	919	940	960	980	*001	*021
214	33 041	062	082	102	122	143	163	183	203	224
215	33 244	264	284	304	325	345	365	385	405	425
216	33 445	465	486	506	526	546	566	586	606	626
217	33 646	666	686	706	726	746	766	786	806	826
218	33 846	866	885	905	925	945	965	985	*005	*025
219	34 044	064	084	104	124	143	163	183	203	223
220	34 242	262	282	301	321	341	361	380	400	420
221	34 439	459	479	498	518	537	557	577	596	616
222	34 635	655	674	694	713	733	753	772	792	811
223	34 830	850	869	889	908	928	947	967	986	*005
224	35 025	044	064	083	102	122	141	160	180	199
225	35 218	238	257	276	295	315	334	353	372	392
226	35 411	430	449	468	488	507	526	545	564	583
227	35 603	622	641	660	679	698	717	736	755	774
228	35 793	813	832	851	870	889	908	927	946	965
229	35 984	*003	*021	*040	*059	*078	*097	*116	*135	*154
230	36 173	192	211	229	248	267	286	305	324	342
231	36 361	380	399	418	436	455	474	493	511	530
232	36 549	568	586	605	624	642	661	680	698	717
233	36 736	754	773	791	810	829	847	866	884	903
234	36 922	940	959	977	996	*014	*033	*051	*070	*088
235	37 107	125	144	162	181	199	218	236	254	273
236	37 291	310	328	346	365	383	401	420	438	457
237	37 475	493	511	530	548	566	585	603	621	639
238	37 658	676	694	712	731	749	767	785	803	822
239	37 840	858	876	894	912	931	949	967	985	*003
240	38 021	039	057	075	093	112	130	148	166	184
241	38 202	220	238	256	274	292	310	328	346	364
242	38 382	399	417	435	453	471	489	507	525	543
243	38 561	578	596	614	632	650	668	686	703	721
244	38 739	757	775	792	810	828	846	863	881	899
245	38 917	934	952	970	987	*005	*023	*041	*058	*076
246	39 094	111	129	146	164	182	199	217	235	252
247	39 270	287	305	322	340	358	375	393	410	428
248	39 445	463	480	498	515	533	550	568	585	602
249	39 620	637	655	672	690	707	724	742	759	777
250	39 794	811	829	846	863	881	898	915	933	950
N	0	1	2	3	4	5	6	7	8	9

Prop. Parts

	22	21
1	2.2	2.1
2	4.4	4.2
3	6.6	6.3
4	8.8	8.4
5	11.0	10.5
6	13.2	12.6
7	15.4	14.7
8	17.6	16.8
9	19.8	18.9

	20
1	2.0
2	4.0
3	6.0
4	8.0
5	10.0
6	12.0
7	14.0
8	16.0
9	18.0

	19
1	1.9
2	3.8
3	5.7
4	7.6
5	9.5
6	11.4
7	13.3
8	15.2
9	17.1

	18
1	1.8
2	3.6
3	5.4
4	7.2
5	9.0
6	10.8
7	12.6
8	14.4
9	16.2

	17
1	1.7
2	3.4
3	5.1
4	6.8
5	8.5
6	10.2
7	11.9
8	13.6
9	15.3

Common Logarithms (Five-Place) of the Natural Numbers 1 to 10,000

Prop. Parts

18
1	1.8
2	3.6
3	5.4
4	7.2
5	9.0
6	10.8
7	12.6
8	14.4
9	16.2

17
1	1.7
2	3.4
3	5.1
4	6.8
5	8.5
6	10.2
7	11.9
8	13.6
9	15.3

16
1	1.6
2	3.2
3	4.8
4	6.4
5	8.0
6	9.6
7	11.2
8	12.8
9	14.4

15
1	1.5
2	3.0
3	4.5
4	6.0
5	7.5
6	9.0
7	10.5
8	12.0
9	13.5

14
1	1.4
2	2.8
3	4.2
4	5.6
5	7.0
6	8.4
7	9.8
8	11.2
9	12.6

N	0	1	2	3	4	5	6	7	8	9
250	39 794	811	829	846	863	881	898	915	933	950
251	39 967	985	*002	*019	*037	*054	*071	*088	*106	*123
252	40 140	157	175	192	209	226	243	261	278	295
253	40 312	329	346	364	381	398	415	432	449	466
254	40 483	500	518	535	552	569	586	603	620	637
255	40 654	671	688	705	722	739	756	773	790	807
256	40 824	841	858	875	892	909	926	943	960	976
257	40 993	*010	*027	*044	*061	*078	*095	*111	*128	*145
258	41 162	179	196	212	229	246	263	280	296	313
259	41 330	347	363	380	397	414	430	447	464	481
260	41 497	514	531	547	564	581	597	614	631	647
261	41 664	681	697	714	731	747	764	780	797	814
262	41 830	847	863	880	896	913	929	946	963	979
263	41 996	*012	*029	*045	*062	*078	*095	*111	*127	*144
264	42 160	177	193	210	226	243	259	275	292	308
265	42 325	341	357	374	390	406	423	439	455	472
266	42 488	504	521	537	553	570	586	602	619	635
267	42 651	667	684	700	716	732	749	765	781	797
268	42 813	830	846	862	878	894	911	927	943	959
269	42 975	991	*008	*024	*040	*056	*072	*088	*104	*120
270	43 136	152	169	185	201	217	233	249	265	281
271	43 297	313	329	345	361	377	393	409	425	441
272	43 457	473	489	505	521	537	553	569	584	600
273	43 616	632	648	664	680	696	712	727	743	759
274	43 775	791	807	823	838	854	870	886	902	917
275	43 933	949	965	981	996	*012	*028	*044	*059	*075
276	44 091	107	122	138	154	170	185	201	217	232
277	44 248	264	279	295	311	326	342	358	373	389
278	44 404	420	436	451	467	483	498	514	529	545
279	44 560	576	592	607	623	638	654	669	685	700
280	44 716	731	747	762	778	793	809	824	840	855
281	44 871	886	902	917	932	948	963	979	994	*010
282	45 025	040	056	071	086	102	117	133	148	163
283	45 179	194	209	225	240	255	271	286	301	317
284	45 332	347	362	378	393	408	423	439	454	469
285	45 484	500	515	530	545	561	576	591	606	621
286	45 637	652	667	682	697	712	728	743	758	773
287	45 788	803	818	834	849	864	879	894	909	924
288	45 939	954	969	984	*000	*015	*030	*045	*060	*075
289	46 090	105	120	135	150	165	180	195	210	225
290	46 240	255	270	285	300	315	330	345	359	374
291	46 389	404	419	434	449	464	479	494	509	523
292	46 538	553	568	583	598	613	627	642	657	672
293	46 687	702	716	731	746	761	776	790	805	820
294	46 835	850	864	879	894	909	923	938	953	967
295	46 982	997	*012	*026	*041	*056	*070	*085	*100	*114
296	47 129	144	159	173	188	202	217	232	246	261
297	47 276	290	305	319	334	349	363	378	392	407
298	47 422	436	451	465	480	494	509	524	538	553
299	47 567	582	596	611	625	640	654	669	683	698
300	47 712	727	741	756	770	784	799	813	828	842

| Prop. Parts | N | 0 | 1 | 2 | 3 | 4 | 5 | 6 | 7 | 8 | 9 |

Common Logarithms (Five-Place) of the Natural Numbers 1 to 10,000

N	0	1	2	3	4	5	6	7	8	9
300	47 712	727	741	756	770	784	799	813	828	842
301	47 857	871	885	900	914	929	943	958	972	986
302	48 001	015	029	044	058	073	087	101	116	130
303	48 144	159	173	187	202	216	230	244	259	273
304	48 287	302	316	330	344	359	373	387	401	416
305	48 430	444	458	473	487	501	515	530	544	558
306	48 572	586	601	615	629	643	657	671	686	700
307	48 714	728	742	756	770	785	799	813	827	841
308	48 855	869	883	897	911	926	940	954	968	982
309	48 996	*010	*024	*038	*052	*066	*080	*094	*108	*122
310	49 136	150	164	178	192	206	220	234	248	262
311	49 276	290	304	318	332	346	360	374	388	402
312	49 415	429	443	457	471	485	499	513	527	541
313	49 554	568	582	596	610	624	638	651	665	679
314	49 693	707	721	734	748	762	776	790	803	817
315	49 831	845	859	872	886	900	914	927	941	955
316	49 969	982	996	*010	*024	*037	*051	*065	*079	*092
317	50 106	120	133	147	161	174	188	202	215	229
318	50 243	256	270	284	297	311	325	338	352	365
319	50 379	393	406	420	433	447	461	474	488	501
320	50 515	529	542	556	569	583	596	610	623	637
321	50 651	664	678	691	705	718	732	745	759	772
322	50 786	799	813	826	840	853	866	880	893	907
323	50 920	934	947	961	974	987	*001	*014	*028	*041
324	51 055	068	081	095	108	121	135	148	162	175
325	51 188	202	215	228	242	255	268	282	295	308
326	51 322	335	348	362	375	388	402	415	428	441
327	51 455	468	481	495	508	521	534	548	561	574
328	51 587	601	614	627	640	654	667	680	693	706
329	51 720	733	746	759	772	786	799	812	825	838
330	51 851	865	878	891	904	917	930	943	957	970
331	51 983	996	*009	*022	*035	*048	*061	*075	*088	*101
332	52 114	127	140	153	166	179	192	205	218	231
333	52 244	257	270	284	297	310	323	336	349	362
334	52 375	388	401	414	427	440	453	466	479	492
335	52 504	517	530	543	556	569	582	595	608	621
336	52 634	647	660	673	686	699	711	724	737	750
337	52 763	776	789	802	815	827	840	853	866	879
338	52 892	905	917	930	943	956	969	982	994	*007
339	53 020	033	046	058	071	084	097	110	122	135
340	53 148	161	173	186	199	212	224	237	250	263
341	53 275	288	301	314	326	339	352	364	377	390
342	53 403	415	428	441	453	466	479	491	504	517
343	53 529	542	555	567	580	593	605	618	631	643
344	53 656	668	681	694	706	719	732	744	757	769
345	53 782	794	807	820	832	845	857	870	882	895
346	53 908	920	933	945	958	970	983	995	*008	*020
347	54 033	045	058	070	083	095	108	120	133	145
348	54 158	170	183	195	208	220	233	245	258	270
349	54 283	295	307	320	332	345	357	370	382	394
350	54 407	419	432	444	456	469	481	494	506	518
N	0	1	2	3	4	5	6	7	8	9

Prop. Parts

15		14		13		12	
1	1.5	1	1.4	1	1.3	1	1.2
2	3.0	2	2.8	2	2.6	2	2.4
3	4.5	3	4.2	3	3.9	3	3.6
4	6.0	4	5.6	4	5.2	4	4.8
5	7.5	5	7.0	5	6.5	5	6.0
6	9.0	6	8.4	6	7.8	6	7.2
7	10.5	7	9.8	7	9.1	7	8.4
8	12.0	8	11.2	8	10.4	8	9.6
9	13.5	9	12.6	9	11.7	9	10.8

Common Logarithms (Five-Place) of the Natural Numbers 1 to 10,000

N	0	1	2	3	4	5	6	7	8	9
350	54 407	419	432	444	456	469	481	494	506	518
351	54 531	543	555	568	580	593	605	617	630	642
352	54 654	667	679	691	704	716	728	741	753	765
353	54 777	790	802	814	827	839	851	864	876	888
354	54 900	913	925	937	949	962	974	986	998	*011
355	55 023	035	047	060	072	084	096	108	121	133
356	55 145	157	169	182	194	206	218	230	242	255
357	55 267	279	291	303	315	328	340	352	364	376
358	55 388	400	413	425	437	449	461	473	485	497
359	55 509	522	534	546	558	570	582	594	606	618
360	55 630	642	654	666	678	691	703	715	727	739
361	55 751	763	775	787	799	811	823	835	847	859
362	55 871	883	895	907	919	931	943	955	967	979
363	55 991	*003	*015	*027	*038	*050	*062	*074	*086	*098
364	56 110	122	134	146	158	170	182	194	205	217
365	56 229	241	253	265	277	289	301	312	324	336
366	56 348	360	372	384	396	407	419	431	443	455
367	56 467	478	490	502	514	526	538	549	561	573
368	56 585	597	608	620	632	644	656	667	679	691
369	56 703	714	726	738	750	761	773	785	797	808
370	56 820	832	844	855	867	879	891	902	914	926
371	56 937	949	961	972	984	996	*008	*019	*031	*043
372	57 054	066	078	089	101	113	124	136	148	159
373	57 171	183	194	206	217	229	241	252	264	276
374	57 287	299	310	322	334	345	357	368	380	392
375	57 403	415	426	438	449	461	473	484	496	507
376	57 519	530	542	553	565	576	588	600	611	623
377	57 634	646	657	669	680	692	703	715	726	738
378	57 749	761	772	784	795	807	818	830	841	852
379	57 864	875	887	898	910	921	933	944	955	967
380	57 978	990	*001	*013	*024	*035	*047	*058	*070	*081
381	58 092	104	115	127	138	149	161	172	184	195
382	58 206	218	229	240	252	263	274	286	297	309
383	58 320	331	343	354	365	377	388	399	410	422
384	58 433	444	456	467	478	490	501	512	524	535
385	58 546	557	569	580	591	602	614	625	636	647
386	58 659	670	681	692	704	715	726	737	749	760
387	58 771	782	794	805	816	827	838	850	861	872
388	58 883	894	906	917	928	939	950	961	973	984
389	58 995	*006	*017	*028	*040	*051	*062	*073	*084	*095
390	59 106	118	129	140	151	162	173	184	195	207
391	59 218	229	240	251	262	273	284	295	306	318
392	59 329	340	351	362	373	384	395	406	417	428
393	59 439	450	461	472	483	494	506	517	528	539
394	59 550	561	572	583	594	605	616	627	638	649
395	59 660	671	682	693	704	715	726	737	748	759
396	59 770	780	791	802	813	824	835	846	857	868
397	59 879	890	901	912	923	934	945	956	966	977
398	59 988	999	*010	*021	*032	*043	*054	*065	*076	*086
399	60 097	108	119	130	141	152	163	173	184	195
400	60 206	217	228	239	249	260	271	282	293	304

Prop. Parts

13		12		11		10	
1	1.3	1	1.2	1	1.1	1	1.0
2	2.6	2	2.4	2	2.2	2	2.0
3	3.9	3	3.6	3	3.3	3	3.0
4	5.2	4	4.8	4	4.4	4	4.0
5	6.5	5	6.0	5	5.5	5	5.0
6	7.8	6	7.2	6	6.6	6	6.0
7	9.1	7	8.4	7	7.7	7	7.0
8	10.4	8	9.6	8	8.8	8	8.0
9	11.7	9	10.8	9	9.9	9	9.0

Common Logarithms (Five-Place) of the Natural Numbers 1 to 10,000

N	0	1	2	3	4	5	6	7	8	9
400	60 206	217	228	239	249	260	271	282	293	304
401	60 314	325	336	347	358	369	379	390	401	412
402	60 423	433	444	455	466	477	487	498	509	520
403	60 531	541	552	563	574	584	595	606	617	627
404	60 638	649	660	670	681	692	703	713	724	735
405	60 746	756	767	778	788	799	810	821	831	842
406	60 853	863	874	885	895	906	917	927	938	949
407	60 959	970	981	991	*002	*013	*023	*034	*045	*055
408	61 066	077	087	098	109	119	130	140	151	162
409	61 172	183	194	204	215	225	236	247	257	268
410	61 278	289	300	310	321	331	342	352	363	374
411	61 384	395	405	416	426	437	448	458	469	479
412	61 490	500	511	521	532	542	553	563	574	584
413	61 595	606	616	627	637	648	658	669	679	690
414	61 700	711	721	731	742	752	763	773	784	794
415	61 805	815	826	836	847	857	868	878	888	899
416	61 909	920	930	941	951	962	972	982	993	*003
417	62 014	024	034	045	055	066	076	086	097	107
418	62 118	128	138	149	159	170	180	190	201	211
419	62 221	232	242	252	263	273	284	294	304	315
420	62 325	335	346	356	366	377	387	397	408	418
421	62 428	439	449	459	469	480	490	500	511	521
422	62 531	542	552	562	572	583	593	603	613	624
423	62 634	644	655	665	675	685	696	706	716	726
424	62 737	747	757	767	778	788	798	808	818	829
425	62 839	849	859	870	880	890	900	910	921	931
426	62 941	951	961	972	982	992	*002	*012	*022	*033
427	63 043	053	063	073	083	094	104	114	124	134
428	63 144	155	165	175	185	195	205	215	225	236
429	63 246	256	266	276	286	296	306	317	327	337
430	63 347	357	367	377	387	397	407	417	428	438
431	63 448	458	468	478	488	498	508	518	528	538
432	63 548	558	568	579	589	599	609	619	629	639
433	63 649	659	669	679	689	699	709	719	729	739
434	63 749	759	769	779	789	799	809	819	829	839
435	63 849	859	869	879	889	899	909	919	929	939
436	63 949	959	969	979	988	998	*008	*018	*028	*038
437	64 048	058	068	078	088	098	108	118	128	137
438	64 147	157	167	177	187	197	207	217	227	237
439	64 246	256	266	276	286	296	306	316	326	335
440	64 345	355	365	375	385	395	404	414	424	434
441	64 444	454	464	473	483	493	503	513	523	532
442	64 542	552	562	572	582	591	601	611	621	631
443	64 640	650	660	670	680	689	699	709	719	729
444	64 738	748	758	768	777	787	797	807	816	826
445	64 836	846	856	865	875	885	895	904	914	924
446	64 933	943	953	963	972	982	992	*002	*011	*021
447	65 031	040	050	060	070	079	089	099	108	118
448	65 128	137	147	157	167	176	186	196	205	215
449	65 225	234	244	254	263	273	283	292	302	312
450	65 321	331	341	350	360	369	379	389	398	408
N	0	1	2	3	4	5	6	7	8	9

Prop. Parts

	11		10		9
1	1.1	1	1.0	1	0.9
2	2.2	2	2.0	2	1.8
3	3.3	3	3.0	3	2.7
4	4.4	4	4.0	4	3.6
5	5.5	5	5.0	5	4.5
6	6.6	6	6.0	6	5.4
7	7.7	7	7.0	7	6.3
8	8.8	8	8.0	8	7.2
9	9.9	9	9.0	9	8.1

Common Logarithms (Five-Place) of the Natural Numbers 1 to 10,000

N	0	1	2	3	4	5	6	7	8	9
450	65 321	331	341	350	360	369	379	389	398	408
451	65 418	427	437	447	456	466	475	485	495	504
452	65 514	523	533	543	552	562	571	581	591	600
453	65 610	619	629	639	648	658	667	677	686	696
454	65 706	715	725	734	744	753	763	772	782	792
455	65 801	811	820	830	839	849	858	868	877	887
456	65 896	906	916	925	935	944	954	963	973	982
457	65 992	*001	*011	*020	*030	*039	*049	*058	*068	*077
458	66 087	096	106	115	124	134	143	153	162	172
459	66 181	191	200	210	219	229	238	247	257	266
460	66 276	285	295	304	314	323	332	342	351	361
461	66 370	380	389	398	408	417	427	436	445	455
462	66 464	474	483	492	502	511	521	530	539	549
463	66 558	567	577	586	596	605	614	624	633	642
464	66 652	661	671	680	689	699	708	717	727	736
465	66 745	755	764	773	783	792	801	811	820	829
466	66 839	848	857	867	876	885	894	904	913	922
467	66 932	941	950	960	969	978	987	997	*006	*015
468	67 025	034	043	052	062	071	080	089	099	108
469	67 117	127	136	145	154	164	173	182	191	201
470	67 210	219	228	237	247	256	265	274	284	293
471	67 302	311	321	330	339	348	357	367	376	385
472	67 394	403	413	422	431	440	449	459	468	477
473	67 486	495	504	514	523	532	541	550	560	569
474	67 578	587	596	605	614	624	633	642	651	660
475	67 669	679	688	697	706	715	724	733	742	752
476	67 761	770	779	788	797	806	815	825	834	843
477	67 852	861	870	879	888	897	906	916	925	934
478	67 943	952	961	970	979	988	997	*006	*015	*024
479	68 034	043	052	061	070	079	088	097	106	115
480	68 124	133	142	151	160	169	178	187	196	205
481	68 215	224	233	242	251	260	269	278	287	296
482	68 305	314	323	332	341	350	359	368	377	386
483	68 395	404	413	422	431	440	449	458	467	476
484	68 485	494	502	511	520	529	538	547	556	565
485	68 574	583	592	601	610	619	628	637	646	655
486	68 664	673	681	690	699	708	717	726	735	744
487	68 753	762	771	780	789	797	806	815	824	833
488	68 842	851	860	869	878	886	895	904	913	922
489	68 931	940	949	958	966	975	984	993	*002	*011
490	69 020	028	037	046	055	064	073	082	090	099
491	69 108	117	126	135	144	152	161	170	179	188
492	69 197	205	214	223	232	241	249	258	267	276
493	69 285	294	302	311	320	329	338	346	355	364
494	69 373	381	390	399	408	417	425	434	443	452
495	69 461	469	478	487	496	504	513	522	531	539
496	69 548	557	566	574	583	592	601	609	618	627
497	69 636	644	653	662	671	679	688	697	705	714
498	69 723	732	740	749	758	767	775	784	793	801
499	69 810	819	827	836	845	854	862	871	880	888
500	69 897	906	914	923	932	940	949	958	966	975

Prop. Parts | N | 0 | 1 | 2 | 3 | 4 | 5 | 6 | 7 | 8 | 9

Prop. Parts

10		9		8	
1	1.0	1	0.9	1	0.8
2	2.0	2	1.8	2	1.6
3	3.0	3	2.7	3	2.4
4	4.0	4	3.6	4	3.2
5	5.0	5	4.5	5	4.0
6	6.0	6	5.4	6	4.8
7	7.0	7	6.3	7	5.6
8	8.0	8	7.2	8	6.4
9	9.0	9	8.1	9	7.2

Common Logarithms (Five-Place) of the Natural Numbers 1 to 10,000

N	0	1	2	3	4	5	6	7	8	9
500	69 897	906	914	923	932	940	949	958	966	975
501	69 984	992	*001	*010	*018	*027	*036	*044	*053	*062
502	70 070	079	088	096	105	114	122	131	140	148
503	70 157	165	174	183	191	200	209	217	226	234
504	70 243	252	260	269	278	286	295	303	312	321
505	70 329	338	346	355	364	372	381	389	398	406
506	70 415	424	432	441	449	458	467	475	484	492
507	70 501	509	518	526	535	544	552	561	569	578
508	70 586	595	603	612	621	629	638	646	655	663
509	70 672	680	689	697	706	714	723	731	740	749
510	70 757	766	774	783	791	800	808	817	825	834
511	70 842	851	859	868	876	885	893	902	910	919
512	70 927	935	944	952	961	969	978	986	995	*003
513	71 012	020	029	037	046	054	063	071	079	088
514	71 096	105	113	122	130	139	147	155	164	172
515	71 181	189	198	206	214	223	231	240	248	257
516	71 265	273	282	290	299	307	315	324	332	341
517	71 349	357	366	374	383	391	399	408	416	425
518	71 433	441	450	458	466	475	483	492	500	508
519	71 517	525	533	542	550	559	567	575	584	592
520	71 600	609	617	625	634	642	650	659	667	675
521	71 684	692	700	709	717	725	734	742	750	759
522	71 767	775	784	792	800	809	817	825	834	842
523	71 850	858	867	875	883	892	900	908	917	925
524	71 933	941	950	958	966	975	983	991	999	*008
525	72 016	024	032	041	049	057	066	074	082	090
526	72 099	107	115	123	132	140	148	156	165	173
527	72 181	189	198	206	214	222	230	239	247	255
528	72 263	272	280	288	296	304	313	321	329	337
529	72 346	354	362	370	378	387	395	403	411	419
530	72 428	436	444	452	460	469	477	485	493	501
531	72 509	518	526	534	542	550	558	567	575	583
532	72 591	599	607	616	624	632	640	648	656	665
533	72 673	681	689	697	705	713	722	730	738	746
534	72 754	762	770	779	787	979	803	811	819	827
535	72 835	843	852	860	868	876	884	892	900	908
536	72 916	925	933	941	949	957	965	973	981	989
537	72 997	*006	*014	*022	*030	*038	*046	*054	*062	*070
538	73 078	086	094	102	111	119	127	135	143	151
539	73 159	167	175	183	191	199	207	215	223	231
540	73 239	247	255	263	272	280	288	296	304	312
541	73 320	328	336	344	352	360	368	376	384	392
542	73 400	408	416	424	432	440	448	456	464	472
543	73 480	488	496	504	512	520	528	536	544	552
544	73 560	568	576	584	592	600	608	616	624	632
545	73 640	648	656	664	672	679	687	695	703	711
546	73 719	727	735	743	751	759	767	775	783	791
547	73 799	807	815	823	830	838	846	854	862	870
548	73 878	886	894	902	910	918	926	933	941	949
549	73 957	965	973	981	989	997	*005	*013	*020	*028
550	74 036	044	052	060	068	076	084	092	099	107
N	0	1	2	3	4	5	6	7	8	9

Prop. Parts

	9		**8**		**7**
1	0.9		0.8		0.7
2	1.8		1.6		1.4
3	2.7		2.4		2.1
4	3.6		3.2		2.8
5	4.5		4.0		3.5
6	5.4		4.8		4.2
7	6.3		5.6		4.9
8	7.2		6.4		5.6
9	8.1		7.2		6.3

Common Logarithms (Five-Place) of the Natural Numbers 1 to 10,000

Prop. Parts	N	0	1	2	3	4	5	6	7	8	9
	550	74 036	044	052	060	068	076	084	092	099	107
	551	74 115	123	131	139	147	155	162	170	178	186
	552	74 194	202	210	218	225	233	241	249	257	265
	553	74 273	280	288	296	304	312	320	327	335	343
	554	74 351	359	367	374	382	390	398	406	414	421
	555	74 429	437	445	453	461	468	476	484	492	500
	556	74 507	515	523	531	539	547	554	562	570	578
	557	74 586	593	601	609	617	624	632	640	648	656
	558	74 663	671	679	687	695	702	710	718	726	733
	559	74 741	749	757	764	772	780	788	796	803	811
	560	74 819	827	834	842	850	858	865	873	881	889
	561	74 896	904	912	920	927	935	943	950	958	966
8	562	74 974	981	989	997	*005	*012	*020	*028	*035	*043
1 0.8	563	75 051	059	066	074	082	089	097	105	113	120
2 1.6	564	75 128	136	143	151	159	166	174	182	189	197
3 2.4	565	75 205	213	220	228	236	243	251	259	266	274
4 3.2	566	75 282	289	297	305	312	320	328	335	343	351
5 4.0	567	75 358	366	374	381	389	397	404	412	420	427
6 4.8	568	75 435	442	450	458	465	473	481	488	496	504
7 5.6	569	75 511	519	526	534	542	549	557	565	572	580
8 6.4	**570**	75 587	595	603	610	618	626	633	641	648	656
9 7.2	571	75 664	671	679	686	694	702	709	717	724	732
	572	75 740	747	755	762	770	778	785	793	800	808
	573	75 815	823	831	838	846	853	861	868	876	884
	574	75 891	899	906	914	921	929	937	944	952	959
	575	75 967	974	982	989	997	*005	*012	*020	*027	*035
	576	76 042	050	057	065	072	080	087	095	103	110
	577	76 118	125	133	140	148	155	163	170	178	185
	578	76 193	200	208	215	223	230	238	245	253	260
	579	76 268	275	283	290	298	305	313	320	328	335
	580	76 343	350	358	365	373	380	388	395	403	410
	581	76 418	425	433	440	448	455	462	470	477	485
7	582	76 492	500	507	515	522	530	537	545	552	559
1 0.7	583	76 567	574	582	589	597	604	612	619	626	634
2 1.4	584	76 641	649	656	664	671	678	686	693	701	708
3 2.1	585	76 716	723	730	738	745	753	760	768	775	782
4 2.8	586	76 790	797	805	812	819	827	834	842	849	856
5 3.5	587	76 864	871	879	886	893	901	908	916	923	930
6 4.2	588	76 938	945	953	960	967	975	982	989	997	*004
7 4.9	589	77 012	019	026	034	041	048	056	063	070	078
8 5.6	**590**	77 085	093	100	107	115	122	129	137	144	151
9 6.3	591	77 159	166	173	181	188	195	203	210	217	225
	592	77 232	240	247	254	262	269	276	283	291	298
	593	77 305	313	320	327	335	342	349	357	364	371
	594	77 379	386	393	401	408	415	422	430	437	444
	595	77 452	459	466	474	481	488	495	503	510	517
	596	77 525	532	539	546	554	561	568	576	583	590
	597	77 597	605	612	619	627	634	641	648	656	663
	598	77 670	677	685	692	699	706	714	721	728	735
	599	77 743	750	757	764	772	779	786	793	801	808
	600	77 815	822	830	837	844	851	859	866	873	880
Prop. Parts	N	0	1	2	3	4	5	6	7	8	9

Common Logarithms (Five-Place) of the Natural Numbers 1 to 10,000

N	0	1	2	3	4	5	6	7	8	9	Prop. Parts
600	77 815	822	830	837	844	851	859	866	873	880	
601	77 887	895	902	909	916	924	931	938	945	952	
602	77 960	967	974	981	988	996	*003	*010	*017	*025	
603	78 032	039	046	053	061	068	075	082	089	097	
604	78 104	111	118	125	132	140	147	154	161	168	
605	78 176	183	190	197	204	211	219	226	233	240	
606	78 247	254	262	269	276	283	290	297	305	312	
607	78 319	326	333	340	347	355	362	369	376	383	
608	78 390	398	405	412	419	426	433	440	447	455	
609	78 462	469	476	483	490	497	504	512	519	526	
610	78 533	540	547	554	561	569	576	583	590	597	
611	78 604	611	618	625	633	640	647	654	661	668	
612	78 675	682	689	696	704	711	718	725	732	739	
613	78 746	753	760	767	774	781	789	796	803	810	
614	78 817	824	831	838	845	852	859	866	873	880	
615	78 888	895	902	909	916	923	930	937	944	951	
616	78 958	965	972	979	986	993	*000	*007	*014	*021	
617	79 029	036	043	050	057	064	071	078	085	092	
618	79 099	106	113	120	127	134	141	148	155	162	
619	79 169	176	183	190	197	204	211	218	225	232	
620	79 239	246	253	260	267	274	281	288	295	302	
621	79 309	316	323	330	337	344	351	358	365	372	
622	79 379	386	393	400	407	414	421	428	435	442	
623	79 449	456	463	470	477	484	491	498	505	511	
624	79 518	525	532	539	546	553	560	567	574	581	
625	79 588	595	602	609	616	623	630	637	644	650	
626	79 657	664	671	678	685	692	699	706	713	720	
627	79 727	734	741	748	754	761	768	775	782	789	
628	79 796	803	810	817	824	831	837	844	851	858	
629	79 865	872	879	886	893	900	906	913	920	927	
630	79 934	941	948	955	962	969	975	982	989	996	
631	80 003	010	017	024	030	037	044	051	058	065	
632	80 072	079	085	092	099	106	113	120	127	134	
633	80 140	147	154	161	168	175	182	188	195	202	
634	80 209	216	223	229	236	243	250	257	264	271	
635	80 277	284	291	298	305	312	318	325	332	339	
636	80 346	353	359	366	373	380	387	393	400	407	
637	80 414	421	428	434	441	448	455	462	468	475	
638	80 482	489	496	502	509	516	523	530	536	543	
639	80 550	557	564	570	577	584	591	598	604	611	
640	80 618	625	632	638	645	652	659	665	672	679	
641	80 686	693	699	706	713	720	726	733	740	747	
642	80 754	760	767	774	781	787	794	801	808	814	
643	80 821	828	835	841	848	855	862	868	875	882	
644	80 889	895	902	909	916	922	929	936	943	949	
645	80 956	963	969	976	983	990	996	*003	*010	*017	
646	81 023	030	037	043	050	057	064	070	077	084	
647	81 090	097	104	111	117	124	131	137	144	151	
648	81 158	164	171	178	184	191	198	204	211	218	
649	81 224	231	238	245	251	258	265	271	278	285	
650	81 291	298	305	311	318	325	331	338	345	351	
N	0	1	2	3	4	5	6	7	8	9	Prop. Parts

Prop. Parts

8		**7**		**6**	
1	0.8	1	0.7	1	0.6
2	1.6	2	1.4	2	1.2
3	2.4	3	2.1	3	1.8
4	3.2	4	2.8	4	2.4
5	4.0	5	3.5	5	3.0
6	4.8	6	4.2	6	3.6
7	5.6	7	4.9	7	4.2
8	6.4	8	5.6	8	4.8
9	7.2	9	6.3	9	5.4

Common Logarithms (Five-Place) of the Natural Numbers 1 to 10,000

Prop. Parts

7

1	0.7
2	1.4
3	2.1
4	2.8
5	3.5
6	4.2
7	4.9
8	5.6
9	6.3

6

1	0.6
2	1.2
3	1.8
4	2.4
5	3.0
6	3.6
7	4.2
8	4.8
9	5.4

N	0	1	2	3	4	5	6	7	8	9
650	81 291	298	305	311	318	325	331	338	345	351
651	81 358	365	371	378	385	391	398	405	411	418
652	81 425	431	438	445	451	458	465	471	478	485
653	81 491	498	505	511	518	525	531	538	544	551
654	81 558	564	571	578	584	591	598	604	611	617
655	81 624	631	637	644	651	657	664	671	677	684
656	81 690	697	704	710	717	723	730	737	743	750
657	81 757	763	770	776	783	790	796	803	809	816
658	81 823	829	836	842	849	856	862	869	875	882
659	81 889	895	902	908	915	921	928	935	941	948
660	81 954	961	968	974	981	987	994	*000	*007	*014
661	82 020	027	033	040	046	053	060	066	073	079
662	82 086	092	099	105	112	119	125	132	138	145
663	82 151	158	164	171	178	184	191	197	204	210
664	82 217	223	230	236	243	249	256	263	269	276
665	82 282	289	295	302	308	315	321	328	334	341
666	82 347	354	360	367	373	380	387	393	400	406
667	82 413	419	426	432	439	445	452	458	465	471
668	82 478	484	491	497	504	510	517	523	530	536
669	82 543	549	556	562	569	575	582	588	595	601
670	82 607	614	620	627	633	640	646	653	659	666
671	82 672	679	685	692	698	705	711	718	724	730
672	82 737	743	750	756	763	769	776	782	789	795
673	82 802	808	814	821	827	834	840	847	853	860
674	82 866	872	879	885	892	898	905	911	918	924
675	82 930	937	943	950	956	963	969	975	982	988
676	82 995	*001	*008	*014	*020	*027	*033	*040	*046	*052
677	83 059	065	072	078	085	091	097	104	110	117
678	83 123	129	136	142	149	155	161	168	174	181
679	83 187	193	200	206	213	219	225	232	238	245
680	83 251	257	264	270	276	283	289	296	302	308
681	83 315	321	327	334	340	347	353	359	366	372
682	83 378	385	391	398	404	410	417	423	429	436
683	83 442	448	455	461	467	474	480	487	493	499
684	83 506	512	518	525	531	537	544	550	556	563
685	83 569	575	582	588	594	601	607	613	620	626
686	83 632	639	645	651	658	664	670	677	683	689
687	83 696	702	708	715	721	727	734	740	746	753
688	83 759	765	771	778	784	790	797	803	809	816
689	83 822	828	835	841	847	853	860	866	872	879
690	83 885	891	897	904	910	916	923	929	935	942
691	83 948	954	960	967	973	979	985	992	998	*004
692	84 011	017	023	029	036	042	048	055	061	067
693	84 073	080	086	092	098	105	111	117	123	130
694	84 136	142	148	155	161	167	173	180	186	192
695	84 198	205	211	217	223	230	236	242	248	255
696	84 261	267	273	280	286	292	298	305	311	317
697	84 323	330	336	342	348	354	361	367	373	379
698	84 386	392	398	404	410	417	423	429	435	442
699	84 448	454	460	466	473	479	485	491	497	504
700	84 510	516	522	528	535	541	547	553	559	566

Prop. Parts	N	0	1	2	3	4	5	6	7	8	9

Common Logarithms (Five-Place) of the Natural Numbers 1 to 10,000

N	0	1	2	3	4	5	6	7	8	9	Prop. Parts
700	84 510	516	522	528	535	541	547	553	559	566	
701	84 572	578	584	590	597	603	609	615	621	628	
702	84 634	640	646	652	658	665	671	677	683	689	
703	84 696	702	708	714	720	726	733	739	745	751	
704	84 757	763	770	776	782	788	794	800	807	813	
705	84 819	825	831	837	844	850	856	862	868	874	
706	84 880	887	893	899	905	911	917	924	930	936	
707	84 942	948	954	960	967	973	979	985	991	997	**7**
708	85 003	009	016	022	028	034	040	046	052	058	1 0.7
709	85 065	071	077	083	089	095	101	107	114	120	2 1.4
710	85 126	132	138	144	150	156	163	169	175	181	3 2.1 4 2.8
711	85 187	193	199	205	211	217	224	230	236	242	5 3.5
712	85 248	254	260	266	272	278	285	291	297	303	6 4.2
713	85 309	315	321	327	333	339	345	352	358	364	7 4.9 8 5.6
714	85 370	376	382	388	394	400	406	412	418	425	9 6.3
715	85 431	437	443	449	455	461	467	473	479	485	
716	85 491	497	503	509	516	522	528	534	540	546	
717	85 552	558	564	570	576	582	588	594	600	606	
718	85 612	618	625	631	637	643	649	655	661	667	
719	85 673	679	685	691	697	703	709	715	721	727	
720	85 733	739	745	751	757	763	769	775	781	788	
721	85 794	800	806	812	818	824	830	836	842	848	
722	85 854	860	866	872	878	884	890	896	902	908	**6**
723	85 914	920	926	932	938	944	950	956	962	968	1 0.6 2 1.2
724	85 974	980	986	992	998	*004	*010	*016	*022	*028	3 1.8
725	86 034	040	046	052	058	064	070	076	082	088	4 2.4
726	86 094	100	106	112	118	124	130	136	141	147	5 3.0 6 3.6
727	86 153	159	165	171	177	183	189	195	201	207	7 4.2
728	86 213	219	225	231	237	243	249	255	261	267	8 4.8
729	86 273	279	285	291	297	303	308	314	320	326	9 5.4
730	86 332	338	344	350	356	362	368	374	380	386	
731	86 392	398	404	410	415	421	427	433	439	445	
732	86 451	457	463	469	475	481	487	493	499	504	
733	86 510	516	522	528	534	540	546	552	558	564	
734	86 570	576	581	587	593	599	605	611	617	623	
735	86 629	635	641	646	652	658	664	670	676	682	
736	86 688	694	700	705	711	717	723	729	735	741	
737	86 747	753	759	764	770	776	782	788	794	800	**5**
738	86 806	812	817	823	829	835	841	847	853	859	1 0.5 2 1.0
739	86 864	870	876	882	888	894	900	906	911	917	3 1.5 4 2.0
740	86 923	929	935	941	947	953	958	964	970	976	5 2.5
741	86 982	988	994	999	*005	*011	*017	*023	*029	*035	6 3.0 7 3.5
742	87 040	046	052	058	064	070	075	081	087	093	8 4.0
743	87 099	105	111	116	122	128	134	140	146	151	9 4.5
744	87 157	163	169	175	181	186	192	198	204	210	
745	87 216	221	227	233	239	245	251	256	262	268	
746	87 274	280	286	291	297	303	309	315	320	326	
747	87 332	338	344	349	355	361	367	373	379	384	
748	87 390	396	402	408	413	419	425	431	437	442	
749	87 448	454	460	466	471	477	483	489	495	500	
750	87 506	512	518	523	529	535	541	547	552	558	
N	0	1	2	3	4	5	6	7	8	9	Prop. Parts

Common Logarithms (Five-Place) of the Natural Numbers 1 to 10,000

N	0	1	2	3	4	5	6	7	8	9
750	87 506	512	518	523	529	535	541	547	552	558
751	87 564	570	576	581	587	593	599	604	610	616
752	87 622	628	633	639	645	651	656	662	668	674
753	87 679	685	691	697	703	708	714	720	726	731
754	87 737	743	749	754	760	766	772	777	783	789
755	87 795	800	806	812	818	823	829	835	841	846
756	87 852	858	864	869	875	881	887	892	898	904
757	87 910	915	921	927	933	938	944	950	955	961
758	87 967	973	978	984	990	996	*001	*007	*013	*018
759	88 024	030	036	041	047	053	058	064	070	076
760	88 081	087	093	098	104	110	116	121	127	133
761	88 138	144	150	156	161	167	173	178	184	190
762	88 195	201	207	213	218	224	230	235	241	247
763	88 252	258	264	270	275	281	287	292	298	304
764	88 309	315	321	326	332	338	343	349	355	360
765	88 366	372	377	383	389	395	400	406	412	417
766	88 423	429	434	440	446	451	457	463	468	474
767	88 480	485	491	497	502	508	513	519	525	530
768	88 536	542	547	553	559	564	570	576	581	587
769	88 593	598	604	610	615	621	627	632	638	643
770	88 649	655	660	666	672	677	683	689	694	700
771	88 705	711	717	722	728	734	739	745	750	756
772	88 762	767	773	779	784	790	795	801	807	812
773	88 818	824	829	835	840	846	852	857	863	868
774	88 874	880	885	891	897	902	908	913	919	925
775	88 930	936	941	947	953	958	964	969	975	981
776	88 986	992	997	*003	*009	*014	*020	*025	*031	*037
777	89 042	048	053	059	064	070	076	081	087	092
778	89 098	104	109	115	120	126	131	137	143	148
779	89 154	159	165	170	176	182	187	193	198	204
780	89 209	215	221	226	232	237	243	248	254	260
781	89 265	271	276	282	287	293	298	304	310	315
782	89 321	326	332	337	343	348	354	360	365	371
783	89 376	382	387	393	398	404	409	415	421	426
784	89 432	437	443	448	454	459	465	470	476	481
785	89 487	492	498	504	509	515	520	526	531	537
786	89 542	548	553	559	564	570	575	581	586	592
787	89 597	603	609	614	620	625	631	636	642	647
788	89 653	658	664	669	675	680	686	691	697	702
789	89 708	713	719	724	730	735	741	746	752	757
790	89 763	768	774	779	785	790	796	801	807	812
791	89 818	823	829	834	840	845	851	856	862	867
792	89 873	878	883	889	894	900	905	911	916	922
793	89 927	933	938	944	949	955	960	966	971	977
794	89 982	988	993	998	*004	*009	*015	*020	*026	*031
795	90 037	042	048	053	059	064	069	075	080	086
796	90 091	097	102	108	113	119	124	129	135	140
797	90 146	151	157	162	168	173	179	184	189	195
798	90 200	206	211	217	222	227	233	238	244	249
799	90 255	260	266	271	276	282	287	293	298	304
800	90 309	314	320	325	331	336	342	347	352	358

Prop. Parts

6	
1	0.6
2	1.2
3	1.8
4	2.4
5	3.0
6	3.6
7	4.2
8	4.8
9	5.4

5	
1	0.5
2	1.0
3	1.5
4	2.0
5	2.5
6	3.0
7	3.5
8	4.0
9	4.5

Common Logarithms (Five-Place) of the Natural Numbers 1 to 10,000

N	0	1	2	3	4	5	6	7	8	9
800	90 309	314	320	325	331	336	342	347	352	358
801	90 363	369	374	380	385	390	396	401	407	412
802	90 417	423	428	434	439	445	450	455	461	466
803	90 472	477	482	488	493	499	504	509	515	520
804	90 526	531	536	542	547	553	558	563	569	574
805	90 580	585	590	596	601	607	612	617	623	628
806	90 634	639	644	650	655	660	666	671	677	682
807	90 687	693	698	703	709	714	720	725	730	736
808	90 741	747	752	757	763	768	773	779	784	789
809	90 795	800	806	811	816	822	827	832	838	843
810	90 849	854	859	865	870	875	881	886	891	897
811	90 902	907	913	918	924	929	934	940	945	950
812	90 956	961	966	972	977	982	988	993	998	*004
813	91 009	014	020	025	030	036	041	046	052	057
814	91 062	068	073	078	084	089	094	100	105	110
815	91 116	121	126	132	137	142	148	153	158	164
816	91 169	174	180	185	190	196	201	206	212	217
817	91 222	228	233	238	243	249	254	259	265	270
818	91 275	281	286	291	297	302	307	312	318	323
819	91 328	334	339	344	350	355	360	365	371	376
820	91 381	387	392	397	403	408	413	418	424	429
821	91 434	440	445	450	455	461	466	471	477	482
822	91 487	492	498	503	508	514	519	524	529	535
823	91 540	545	551	556	561	566	572	577	582	587
824	91 593	598	603	609	614	619	624	630	635	640
825	91 645	651	656	661	666	672	677	682	687	693
826	91 698	703	709	714	719	724	730	735	740	745
827	91 751	756	761	766	772	777	782	787	793	798
828	91 803	808	814	819	824	829	834	840	845	850
829	91 855	861	866	871	876	882	887	892	897	903
830	91 908	913	918	924	929	934	939	944	950	955
831	91 960	965	971	976	981	986	991	997	*002	*007
832	92 012	018	023	028	033	038	044	049	054	059
833	92 065	070	075	080	085	091	096	101	106	111
834	92 117	122	127	132	137	143	148	153	158	163
835	92 169	174	179	184	189	195	200	205	210	215
836	92 221	226	231	236	241	247	252	257	262	267
837	92 273	278	283	288	293	298	304	309	314	319
838	92 324	330	335	340	345	350	355	361	366	371
839	92 376	381	387	392	397	402	407	412	418	423
840	92 428	433	438	443	449	454	459	464	469	474
841	92 480	485	490	495	500	505	511	516	521	526
842	92 531	536	542	547	552	557	562	567	572	578
843	92 583	588	593	598	603	609	614	619	624	629
844	92 634	639	645	650	655	660	665	670	675	681
845	92 686	691	696	701	706	711	716	722	727	732
846	92 737	742	747	752	758	763	768	773	778	783
847	92 788	793	799	804	809	814	819	824	829	834
848	92 840	845	850	855	860	865	870	875	881	886
849	92 891	896	901	906	911	916	921	927	932	937
850	92 942	947	952	957	962	967	973	978	983	988
N	0	1	2	3	4	5	6	7	8	9

Prop. Parts

6
1	0.6
2	1.2
3	1.8
4	2.4
5	3.0
6	3.6
7	4.2
8	4.8
9	5.4

5
1	0.5
2	1.0
3	1.5
4	2.0
5	2.5
6	3.0
7	3.5
8	4.0
9	4.5

Common Logarithms (Five-Place) of the Natural Numbers 1 to 10,000

Prop. Parts:

6

1	0.6
2	1.2
3	1.8
4	2.4
5	3.0
6	3.6
7	4.2
8	4.8
9	5.4

5

1	0.5
2	1.0
3	1.5
4	2.0
5	2.5
6	3.0
7	3.5
8	4.0
9	4.5

4

1	0.4
2	0.8
3	1.2
4	1.6
5	2.0
6	2.4
7	2.8
8	3.2
9	3.6

N	0	1	2	3	4	5	6	7	8	9
850	92 942	947	952	957	962	967	973	978	983	988
851	92 993	998	*003	*008	*013	*018	*024	*029	*034	*039
852	93 044	049	054	059	064	069	075	080	085	090
853	93 095	100	105	110	115	120	125	131	136	141
854	93 146	151	156	161	166	171	176	181	186	192
855	93 197	202	207	212	217	222	227	232	237	242
856	93 247	252	258	263	268	273	278	283	288	293
857	93 298	303	308	313	318	323	328	334	339	344
858	93 349	354	359	364	369	374	379	384	389	394
859	93 399	404	409	414	420	425	430	435	440	445
860	93 450	455	460	465	470	475	480	485	490	495
861	93 500	505	510	515	520	526	531	536	541	546
862	93 551	556	561	566	571	576	581	586	591	596
863	93 601	606	611	616	621	626	631	636	641	646
864	93 651	656	661	666	671	676	682	687	692	697
865	93 702	707	712	717	722	727	732	737	742	747
866	93 752	757	762	767	772	777	782	787	792	797
867	93 802	807	812	817	822	827	832	837	842	847
868	93 852	857	862	867	872	877	882	887	892	897
869	93 902	907	912	917	922	927	932	937	942	947
870	93 952	957	962	967	972	977	982	987	992	997
871	94 002	007	012	017	022	027	032	037	042	047
872	94 052	057	062	067	072	077	082	086	091	096
873	94 101	106	111	116	121	126	131	136	141	146
874	94 151	156	161	166	171	176	181	186	191	196
875	94 201	206	211	216	221	226	231	236	240	245
876	94 250	255	260	265	270	275	280	285	290	295
877	94 300	305	310	315	320	325	330	335	340	345
878	94 349	354	359	364	369	374	379	384	389	394
879	94 399	404	409	414	419	424	429	433	438	443
880	94 448	453	458	463	468	473	478	483	488	493
881	94 498	503	507	512	517	522	527	532	537	542
882	94 547	552	557	562	567	571	576	581	586	591
883	94 596	601	606	611	616	621	626	630	635	640
884	94 645	650	655	660	665	670	675	680	685	689
885	94 694	699	704	709	714	719	724	729	734	738
886	94 743	748	753	758	763	768	773	778	783	787
887	94 792	797	802	807	812	817	822	827	832	836
888	94 841	846	851	856	861	866	871	876	880	885
889	94 890	895	900	905	910	915	919	924	929	934
890	94 939	944	949	954	959	963	968	973	978	983
891	94 988	993	998	*002	*007	*012	*017	*022	*027	*032
892	95 036	041	046	051	056	061	066	071	075	080
893	95 085	090	095	100	105	109	114	119	124	129
894	95 134	139	143	148	153	158	163	168	173	177
895	95 182	187	192	197	202	207	211	216	221	226
896	95 231	236	240	245	250	255	260	265	270	274
897	95 279	284	289	294	299	303	308	313	318	323
898	95 328	332	337	342	347	352	357	361	366	371
899	95 376	381	386	390	395	400	405	410	415	419
900	95 424	429	434	439	444	448	453	458	463	468

Prop. Parts	N	0	1	2	3	4	5	6	7	8	9

Appendix Table I

Common Logarithms (Five-Place) of the Natural Numbers 1 to 10,000

N	0	1	2	3	4	5	6	7	8	9	Prop. Parts
900	95 424	429	434	439	444	448	453	458	463	468	
901	95 472	477	482	487	492	497	501	506	511	516	
902	95 521	525	530	535	540	545	550	554	559	564	
903	95 569	574	578	583	588	593	598	602	607	612	
904	95 617	622	626	631	636	641	646	650	655	660	
905	95 665	670	674	679	684	689	694	698	703	708	
906	95 713	718	722	727	732	737	742	746	751	756	
907	95 761	766	770	775	780	785	789	794	799	804	
908	95 809	813	818	823	828	832	837	842	847	852	
909	95 856	861	866	871	875	880	885	890	895	899	
910	95 904	909	914	018	923	928	933	938	942	947	
911	95 952	957	961	966	971	976	980	985	990	995	
912	95 999	*004	*009	*014	*019	*023	*028	*033	*038	*042	**5**
913	96 047	052	057	061	066	071	076	080	085	090	1 0.5
914	96 095	099	104	109	114	118	123	128	133	137	2 1.0
915	96 142	147	152	156	161	166	171	175	180	185	3 1.5
916	96 190	194	199	204	209	213	218	223	227	232	4 2.0
917	96 237	242	246	251	256	261	265	270	275	280	5 2.5
918	96 284	289	294	298	303	308	313	317	322	327	6 3.0
919	96 332	336	341	346	350	355	360	365	369	374	7 3.5
920	96 379	384	388	393	398	402	407	412	417	421	8 4.0
921	96 426	431	435	440	445	450	454	459	464	468	9 4.5
922	96 473	478	483	487	492	497	501	506	511	515	
923	96 520	525	530	534	539	544	548	553	558	562	
924	96 567	572	577	581	586	591	595	600	605	609	
925	96 614	619	624	628	633	638	642	647	652	656	
926	96 661	666	670	675	680	685	689	694	699	703	
927	96 708	713	717	722	727	731	736	741	745	750	
928	96 755	759	764	769	774	778	783	788	792	797	
929	96 802	806	811	816	820	825	830	834	839	844	
930	96 848	853	858	862	867	872	876	881	886	890	
931	96 895	900	904	909	914	918	923	928	932	937	
932	96 942	946	951	956	960	965	970	974	979	984	**4**
933	96 988	993	997	*002	*007	*011	*016	*021	*025	*030	1 0.4
934	97 035	039	044	049	053	058	063	067	072	077	2 0.8
935	97 081	086	090	095	100	104	109	114	118	123	3 1.2
936	97 128	132	137	142	146	151	155	160	165	169	4 1.6
937	97 174	179	183	188	192	197	202	206	211	216	5 2.0
938	97 220	225	230	234	239	243	248	253	257	262	6 2.4
939	97 267	271	276	280	285	290	294	299	304	308	7 2.8
940	97 313	317	322	327	331	336	340	345	350	354	8 3.2
941	97 359	364	368	373	377	382	387	391	396	400	9 3.6
942	97 405	410	414	419	424	428	433	437	442	447	
943	97 451	456	460	465	470	474	479	483	488	493	
944	97 497	502	506	511	516	520	525	529	534	539	
945	97 543	548	552	557	562	566	571	575	580	585	
946	97 589	594	598	603	607	612	617	621	626	630	
947	97 635	640	644	649	653	658	663	667	672	676	
948	97 681	685	690	695	699	704	708	713	717	722	
949	97 727	731	736	740	745	749	754	759	763	768	
950	97 772	777	782	786	791	795	800	804	809	813	
N	0	1	2	3	4	5	6	7	8	9	Prop. Parts

Common Logarithms (Five-Place) of the Natural Numbers 1 to 10,000

N	0	1	2	3	4	5	6	7	8	9
950	97 772	777	782	786	791	795	800	804	809	813
951	97 818	823	827	832	836	841	845	850	855	859
952	97 864	868	873	877	882	886	891	896	900	905
953	97 909	914	918	923	928	932	937	941	946	950
954	97 955	959	964	968	973	978	982	987	991	996
955	98 000	005	009	014	019	023	028	032	037	041
956	98 046	050	055	059	064	068	073	078	082	087
957	98 091	096	100	105	109	114	118	123	127	132
958	98 137	141	146	150	155	159	164	168	173	177
959	98 182	186	191	195	200	204	209	214	218	223
960	98 227	232	236	241	245	250	254	259	263	268
961	98 272	277	281	286	290	295	299	304	308	313
962	98 318	322	327	331	336	340	345	349	354	358
963	98 363	367	372	376	381	385	390	394	399	403
964	98 408	412	417	421	426	430	435	439	444	448
965	98 453	457	462	466	471	475	480	484	489	493
966	98 498	502	507	511	516	520	525	529	534	538
967	98 543	547	552	556	561	565	570	574	579	583
968	98 588	592	597	601	605	610	614	619	623	628
969	98 632	637	641	646	650	655	659	664	668	673
970	98 677	682	686	691	695	700	704	709	713	717
971	98 722	726	731	735	740	744	749	753	758	762
972	98 767	771	776	780	784	789	793	798	802	807
973	98 811	816	820	825	829	834	838	843	847	851
974	98 856	860	865	869	874	878	883	887	892	896
975	98 900	905	909	914	918	923	927	932	936	941
976	98 945	949	954	958	963	967	972	976	981	985
977	98 989	994	998	*003	*007	*012	*016	*021	*025	*029
978	99 034	038	043	047	052	056	061	065	069	074
979	99 078	083	087	092	096	100	105	109	114	118
980	99 123	127	131	136	140	145	149	154	158	162
981	99 167	171	176	180	185	189	193	198	202	207
982	99 211	216	220	224	229	233	238	242	247	251
983	99 255	260	264	269	273	277	282	286	291	295
984	99 300	304	308	313	317	322	326	330	335	339
985	99 344	348	352	357	361	366	370	374	379	383
986	99 388	392	396	401	405	410	414	419	423	427
987	99 432	436	441	445	449	454	458	463	467	471
988	99 476	480	484	489	493	498	502	506	511	515
989	99 520	524	528	533	537	542	546	550	555	559
990	99 564	568	572	577	581	585	590	594	599	603
991	99 607	612	616	621	625	629	634	638	642	647
992	99 651	656	660	664	669	673	677	682	686	691
993	99 695	699	704	708	712	717	721	726	730	734
994	99 739	743	747	752	756	760	765	769	774	778
995	99 782	787	791	795	800	804	808	813	817	822
996	99 826	830	835	839	843	848	852	856	861	865
997	99 870	874	878	883	887	891	896	900	904	909
998	99 913	917	922	926	930	935	939	944	948	952
999	99 957	961	965	970	974	978	983	987	991	996
1000	00 000	004	009	013	017	022	026	030	035	039

Prop. Parts

	5
1	0.5
2	1.0
3	1.5
4	2.0
5	2.5
6	3.0
7	3.5
8	4.0
9	4.5

	4
1	0.4
2	0.8
3	1.2
4	1.6
5	2.0
6	2.4
7	2.8
8	3.2
9	3.6

Random Numbers*

Line	(1)	(2)	(3)	(4)	(5)	(6)	(7)	(8)
1	78994	36244	02673	25475	84953	61793	50243	63423
2	04909	58485	70686	93930	34880	73059	06823	80257
3	46582	73570	33004	51795	86477	46736	60460	70345
4	29242	89792	88634	60285	07190	07795	27011	85941
5	68104	81339	97090	20601	78940	20228	22803	96070
6	17156	02182	82504	19880	93747	80910	78260	25136
7	50711	94789	07171	02103	99057	98775	37997	18325
8	39449	52409	75095	77720	39729	03205	09313	43545
9	75629	82729	76916	72657	58992	32756	01154	84890
10	01020	55151	36132	51971	32155	60735	64867	35424
11	08337	89989	24260	08618	66798	25889	52860	57375
12	76829	47229	19706	30094	69430	92399	98749	22081
13	39708	30641	21267	56501	95182	72442	21445	17276
14	89836	55817	56747	75195	06818	83043	47403	58266
15	25903	61370	66081	54076	67442	52964	23823	02718
16	71345	03422	01015	68025	19703	77313	04555	83425
17	61454	92263	14647	08473	34124	10740	40839	05620
18	80376	08909	30470	40200	46558	61742	11643	92121
19	45144	54373	05505	90074	24783	86299	20900	15144
20	12191	88527	58852	51175	11534	87218	04876	85584
21	62936	59120	73957	35969	21598	47287	39394	08778
22	31588	96798	43668	12611	01714	77266	55079	24690
23	20787	96048	84726	17512	39450	43618	30629	24356
24	45603	00745	84635	43079	52724	14262	05750	89373
25	31606	64782	34027	56734	09365	20008	93559	78384
26	10452	33074	76718	99556	16026	00013	78411	95107
27	37016	64633	67301	50949	91298	74968	73631	57397
28	66725	97865	25409	37498	00816	99262	14471	10232
29	07380	74438	82120	17890	40963	55757	13492	68294
30	71621	57688	58256	47702	74724	89419	08025	68519
31	03466	13263	23917	20417	11315	52805	33072	07723
32	12692	32931	97387	34822	53775	91674	76549	37635
33	52192	30941	44998	17833	94563	23062	95725	38463
34	56691	72529	66063	73570	86860	68125	40436	31303
35	74952	43041	58869	15677	78598	43520	97521	83248
36	18752	43693	32867	53017	22661	39610	03796	02622
37	61691	04944	43111	28325	82319	65589	66048	98498
38	49197	63948	38947	60207	70667	39843	60607	15328
39	19436	87291	71684	74859	76501	93456	95714	92518
40	39143	64893	14606	13543	09621	68301	69817	52140
41	82244	67549	76491	09761	74494	91307	64222	66592
42	55847	56155	42878	23708	97999	40131	52360	90390
43	94095	95970	07826	25991	37584	56966	68623	83454
44	11751	69469	25521	44097	07511	88976	30122	67542
45	69902	08995	27821	11758	64989	61902	32121	28165
46	21850	25352	25556	92161	23592	43294	10479	37879
47	75850	46992	25165	55906	62339	88958	91717	15756
48	29648	22086	42581	85677	20251	39641	65786	80689
49	82740	28443	42734	25518	82827	35825	90288	32911
50	36842	42092	52075	83926	·42875	71500	69216	01350

* A portion of page 5 of *Table of 105,000 Random Decimal Digits* constructed by H. Burke Horton and R. Tynes Smith III, for the Bureau of Transport Economics and Statistics, Interstate Commerce Commission. Reproduced here with the permission of W. H. S. Stevens, Director of that Bureau.

Squares, Square Roots, and Reciprocals

n	n^2	$\sqrt{n}$	$\sqrt{10n}$	$1/n$	n	n^2	$\sqrt{n}$	$\sqrt{10n}$	$1/n$
1	1	1.000	3.162	1.00000	51	2601	7.141	22.583	.01961
2	4	1.414	4.472	.50000	52	2704	7.211	22.804	.01923
3	9	1.732	5.477	.33333	53	2809	7.280	23.022	.01887
4	16	2.000	6.325	.25000	54	2916	7.348	23.238	.01852
5	25	2.236	7.071	.20000	55	3025	7.416	23.452	.01818
6	36	2.449	7.746	.16667	56	3136	7.483	23.664	.01786
7	49	2.646	8.367	.14286	57	3249	7.550	23.875	.01754
8	64	2.828	8.944	.12500	58	3364	7.616	24.083	.01724
9	81	3.000	9.487	.11111	59	3481	7.681	24.290	.01695
10	100	3.162	10.000	.10000	60	3600	7.746	24.495	.01667
11	121	3.317	10.488	.09091	61	3721	7.810	24.698	.01639
12	144	3.464	10.954	.08333	62	3844	7.874	24.900	.01613
13	169	3.606	11.402	.07692	63	3969	7.937	25.100	.01587
14	196	3.742	11.832	.07143	64	4096	8.000	25.298	.01562
15	225	3.873	12.247	.06667	65	4225	8.062	25.495	.01538
16	256	4.000	12.649	.06250	66	4356	8.124	25.690	.01515
17	289	4.123	13.038	.05882	67	4489	8.185	25.884	.01493
18	324	4.243	13.416	.05556	68	4624	8.246	26.077	.01471
19	361	4.359	13.784	.05263	69	4761	8.307	26.268	.01449
20	400	4.472	14.142	.05000	70	4900	8.367	26.458	.01429
21	441	4.583	14.491	.04762	71	5041	8.426	26.646	.01408
22	484	4.690	14.832	.04545	72	5184	8.485	26.833	.01389
23	529	4.796	15.166	.04348	73	5329	8.544	27.019	.01370
24	576	4.899	15.492	.04167	74	5476	8.602	27.203	.01351
25	625	5.000	15.811	.04000	75	5625	8.660	27.386	.01333
26	676	5.099	16.125	.03846	76	5776	8.718	27.568	.01316
27	729	5.196	16.432	.03704	77	5929	8.775	27.749	.01299
28	784	5.292	16.733	.03571	78	6084	8.832	27.928	.01282
29	841	5.385	17.029	.03448	79	6241	8.888	28.107	.01266
30	900	5.477	17.321	.03333	80	6400	8.944	28.284	.01250
31	961	5.568	17.607	.03226	81	6561	9.000	28.460	.01235
32	1024	5.657	17.889	.03125	82	6724	9.055	28.636	.01220
33	1089	5.745	18.166	.03030	83	6889	9.110	28.810	.01205
34	1156	5.831	18.439	.02941	84	7056	9.165	28.983	.01190
35	1225	5.916	18.708	.02857	85	7225	9.220	29.155	.01176
36	1296	6.000	18.974	.02778	86	7396	9.274	29.326	.01163
37	1369	6.083	19.235	.02703	87	7569	9.327	29.496	.01149
38	1444	6.164	19.494	.02632	88	7744	9.381	29.665	.01136
39	1521	6.245	19.748	.02564	89	7921	9.434	29.833	.01124
40	1600	6.325	20.000	.02500	90	8100	9.487	30.000	.01111
41	1681	6.403	20.248	.02439	91	8281	9.539	30.166	.01099
42	1764	6.481	20.494	.02381	92	8464	9.592	30.332	.01087
43	1849	6.557	20.736	.02326	93	8649	9.644	30.496	.01075
44	1936	6.633	20.976	.02273	94	8836	9.695	30.659	.01064
45	2025	6.708	21.213	.02222	95	9025	9.747	30.822	.01053
46	2116	6.782	21.448	.02174	96	9216	9.798	30.984	.01042
47	2209	6.856	21.679	.02128	97	9409	9.849	31.145	.01031
48	2304	6.928	21.909	.02083	98	9604	9.899	31.305	.01020
49	2401	7.000	22.136	.02041	99	9801	9.950	31.464	.01010
50	2500	7.071	22.361	.02000	100	10000	10.000	31.623	.01000

Appendix Table IV

Table of Areas under the Normal Curve

Each entry in this table is the proportion of the total area (N) under a normal curve which lies under the segment between the mean and x/σ standard deviations from the mean. Example: $N = 400$, $x = X - \bar{X} = 31$, $\sigma = 20$, $x/\sigma = 1.55$. Then $A = 0.4394 \times 400 = 175.76$. This is the required area.

x/σ	.00	.01	.02	.03	.04	.05	.06	.07	.08	.09
0.0	.0000	.0040	.0080	.0120	.0160	.0199	.0239	.0279	.0319	.0359
0.1	.0398	.0438	.0478	.0517	.0557	.0596	.0636	.0675	.0714	.0753
0.2	.0793	.0832	.0871	.0910	.0948	.0987	.1026	.1064	.1103	.1141
0.3	.1179	.1217	.1255	.1293	.1331	.1368	.1406	.1443	.1480	.1517
0.4	.1554	.1591	.1628	.1664	.1700	.1726	.1772	.1808	.1844	.1879
0.5	.1915	.1950	.1985	.2019	.2054	.2088	.2123	.2157	.2190	.2224
0.6	.2257	.2291	.2324	.2357	.2389	.2422	.2454	.2486	.2518	.2549
0.7	.2580	.2612	.2642	.2673	.2704	.2734	.2764	.2794	.2823	.2852
0.8	.2881	.2910	.2939	.2967	.2995	.3023	.3051	.3078	.3106	.3133
0.9	.3159	.3186	.3212	.3238	.3264	.3289	.3315	.3340	.3365	.3389
1.0	.3413	.3438	.3461	.3485	.3508	.3531	.3554	.3577	.3599	.3621
1.1	.3643	.3665	.3686	.3708	.3729	.3749	.3770	.3790	.3810	.3830
1.2	.3849	.3869	.3888	.3907	.3925	.3944	.3962	.3980	.3997	.4015
1.3	.4032	.4049	.4066	.4082	.4099	.4115	.4131	.4147	.4162	.4177
1.4	.4192	.4207	.4222	.4236	.4251	.4265	.4279	.4292	.4306	.4319
1.5	.4332	.4345	.4357	.4370	.4382	.4394	.4406	.4418	.4429	.4441
1.6	.4452	.4463	.4474	.4484	.4495	.4505	.4515	.4525	.4535	.4545
1.7	.4554	.4564	.4573	.4582	.4591	.4599	.4608	.4616	.4625	.4633
1.8	.4641	.4649	.4656	.4664	.4671	.4678	.4686	.4693	.4699	.4706
1.9	.4713	.4719	.4726	.4732	.4738	.4744	.4750	.4756	.4761	.4767
2.0	.4772	.4778	.4783	.4788	.4793	.4798	.4803	.4808	.4812	.4817
2.1	.4821	.4826	.4830	.4834	.4838	.4842	.4846	.4850	.4854	.4857
2.2	.4861	.4864	.4868	.4871	.4875	.4878	.4881	.4884	.4887	.4890
2.3	.4893	.4896	.4898	.4901	.4904	.4906	.4909	.4911	.4913	.4916
2.4	.4918	.4920	.4922	.4925	.4927	.4929	.4931	.4932	.4934	.4936
2.5	.4938	.4940	.4941	.4943	.4945	.4946	.4948	.4949	.4951	.4952
2.6	.4953	.4955	.4956	.4957	.4959	.4960	.4961	.4962	.4963	.4964
2.7	.4965	.4966	.4967	.4968	.4969	.4970	.4971	.4972	.4973	.4974
2.8	.4974	.4975	.4976	.4977	.4977	.4978	.4979	.4979	.4980	.4981
2.9	.4981	.4982	.4982	.4983	.4984	.4984	.4985	.4985	.4986	.4986
3.0	.49865	.4987	.4987	.4988	.4988	.4989	.4989	.4989	.4990	.4990
3.1	.49903	.4991	.4991	.4991	.4992	.4992	.4992	.4992	.4993	.4993
3.2	.4993129	.4993	.4994	.4994	.4994	.4994	.4994	.4995	.4995	.4995
3.3	.4995166	.4995	.4995	.4996	.4996	.4996	.4996	.4996	.4996	.4997
3.4	.4996631	.4997	.4997	.4997	.4997	.4997	.4997	.4997	.4998	.4998
3.5	.4997674	.4998	.4998	.4998	.4998	.4998	.4998	.4998	.4998	.4998
3.6	.4998409	.4998	.4999	.4999	.4999	.4999	.4999	.4999	.4999	.4999
3.7	.4998922	.4999	.4999	.4999	.4999	.4999	.4999	.4999	.4999	.4999
3.8	.4999277	.4999	.4999	.4999	.4999	.4999	.4999	.5000	.5000	.5000
3.9	.4999519	.5000	.5000	.5000	.5000	.5000	.5000	.5000	.5000	.5000
4.0	.4999683									
4.5	.4999966									
5.0	.4999997133									

Source: Frederick E. Croxton and Dudley J. Cowden, *Practical Business Statistics* (2d ed.; New York: Prentice-Hall, Inc., 1948), p. 511. Reprinted by permission of the publisher.

Through $x/\sigma = 2.99$, from Rugg's *Statistical Methods Applied to Education*, by arrangement with the publishers, Houghton Mifflin Company. A much more detailed table of normal curve areas is given in Federal Works Agency, Work Projects Administration for the City of New York, *Tables of Probability Functions* (New York: National Bureau of Standards, 1942), Vol. II, pp. 2–238. The values shown are for areas $\pm x/\sigma$ from μ and are thus twice those shown in our table above. In this appendix values for $x/\sigma = 3.00$ through 5.00 were computed from the latter source.

Table of "Student's" Distribution

This table shows:
Values of t

Degrees of Freedom	Level of Significance												
	.9	.8	.7	.6	.5	.4	.3	.2	.1	.05	.02	.01	.001
1	.158	.325	.510	.727	1.000	1.376	1.963	3.078	6.314	12.706	31.821	63.657	636.619
2	.142	.289	.445	.617	.816	1.061	1.386	1.886	2.910	4.303	6.965	9.925	31.598
3	.137	.277	.424	.584	.765	.978	1.250	1.638	2.353	3.182	4.541	5.841	12.941
4	.134	.271	.414	.569	.741	.941	1.190	1.533	2.132	2.776	3.747	4.604	8.610
5	.132	.267	.408	.559	.727	.920	1.156	1.476	2.015	2.571	3.365	4.032	6.859
6	.131	.265	.404	.553	.718	.906	1.134	1.440	1.943	2.447	3.143	3.707	5.959
7	.130	.263	.402	.549	.711	.896	1.119	1.415	1.895	2.365	2.998	3.499	5.405
8	.130	.262	.399	.546	.706	.889	1.108	1.397	1.860	2.306	2.896	3.355	5.041
9	.129	.261	.398	.543	.703	.883	1.100	1.383	1.833	2.262	2.821	3.250	4.781
10	.129	.260	.397	.542	.700	.879	1.093	1.372	1.812	2.228	2.764	3.169	4.587
11	.129	.260	.396	.540	.697	.876	1.088	1.363	1.796	2.201	2.718	3.106	4.437
12	.128	.259	.395	.539	.695	.873	1.083	1.356	1.782	2.179	2.681	3.055	4.318
13	.128	.259	.394	.538	.694	.870	1.079	1.350	1.771	2.160	2.650	3.012	4.221
14	.128	.258	.393	.537	.692	.868	1.076	1.345	1.761	2.145	2.624	2.977	4.140
15	.128	.258	.393	.536	.691	.866	1.074	1.341	1.753	2.131	2.602	2.947	4.073
16	.128	.258	.392	.535	.690	.865	1.071	1.337	1.746	2.120	2.583	2.921	4.015
17	.128	.257	.392	.534	.689	.863	1.069	1.333	1.740	2.110	2.567	2.898	3.965
18	.127	.257	.392	.534	.688	.862	1.067	1.330	1.734	2.101	2.552	2.878	3.922
19	.127	.257	.391	.533	.688	.861	1.066	1.328	1.729	2.093	2.539	2.861	3.883
20	.127	.257	.391	.533	.687	.860	1.064	1.325	1.725	2.086	2.528	2.845	3.850
21	.127	.257	.391	.532	.686	.859	1.063	1.323	1.721	2.080	2.518	2.831	3.819
22	.127	.256	.390	.532	.686	.858	1.061	1.321	1.717	2.074	2.508	2.819	3.792
23	.127	.256	.390	.532	.685	.858	1.060	1.319	1.714	2.069	2.500	2.807	3.767
24	.127	.256	.390	.531	.685	.857	1.059	1.318	1.711	2.064	2.492	2.797	3.745
25	.127	.256	.390	.531	.684	.856	1.058	1.316	1.708	2.060	2.485	2.787	3.725
26	.127	.256	.390	.531	.684	.856	1.058	1.315	1.706	2.056	2.479	2.779	3.707
27	.127	.256	.389	.531	.684	.855	1.057	1.314	1.703	2.052	2.473	2.771	3.690
28	.127	.256	.389	.530	.683	.855	1.056	1.313	1.701	2.048	2.467	2.763	3.674
29	.127	.256	.389	.530	.683	.854	1.055	1.311	1.699	2.045	2.462	2.756	3.659
30	.127	.256	.389	.530	.683	.854	1.055	1.310	1.697	2.042	2.457	2.750	3.646
40	.126	.255	.388	.529	.681	.851	1.050	1.303	1.684	2.021	2.423	2.704	3.551
60	.126	.254	.387	.527	.679	.848	1.046	1.296	1.671	2.000	2.390	2.660	3.460
120	.126	.254	.386	.526	.677	.845	1.041	1.289	1.658	1.980	2.358	2.617	3.373
∞	.126	.253	.385	.524	.674	.842	1.036	1.282	1.645	1.960	2.326	2.576	3.291

SOURCE: This table is reprinted from Table III of Fisher and Yates, *Statistical Tables for Biological, Agricultural, and Medical Research*, published by Oliver and Boyd, Ltd., Edinburgh, by permission of the authors and publishers.

Table of the Distribution of Chi-Square
Values of x^2

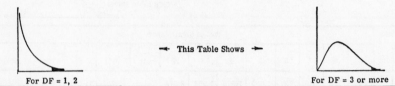

← This Table Shows →

For DF = 1, 2   For DF = 3 or more

Degrees of Freedom DF	Level of Significance								
	.99	.98	.95	.90	.50	.10	.05	.02	.01
1	.000157	.000628	.00393	.0158	.455	2.706	3.841	5.412	6.635
2	.0201	.0404	.103	.211	1.386	4.605	5.991	7.824	9.210
3	.115	.185	.352	.584	2.366	6.251	7.815	9.837	11.345
4	.297	.429	.711	1.064	3.357	7.779	9.488	11.668	13.277
5	.554	.752	1.145	1.610	4.351	9.236	11.070	13.388	15.086
6	.872	1.134	1.635	2.204	5.348	10.645	12.592	15.033	16.812
7	1.239	1.564	2.167	2.833	6.346	12.017	14.067	16.622	18.475
8	1.646	2.032	2.733	3.490	7.344	13.362	15.507	18.168	20.090
9	2.088	2.532	3.325	4.168	8.343	14.684	16.919	19.679	21.666
10	2.558	3.059	3.940	4.865	9.342	15.987	18.307	21.161	23.209
11	3.053	3.609	4.575	5.578	10.341	17.275	19.675	22.618	24.725
12	3.571	4.178	5.226	6.304	11.340	18.549	21.026	24.054	26.217
13	4.107	4.765	5.892	7.042	12.340	19.812	22.362	25.472	27.688
14	4.660	5.368	6.571	7.790	13.339	21.064	23.685	26.873	29.141
15	5.229	5.985	7.261	8.547	14.339	22.307	24.996	28.259	30.578
16	5.812	6.614	7.962	9.312	15.338	23.542	26.296	29.633	32.000
17	6.408	7.255	8.672	10.085	16.338	24.769	27.587	30.995	33.409
18	7.015	7.906	9.390	10.865	17.338	25.989	28.869	32.346	34.805
19	7.633	8.567	10.117	11.651	18.338	27.204	30.144	33.687	36.191
20	8.260	9.237	10.851	12.443	19.337	28.412	31.410	35.020	37.566
21	8.897	9.915	11.591	13.240	20.337	29.615	32.671	36.343	38.932
22	9.542	10.600	12.338	14.041	21.337	30.813	33.924	37.659	40.289
23	10.196	11.293	13.091	14.848	22.337	32.007	35.172	38.968	41.638
24	10.856	11.992	13.848	15.659	23.337	33.196	36.415	40.270	42.980
25	11.524	12.697	14.611	16.473	24.337	34.382	37.652	41.566	44.314
26	12.198	13.409	15.379	17.292	25.336	35.563	38.885	42.856	45.642
27	12.879	14.125	16.151	18.114	26.336	36.741	40.113	44.140	46.963
28	13.565	14.847	16.928	18.939	27.336	37.916	41.337	45.419	48.278
29	14.256	15.574	17.708	19.768	28.336	39.087	42.557	46.693	49.588
30	14.953	16.306	18.493	20.599	29.336	40.256	43.773	47.962	50.892

For larger values of degrees of freedom, the quantity $\sqrt{2x^2}$ may be assumed to be approximately normally distributed with mean $\sqrt{2DF - 1}$ and standard deviation 1. Thus the statistic, $\sqrt{2x^2} - \sqrt{2DF - 1}$, may be taken to have the standard normal distribution.

SOURCE: This table is reprinted from Table III of Fisher, *Statistical Methods for Research Workers*, published by Oliver and Boyd, Ltd., Edinburgh, by permission of author and publishers.

Table of Values of r for Values of z

z	.00	.01	.02	.03	.04	.05	.06	.07	.08	.09
.0	.0000	.0100	.0200	.0300	.0400	.0500	.0599	.0699	.0798	.0898
.1	.0997	.1096	.1194	.1293	.1391	.1489	.1587	.1684	.1781	.1878
.2	.1974	.2070	.2165	.2260	.2355	.2449	.2543	.2636	.2729	.2821
.3	.2913	.3004	.3095	.3185	.3275	.3364	.3452	.3540	.3627	.3714
.4	.3800	.3885	.3969	.4053	.4136	.4219	.4301	.4382	.4462	.4542
.5	.4621	.4700	.4777	.4854	.4930	.5005	.5080	.5154	.5227	.5299
.6	.5370	.5441	.5511	.5581	.5649	.5717	.5784	.5850	.5915	.5980
.7	.6044	.6107	.6169	.6231	.6291	.6352	.6411	.6469	.6527	.6584
.8	.6640	.6696	.6751	.6805	.6858	.6911	.6963	.7014	.7064	.7114
.9	.7163	.7211	.7259	.7306	.7352	.7398	.7443	.7487	.7531	.7574
1.0	.7616	.7658	.7699	.7739	.7779	.7818	.7857	.7895	.7932	.7969
1.1	.8005	.8041	.8076	.8110	.8144	.8178	.8210	.8243	.8275	.8306
1.2	.8337	.8367	.8397	.8426	.8455	.8483	.8511	.8538	.8565	.8591
1.3	.8617	.8643	.8663	.8693	.8717	.8741	.8764	.8787	.8810	.8832
1.4	.8854	.8875	.8896	.8917	.8937	.8957	.8977	.8996	.9015	.9033
1.5	.9052	.9069	.9087	.9104	.9121	.9138	.9154	.9170	.9186	.9202
1.6	.9217	.9232	.9246	.9261	.9275	.9289	.9302	.9316	.9329	.9342
1.7	.9354	.9367	.9379	.9391	.9402	.9414	.9425	.9436	.9447	.9458
1.8	.9468	.9478	.9498	.9488	.9508	.9518	.9527	.9536	.9545	.9554
1.9	.9562	.9571	.9579	.9587	.9595	.9603	.9611	.9619	.9626	.9633
2.0	.9640	.9647	.9654	.9661	.9668	.9674	.9680	.9687	.9693	.9699
2.1	.9705	.9710	.9716	.9722	.9727	.9732	.9738	.9743	.9748	.9753
2.2	.9757	.9762	.9767	.9771	.9776	.9780	.9785	.9789	.9793	.9797
2.3	.9801	.9805	.9809	.9812	.9816	.9820	.9823	.9827	.9830	.9834
2.4	.9837	.9840	.9843	.9846	.9849	.9852	.9855	.9858	.9861	.9863
2.5	.9866	.9869	.9871	.9874	.9876	.9879	.9881	.9884	.9886	.9888
2.6	.9890	.9892	.9895	.9897	.9899	.9901	.9903	.9905	.9906	.9908
2.7	.9910	.9912	.9914	.9915	.9917	.9919	.9920	.9922	.9923	.9925
2.8	.9926	.9928	.9929	.9931	.9932	.9933	.9935	.9936	.9937	.9938
2.9	.9940	.9941	.9942	.9943	.9944	.9945	.9946	.9947	.9949	.9950
3.0	.9951									
4.0	.9993									
5.0	.9999									

INDEX

Acceptance, areas of, test of significance, 191–193

Accuracy of estimates, 285–288

Actual-deviations method, calculation of arithmetic means, grouped data 82–84

Addition, rounding in, 409

Aggregates price index, relative of, 310–311
weighted, relative of, 313–314

Analysis, time-series, importance of, 331–333

Antilogarithms, finding, 401

Arithmetic mean (measure of central tendency), 76–87
calculation of, grouped data, 81–86
actual-deviation method, 82–84
basic method, 82
step-deviations method, 84–86
ungrouped data, 77–78
use of, when, 86–87
weighted, 78–81

Average, in computing seasonal variances, 369
form of, deciding on, construction of index numbers, 321–322
moving, measuring time-series trend, 338–341
of relatives price index, 311–312
of weighted relatives price index, 314–316

Average deviation, measure of dispersion, calculating, 114–116
usefulness of, 116

Bar charts, 35–40

Base, choosing, construction of index numbers, 319–321
small, distortions caused by, 397–398

Basic method, calculation of arithmetic mean, grouped data, 82

Binomial distribution, 225–239
applications, 230–232
formula, a general, 228–230
mean of, 232–234
normal curve approximation to the binomial, 234–239
standard deviation of, 232–234

Business, cycle, forecasting, 385–387
normal curve in, 143

Central tendency, measures of, 75–101
arithmetic mean, 76–87
calculation of, grouped data, 81–86;
ungrouped data, 77–78

use of, when, 86–87
weighted, 78–81
comparison of, 101
geometric mean, 87–91
calculation of, grouped data, 89–91;
ungrouped data, 88–89
median, 91–97
calculation of, grouped data, 94–97;
ungrouped data, 93–94
mode, 97–101
calculation of, grouped data, 98–101;
ungrouped data, 97–98

Change, percentage of, 394–395

Changing seasonal variables, 369–370

Characteristic of a number, determining, 400

Charts, 35–46
bar, 35–40
control, quality control, 267
graphs and, 35–46
line, 40–41
pie, 41
rules, general, 28–29
semilogarithmic, 41–46

Chi-square distribution, 244–255
examples, marketing, 249–252
personnel, 248–249
production, 252–255
theoretical, 245–247
sample size, 255

Class, interval, selecting, frequency distribution, 55–58
limits, defining, frequency distribution, 58

Cluster sampling, 269–270

Coefficient, of correlation, measure of correlation, 291–293
of determination, measure of correlation, 291
of variation, relative dispersion, 119–120

Commodities to be included, deciding, construction of index numbers, 317

Common index numbers, 322–324
consumer price index, 322–323
industrial production index, 324
wholesale price index, 323–324

Complete-experiment probability situations, 139–140

Confidence intervals, sampling application, 170–184
confidence levels, possible, 176–178
size of interval and relation between, 178–180
determination of, 171–173

interpretation of, 173–176
proportions, 244
sample size and, 181–183
size of, relation between confidence level and, 178–180
standard error of the mean and, 180–181
unknown σ, small n, and the t distribution, 208–209
Confidence levels, possible, 176–178
size of confidence interval, relation between, 178–180
Consumer price index, 322–323
Continuous data, 59, 223
Control, charts, quality control, 267
quality (*see* Quality control)
statistics and, 5
Correlation, 277–300
coefficient of, 291–293
estimates, accuracy of, 285–288
standard error of, 285–288
forecasting and, 299–300
measures of, calculation of, 288–293
coefficient of correlation 291–293
coefficient of determination, 291
r, significance, 296–299
regression line, 281–285
relations, other, 293–294
scattergram, 279–281
short-cut methods, 295–296
z transformation, 297–299
Cumulative frequency distributions, 59–60
Curve, the, graphing, frequency distributions, 63
leptokurtic, 123
Lorenz, frequency distributions, 65–67
mesokurtic, 123
normal, 123, 142–148
approximation to the binomial, 234–239
in business, 143
frequency distributions, 64
probability and, 148
standard deviation and, 143–145
table of areas, 143, 145–148
platykurtic, 123
time-series data, selection of type to be fitted to, 347–348
Cyclical movements, measuring, 377–387
business cycle, forecasting, 385–387
National Bureau method, 380–384
residual method, 378–380
Cyclical variations, comparing, 379–380
time-series trend, 335–336

Data, continuous, 59, 223
discrete or discontinuous, frequency distributions from, 59

grouped, arithmetic mean, calculation of, 81–86
geometric mean, calculation of, 89–91
median, calculation of, 94–97
mode, calculation of, 98–101
standard deviation, 118–119
primary, 11–12
collecting, 12–13
qualitative, sampling applications, 223–255
binomial distribution, 225–239
chi-square distribution, 244–255
probability theorems, 223–225
proportions, 239–244
secondary, 11–12
sources of, 11–12
ungrouped, arithmetic mean, calculation of, 77–78
calculation of, 97–98
geometric mean, calculation of, 88–89
median, calculation of, 93–94
standard deviation, 117–118
Design, sample, 267–271
directed samples, 270–271
restricted random sampling, 269–270
unrestricted random sampling, 268–269
Determination, coefficient of, measure of correlation, 291
Deviation, of binomial distribution, 232–234
measures of dispersion, calculating, average, 114–116
standard, 116–119
standard, normal curve and, 143–145
sampling distribution of the mean, 161–164
Difference, between two means, significance of, 199–202
significant, test of significance, 187–189
Directed samples, sample design, 270–271
Discrete data, frequency distributions from, 59
Dispersion, measures of, 108–120
deviation, calculating, average, 114–116; standard, 116–119
percentiles, 113–114
quartiles, 109–113
interquartile range, 113
Q_1, Q_2, Q_3, calculation of, 111–112
semi-interquartile range, 113
range, 108–109
relative, 119–120
coefficient of variation, 119–120
Distortion caused by small bases, 395–396
Distribution, binomial, 225–239
applications, 230–232
deviation, standard, 232–234
formula, a general, 228–230
mean, 232–234

Distribution, binomial (*cont.*)
  normal curve approximation to the bi-
    nomial, 234–239
  chi-square, 244–255
    marketing, example from, 249–252
    personnel, example from, 248–249
    production, example from, 252–255
    sample size, 255
    theoretical example, 245–247
  frequency (*see* Frequency distributions)
  of the mean, sampling, 152–164
    mean of, 157–158
    shape of, 158–161
    standard deviation of, 161–164
  t distribution, 207–208
Division, rounding in, 409

Editing seasonal variations, preliminary,
    356–357
Equations, simple, solving, 396–399
Error, of the mean, standard, confidence in-
    tervals and, 180–181
  standard, of estimate, 285–288
  type I and type II, tests of significance,
    195–199
Estimates, accuracy of, 285–288
  standard error of, 285–288
Exploration, statistics and, 6–7
Extrapolation of time-series trend, 348–349

Figures, rounding, 407
  significant, 406
    indication of, 410
Forecasting, 277–387
  business cycle, 385–387
  correlation, 277–300
    estimates, accuracy of, 285–288
    measures of, calculation of, 288–293
    r, significance of, 296–299
    regression line, 281–285
    scattergram, 279–281
    short-cut methods, 295–296
    z transformation, 297–299
  cyclical movements, measuring, 377–387
    business cycle, 385–387
    National Bureau method, 380–384
    residual method, 378–380
  index numbers, 309–324
    common, 322–324
    construction methods, 310–316
    construction problems, 316–322
    price index (*see* Price index)
    quantity index, 322
    value index, 322
  seasonal variations, measuring, 356–371
    average in computing, 369
    changing, 369–370
    editing, preliminary, 356–357
    isolating, problem of, 357

    median link-relative method of meas-
      uring, 365–368
    period of, selecting, 368
    ratio-to-the-moving-average method
      of measuring, 360–365
    ratio-to-trend method of measuring,
      357–360
    seasonal indexes and planning, 371
    seasonal influences, eliminating, 370–
      371
  statistics and, 4–5
  time-series trend, 331–349
    analysis, importance of, 331–333
    composition of, mathematical statement
      of, 337–338
    curve to be fitted, selection of type of,
      347–348
    extrapolation of, 348–349
    measuring, methods of, 338–347
    period of, choice of, 348
    variation, elements of, 333–338
Form, of average, deciding on, construction
    of index numbers, 321–322
  of index, deciding, 319
Frequency distributions, 52–67
  construction of, 55–59
    class interval, selecting, 55–58
    class limits, defining, 58
    tabulation of frequencies, 58–59
  cumulative, 59–60
  discrete data, from, 59
  graphing, 60–64
    curve, 63
    histogram, 60–61
    ogives, 63–64
    polygon, 61–63
  types of, 64–67
    J-shaped, 65
    Lorenz curve, 65–67
    normal curve, 64
    U-shaped, 65

Geometric mean (measure of central tend-
    ency), 87–91
  calculation of, grouped data, 89–91
    ungrouped data, 88–89
Geometric straight line, fitting, measuring
    time-series trend, 346–347
Graphs and graphing, charts and, 35–46
  frequency distributions, 60–64
    curve, 63
    histogram, 60–61
    ogives, 63–64
    polygon, 61–63
Grouped data, arithmetic mean, calculation
    of, 81–86
    actual-deviations method, 82–84
    basic method, 82

step-deviations method, 84–86
geometric mean, calculation of, 89–91
median, calculation of, 94–97
mode, calculation of, 98–101
standard deviation, 118–119

Histogram, graphing frequency distributions, 60–61

Inaccuracy in sampling results, sources of, 13–14
Incomplete-experiment probability situations, 137–139
Index, consumer price, 322–323
industrial production, 324
numbers (*see* Index numbers)
price (*see* Price index)
quantity, 322
seasonal, and planning, 371
value, 322
wholesale price, 323–324
Index numbers, 309–324
common, 322–324
consumer price index, 322–323
industrial production index, 324
wholesale price index, 323–324
construction methods, 310–316
average of relatives price index, 311–312
average of weighted relatives price index, 314–316
relative of aggregates price index, 310–311
relative of weighted aggregates price index, 313–314
construction problems, 316–322
base, choosing, 319–321
commodities to be included, deciding, 317
form of average, deciding on, 321–322
form of index, deciding, 319
purpose, defining, 317
weights, determining, 318–319
price index (*see* Price index)
quantity index, 322
value index, 322
Indication of significance, 408
Industrial production index, 324
Inference, statistical, 133–273
normal curve, 142–148
in business, 143
probability and, 148
standard deviation and, 143–145
table of areas, 143, 145–148
probability, 134–141
normal curve and, 148
ratio, range and limits of, 140–141
situations, 136–140
terminology, 135

quality control, 260–267
control charts, 267
pattern, recognition of, 262–263
"piece-to-piece" variation, 262
prediction ability, 263–265
sample and universe, relation between, 265–266
sample design, 267–271
directed samples, 270–271
restricted random sampling, 269–270
unrestricted random sampling, 268–269
sample measures and, other, 271
sampling, 148–164
applications, 170–212, 223–255
binomial distribution, 225–239
chi-square distribution, 244–255
confidence intervals, 170–184
distribution of the mean, 152–264
experiment, a simple, 151–152
probability theorems, 223–225
proportions, 239–244
qualitative data, 223–225
simple random, 150
tests of significance, 184–202
unknown σ, small n, and the t distribution, 206–211
unknown σ and large n, 202–206
sampling theory, population, learning about, 149–150
Information, securing, techniques of, 14–19
interviews, 15–17
questioning procedure, proper, 17–19
questionnaires, 15–17
Interpolation, 400–401
Interquartile range, measure of dispersion, calculating, 113
Interviews, information through, securing, 15–17
Investigation, statistical, conducting, 7–22
data, primary and secondary, and sources of, 11–12
inaccuracy in sampling results, sources of, 13–14
information, securing, techniques of, 14–19
interviews, 15–17
primary data, collecting, 12–13
problem, defining and limiting, 7–9
questioning procedure, proper, 17–19
questionnaires, 15–17
questions, forms of, 19–21
tabulation, 21–22
terms, definition of, 9–11
Irregular factors, time-series trend variation, 336
Isolation of seasonal variables, problem of, 357

J-shaped frequency distribution, 65

Kurtosis, measure of, 122–123

Large n, unknown σ and, sampling application, 202–206
Law of normality, 143
Least square lines, fitting, measuring time-series trend, 341–345
Leptokurtic curve, 123
Limitation, probability ratio, 140–141
    residual method of measuring cyclical movements, 379
Line charts, 40–41
Logarithms, 399–404
    antilogarithms, finding, 402
    characteristic, determining, 400
    extracting roots with, 402
    finding, examples of, 400
    interpolation, 400–401
    multiplication with use of, 401–402
    raising powers with, 402
    slide rule, 402–404
Lorenz curve frequency distribution, 65–67

Manual trend-fitting, measuring time-series trend, 338
Marketing, chi-square distribution, example from, 249–252
Mean, arithmetic (see Arithmetic mean)
    of binomial distribution, 232–234
    difference between two, significance of, 199–202
    distribution of the, sampling, 152–164
        mean of, 157–158
        shape of, 158–161
        standard deviation of, 161–164
    geometric (see Geometric mean)
    standard error of, confidence intervals and, 180–181
Measures and measuring, central tendency, 75–101
    arithmetic mean, 76–87
    comparison of, 101
    geometric mean, 87–91
    median, 91–97
    mode, 97–101
    of correlation, calculation of, 288–293
        coefficient of correlation, 291–293
        coefficient of determination, 291
    cyclical movements, 377–387
        business cycle, forecasting, 385–387
        National Bureau method, 380–384
        residual method, 378–380
    dispersion, 108–120
        average deviation, 114–116
        percentiles, 113–114
        quartiles, 109–113
        range, 108–109

relative, 119–120
standard deviation, 116–319
kurtosis, 122–123
seasonal variations, 356–371
    average in computing, 369
    editing, preliminary, 356–357
    isolating, problem of, 357
    median link-relative method, 365–368
    period of, selecting, 368
    ratio-to-the-moving-average method, 360–365
    ratio-to-trend method, 357–360
    seasonal indexes and planning, 371
    seasonal influences, eliminating, 370–371
skewness, 120–122
time-series trend, 338–347
    annual trend values, conversion to monthly values, 345
    geometric straight line, fitting, 346–347
    least square lines, fitting, 341–345
    manual trend-fitting, 338
    moving averages, 338–341
Median, measure of central tendency, 91–97
    calculation of, grouped data, 94–97
        ungrouped data, 93–94
Median link-relative method, measuring seasonal variations, 365–368
Mesokurtic curve, 123
Mode, measure of central tendency, 97–101
    calculation of, grouped data, 98–101
        ungrouped data, 97–98
Moving averages, measuring time-series trend, 338–341
Multiple-choice questions, 19–20
Multiplication, rounding in, 409

n (see Large n; Small n)
National Bureau method, measuring cyclical movements, 380–384
    reference cycles, 383–384
    specific cycles, 380–383
Normal curve, 123, 142–148
    approximation to the binomial, 234–239
    in business, 143
    frequency distributions, 64
    probability and, 148
    standard deviation and, 143–145
    table of areas, 143, 145–148
Normality, law of, 143

Ogives, graphing, frequency distributions, 63–64
One-tailed tests, two-tailed versus, 194–195
Open questions, 21

Pattern, recognition of, quality control, 262–263
Percent changes in percentages, 398

Percentages, 396–398
  of change, 394–395
  distortions caused by small bases, 395–396
  percent changes in, 396
Percentiles, measures of dispersion, 113–114
Period of time-series trend, choice of, 348
Personnel, chi-square distribution example from, 248–249
Pie charts, 41
"Piece-to-piece" variation, quality control, 262
Platykurtic curve, 123
Polygon, graphing, frequency distributions, 61–63
Population, sampling, 149–150
Powers, raising, with logarithms, 404
Predetermined probability situations, 136–137
Prediction, quality control, 263–265
Price index, average of relatives, 311–312
  consumer, 322–323
  relative of aggregates, 310–311
  weighted aggregates, relative of, 313–314
  weighted relatives, average of, 314–316
  wholesale, 323–324
Primary data, 11–12
  collecting, 12–13
Probability, 134–141
  normal curve and, 148
  ratio, range and limits of, 140–141
  situations, 136–140
    applications, 140
    complete-experiment, 139–140
    incomplete-experiment, 137–139
    predetermined, 136–137
  terminology, 135
  theorems, 223–225
Problem, defining, 7–9
  limiting, 7–9
Production, chi-square distribution, example from, 252–255
Proportions, 239–244
  confidence intervals, 244
  tests of significance, 243

Q_1, Q_2, Q_3, calculation of, 111–112
Qualitative data, sampling applications, 223–255
  binomial distribution, 225–239
    applications, 230–232
    deviation, mean and standard, 232–234
    formula, a general, 228–230
    normal curve approximation to the binomial, 234–239
  chi-square distribution, 244–245
    marketing, example from, 249–252
    personnel, example from, 248–249

  production, example from, 252–255
    sample size, 255
    theoretical example, 245–247
  probability theorems, 223–225
  proportions, 239–244
    confidence intervals, 244
    tests of significance, 243
Quality control, statistical, 5, 260–267
  control charts, 267
  pattern, recognition of, 262–263
  "piece-to-piece" variation, 262
  prediction ability, 263–265
  sample and universe, relation between, 265–266
Quanity index, 322
Quartiles, measures of dispersion, 109–113
  interquartile range, 113
  Q_1, Q_2, Q_3, calculation of, 111–112
  semi-interquartile range, 113
Questioning procedure, proper, information through, securing, 17–19
Questionnaires, information through, securing, 15–17
Questions, forms of, 19–21
  multiple-choice, 19–20
  open, 21
  specific-information, 20–21
  "yes or no," 20

r, significance of, correlation, 296–299
  sample size and, 299
  values of, other than 0, tests of hypotheses concerning, 299
Random factors, time-series trend variation, 336
Random sampling, restricted, 269–270
  simple, 150
  unrestricted, 268–269
Range, interquartile, calculating, 113
  measure of dispersion, 108–109
  probability ratio, 140–141
  semi-interquartile, calculating, 113
Ratio-to-the-moving-average method, measuring seasonal variations, 360–365
Ratio-to-trend method, measuring seasonal variables, 357–360
  adjusting seasonal indexes to total 1200 percent, 359–360
  appraisal of, 360
Ratios, 393–394
  probability, range and limits of, 140–141
Regression line, correlation, 281–285
Rejection, areas of, test of significance, 191–193
Relative of aggregates price index, 310–311
Relative of weighted aggregates price index, 313–314

Relative dispersion, 119–120
  coefficient of variation, 119–120
Relatives price index, weighted, average of,
    314–316
Residual method, measuring cyclical move-
    ments, 378–380
  cyclical variations, comparing, 379–380
  limitations of, 379
Restricted random sampling, sample design,
    269–270
Roots (*see* Square roots)
Rounding, in addition and subtraction, 407
  in multiplication and division, 407

Sample(s), design, 267–271
  directed samples, 270–271
  restricted random, 269–270
  unrestricted random, 268–269
  directed, sample design, 270–271
  size of, chi-square distribution, 255
    confidence intervals and, 181–183
    fixed, type I and type II, errors for, 197–
      198
    significance or r and, 299
  universe and, relation between, quality con-
    trol, 265–266
Sampling, applications, 170–212
  confidence intervals, 170–184
  qualitative data, 223–255
  tests of significance, 184–202
  unknown σ, small n, and the t distribu-
    tion, 206–211
  unknown σ and large n, 202–206
  confidence intervals, 170–184
    confidence levels, possible, 176–178
    determination of, 171–173
    interpretation of, 173–176
    proportions, 244
    sample size and, 181–183
    size of, relation between confidence level
      and, 178–180
    standard error of the mean and, 180–181
    unknown σ, small n, and the t distribu-
      tion, 209–211
  distribution of the mean, 152–164
    mean of, 157–158
    shape of, 158–161
    standard deviation of, 161–164
  experiment, a simple, 151–152
  population, learning about, 149–150
  qualitative data, 223–255
    binomial distribution, 225–239
    chi-square distribution, 244–255
    probability theorems, 223–225
    proportions, 239–244
  quality control, statistical, 260–267
    control charts, 267
    pattern, recognition of, 262–263

    "piece-to-piece" variation, 262
    prediction ability, 263–265
    sample and universe, relation between,
      265–266
  random restricted, 269–270
  simple, 150
  unrestricted, 268–269
  results, inaccuracy in, sources of, 13–14
  sample design, 267–271
    directed samples, 270–271
    restricted random sampling, 269–270
    unrestricted random sampling, 268–269
  tests of significance, 184–202
    areas of acceptance and rejection, 191–
      193
    difference, a significant, 187–189
    difference between two means, signifi-
      cance of, 199–202
    errors, type I and type II, 195–199
    one-tailed versus two-tailed tests, 194–
      195
    proportions, 243
    sampling variation, 185–187
    significance level, 189–191
    unknown σ, small n, and the t distribu-
      tion, 209–211
  theory, 148–164
  variation, test of significance, 185–187
Scattergram, 279–281
Schedules, 15
Seasonal indexes and planning, 371
Seasonal influences, eliminating, 370–371
Seasonal trend, time-series variation, 333–334
Seasonal variations, measuring, 356–371
  average in computing, 369
  changing, 369–370
  editing, preliminary, 356–357
  isolating, problem of, 357
  median link-relative method, 365–368
  period of, selecting, 368
  ratio-to-the-moving-average method,
    360–365
  ratio-to-trend method, 357–360
  seasonal indexes and planning, 371
  seasonal influences, eliminating, 370–371
  time-series trend, 334–335
Secondary data, 11–12
Semi-interquartile range, measure of disper-
    sion, calculating, 113
Semilogarithmic charts, 41–46
Shape of sampling distribution of the mean,
    158–161
Short-cut methods, correlation, 295–296
Significance, tests of, sampling application,
    184–202
  areas of acceptance and rejection, 191–
    193
  difference, a significant, 187–189

difference between two means, significance of, 199–200
errors, type I and type II, 195–199
one-tailed versus two-tailed tests, 194–195
proportions, 243
sampling variation, 185–187
significance level, 189–191
unknown σ, small n, and the t distribution, 209–211
Significance level, test of significance, 189–191
Significant figures, 406
indication of, 408
Simple equations, solving, 396–399
Simple random sampling, 150
Situations, probability, 136–140
applications, 140
complete-experiment, 139–140
incomplete-experiment, 137–139
predetermined, 136–137
Skewness, measures of, 120–122
Slide rule, 402–404
Small n, unknown σ, and the t distribution, sampling application, 206–211
Sources, of data, 11–12
of inaccuracy in sampling results, 13–14
Specific-information questions, 20–21
Square roots, extracting, with logarithms, 402
finding, 404–406
longhand technique, 405–406
table of, 404–405
Squares, table of 404–405
Standard deviation, binomial distribution, 232–234
measure of dispersion, calculating, 116–119
grouped data, 118–119
ungrouped data, 117–118
normal curve and, 143–145
sampling distribution of the mean, 161–164
Standard error, of estimate, 285–288
of the mean, confidence intervals and, 180–181
Statistical inference (*see* Inference)
Statistics, control and, 5
exploration and, 6–7
forecasting and, 4–5
nature of, 3–4
Step-deviations method, calculation of arithmetic mean, grouped data, 84–86
Straight line, geometric fitting, measuring time-series trend, 346–347
Stratified sampling, 269–270
Subtraction, rounding in, 409
Systematic sampling, 269–270

Tables, 29–34
areas, normal curve, 143, 145–148
parts of, 30

rules, general, 28–29
squares and square roots, 404–405
Tabulation, 21–22
frequencies, 58–59
distribution, 207–208
Terms, definition of, 9–11
Tests of significance, sampling application, 184–202, 243
areas of acceptance and rejection, 191–193
difference between two means, significance of, 199–202
errors, type I and type II, 195–199
one-tailed versus two-tailed tests, 194–195
proportions, 243
sampling variation, 185–187
significance level, 189–191
t difference, a significant, 187–189
unknown σ, small n, and the t distribution, 209–211
Time-series trend, 331–349
analysis, importance of, 331–333
composition of, mathematical statement of, 337–338
curve to be fitted, selection of type of, 347–348
extrapolation of, 348–349
measuring, method of, 338–347
annual trend values, conversion to monthly values, 345
geometric straight line, fitting, 346–347
least square lines, fitting, 341–345
manual trend-fitting, 338
moving averages, 338–341
period of, choice of, 348
variation, elements of, 333–338
classification, problems of, 336–337
cyclical, 335–336
irregular or random factors, 336
seasonal, 334–335
secular trend, 333–334
Two-tailed tests, one-tailed versus, 194–195
Type I and II errors, 195–199

Ungrouped data, arithmetic mean, calculation of, 77–78
geometric mean, calculation of, 88–89
median, calculation of, 93–94
mode, calculation of, 97–98
standard deviation, 117–118
Universe, 13
sample and, relation between, quality control, 265–266
Unknown σ, large n and, sampling application, 202–206
small n, and the t distribution, sampling application, 206–211

446   INDEX

Unrestricted random sampling, sampling
    design, 268–269
U-shaped frequency distribution, 65

Value index, 322
Values, time-series trend, converting
    annual to monthly, 345
Variation(s), coefficient of, relative disper-
    sion, 119–120
  cyclical, comparing, 379–380
    time-series trend, 335–336
  "piece-to-piece," quality control, 262
  sampling, test of significance, 185–187
  seasonal, average in computing, 369
    changing, 369–370
    editing, preliminary, 356–357
    isolating, problem of, 357
    measuring, 356–371
      median link-relative method, 365–368
      ratio-to-the-moving-average method,
        360–365
      ratio-to-trend method, 357–360

period of, selecting, 368
seasonal indexes and planning, 371
seasonal influences, eliminating, 370–371
time-series trend, 334–335
time-series, elements of, 333–338
    classification, problems of, 336–337
    cyclical, 335–336
    irregular or random factors, 336
    seasonal, 334–335
    secular trend, 333–334

Weighted aggregates price index, relative of,
    313–314
Weighted arithmetic mean, 78–81
Weighted relatives price index, average of,
    314–316
Weights, determining, construction of index
    numbers, 318–319
Wholesale price index, 323–324

"Yes or no" questions, 20

z transformation, correlation, 297–299